What People Are Saying
Food for Freedom

"In his excellent follow-up to *The World Peace Diet*, Dr. Will Tuttle eloquently explains in *Food for Freedom* that we reap what we sow. He explores and demonstrates how human freedom is inextricably inter-connected to our granting freedom to all sentient beings." —**Dawn Lester & David Parker**, authors, *What Really Makes You Ill?*

"*Food for Freedom* is Dr. Will Tuttle's next spiritually uplifting and life-changing gem after *The World Peace Diet*. A must read for everybody who cares about freedom, spiritual evolution and a future worth living!" —**Stefan Wolf**, creator of the documentary film *A New We*.

"Dr. Will Tuttle and his wife Madeleine have created over many years a unique litany of information and thoughtful contributions for human-kind that is, in my experience, unmatched. Their musical performances and their love for us fellow human beings are heartfelt, as many who have heard their presentations and performances will say. Recording their thoughts and their honest sense of food and its relationship to human health and our welfare into this book is a treasure, as any reader will find." —**Dr. T. Colin Campbell**, best-selling author and Professor Emeritus of Nutritional Biochemistry at Cornell University

"*Food for Freedom* is an outstanding book of the vegan way of life as an expression of all aspects of our true human nature at its highest level. Dr. Will Tuttle creates a scientific and wisdom-filled explanation of the vegan way that has been rarely expressed in one place. This book is a holistic work of art, science, and basic spiritual wisdom that will help readers develop a fully illuminated world view on the vegan way of life." —**Dr. Gabriel Cousens, M.D.**, world recognized Essene teacher and author

"Dr. Tuttle's devotion to human and planetary health is unquestionable, and in this new offering *Food for Freedom,* he further expounds and expands on the multitude of purposeful reasons that we must all embrace profound change." —**Dr. Brian Clement**, best-selling author, and director, Hippocrates Wellness

"Dr. Tuttle has done it again. His *World Peace Diet* masterpiece, acclaimed around the world and translated into many languages, shocked readers into a new awareness of the sacredness of all life and our urgent need to end human violence toward animals, the Earth and each other. *Food For Freedom* not only elegantly expands on the WPD teachings, but also boldly addresses the myriad crises that seem to have engulfed the world in these last few years. With hundreds of references and resources, *Food for Freedom* elucidates where we are, how we got here, how we can face the truth of what is really happening and how we can finally bring freedom, peace and joy to our own hearts, to each other and to all beings. May freedom and wisdom be with you as you read this guide to our true destiny." —**Judy McCoy Carman**, author, *Peace to All Beings* and *Homo Ahimsa*

"*Food for Freedom* is a brilliant, effortless read that is at the same time specific and all-encompassing. Dr. Tuttle connects the dots between animal herding, enslavement, and slaughter, and our own bondage and servitude at the hands of the wealthy few. His detailed descriptions of technical, political, and industrial tactics used to brainwash and control us are unparalleled. He reminds us of the spiritual awareness born within each of us that can be tapped into and used to inspire us to find our own life's calling and make this world a better place for all life on this wondrous planet." —**Britt Lind**, founder, Kindness and Science in Action

"I'm very grateful for Dr. Will Tuttle's courage to write *Food for Freedom: How We Can Reclaim Our Health and Rescue Our World.* This revolutionary book offers brilliant ideas that are vital to be put into action now. Our health freedom rights and the requirement for a world-wide transition to a vegan life are masterful concepts fundamental to sustaining our existence on planet Earth. If you wish to feel healthier and happier with your decision to respect all life forms, do jump on the opportunity to be transformed by this book." —**Karen Ranzi**, M.A., award-winning author of *Creating Healthy Children* and *Heal and Prevent Autism*

"*Food for Freedom* is an indispensable resource for anyone seeking true health and wellbeing in all its forms. A liberating and empowering masterpiece that takes vegans and non-vegans alike through a journey of self-awakening and ultimate sovereignty." —**Margarita Restrepo**, founder and editor-in-chief, *Naked Food Magazine*

"In *Food for Freedom*, Dr. Will Tuttle masterfully educates us on the multifaceted ways in which we as a society have become indoctrinated into accepting both mistreatment of animals and normalization of pharmaceutical dominance in our lives in the names of nutrition and health, while actually robbing us of both. He does this in such an empowering and insightful way that ignites our innate wisdom and compassion, providing us with practical solutions for overcoming food and drug addictions and transforming our lives for the betterment of ourselves and all of God's precious creatures. A very worthwhile read!" —**Dr. Armaiti May**, founder, Veterinary Association for the Protection of Animals

"*Food for Freedom* is a must-read for anyone who wants to help advance abundance and joy for all. This book highlights the Golden Rule and the boomerang effect, thus leading to freedom and an end to the cycle of suffering. —**Marlene Narrow**, Founder, *Vegan Nation Radio*

"Enlightening, thought-provoking, and superb work of literature: *Food for Freedom* confronts the reader with the undeniable causes for our modern slavery. Scholarly and poetic, this book will engage every level of your being. If you care about freedom, it is the most compelling contemporary exploration into the topic. Not only because its contents masterfully reveal the ancient origins of war and violence, but because the writer himself has fully embodied his teaching and walks this Earth as a true ambassador for peace. This groundbreaking work of defining the corresponding five dimensions of health and freedom provides an actual roadmap for the new civilization." —**Henna Maria,** peace activist, poet, medicine woman

"Dr. Will Tuttle is one of the most well informed & original thinkers that I have ever met! He embodies an ideal blend of academic brilliance, compassion & spiritual activism. His new book, *Food for Freedom*, is certain to inform, enlighten & liberate countless souls." —**Meenakshi Angel Honig,** acclaimed yoga instructor & author, *The Soulution*

"Reading *Food for Freedom*, I had the same experience I had reading Will Tuttle's earlier amazing book, *The World Peace Diet,* of being stunned and happily blown away by the clarification and expansion of what I have learned over the decades. *Food for Freedom* goes beyond *The World Peace Diet* in that it reminds me that everything I do, think, feel, use, eat, wear, and buy has direct impacts that go far beyond my personal sphere." —**Veda Stram,** author, *What to Eat When You Don't Eat Animals*

"*Food for Freedom* is a work revealing the complete interconnection of all levels of existence. Dr. Tuttle's work explores how what we do, think, feel and put in our body can help us find the solution to the problem of freedom. This book is a must for those who are aligned with the unfolding journey of light." —**Michele Lastella,** journalist and film director

"Dr. Will Tuttle's enlightening book brings a crucially important message for our time. As humanity stands on the precipice of bondage to an Orwellian technocratic superstate, *Food for Freedom* uncovers the layers of misperception that have clouded our minds. It deprograms us from flawed beliefs that have degraded our world and allowed our freedom to become imperiled. This timely book synthesizes a new framework of common ground between two evolutionary directions that have not always been in alignment: the search for personal sovereignty and human freedom, and the necessity to liberate all sentient beings. *Food for Freedom* shows that these two are in fact interwoven." —**Dr. Nicky Hind,** composer, pianist

FOOD
—FOR—
FREEDOM

*Reclaiming Our Health and
Rescuing Our World*

WILL TUTTLE, Ph.D.

Karuna • Middletown, CA

Food for Freedom:
Reclaiming Our Health and Rescuing Our World

Karuna
Middletown, CA
www.foodforfreedom.net

Front cover art by Madeleine Tuttle

ISBN: 979-8-9902104-0-0
Library of Congress Control Number: 2024905343

Disclaimer:
The ideas and suggestions in this book are intended for educational purposes only. The information provided in this book is for personal and spiritual development. It does not constitute medical advice. This book is not intended to replace medical advice, or to diagnose, prescribe or treat any disease, condition or injury.

TABLE OF CONTENTS

CHAPTER SIX

THE BENEFITS OF DEEP VEGANISM

CHAPTER SEVEN

DARK INSTITUTIONS, FOOD, AND FREEDOM

CHAPTER EIGHT

THE VACCA-CINATION OF HUMANITY

CHAPTER NINE

THE METAPHYSICS OF MASKS

INTRODUCTION

⌒⌒

"Untruth corrodes the soul; truth nourishes it."
—MAHATMA GANDHI

Food and Freedom

This book is an exploration into the underlying cultural food narratives in our society, and how they have eroded our freedom, health, spirituality, and awareness. It aims to provide alternatives that promote these qualities, and to offer a wide range of practical steps we can each take to reinvigorate and liberate our lives and our culture. The basic idea is that we have all been wounded from infancy onward, compelled to participate in our culture's defining social ritual—our meals. With insufficient awareness of the consequences of our routine mistreatment of animals for food, we are causing an ongoing cascade of events and conditions that are harmful to us on every level.

For example, most of us understand that we are being increasingly confronted by weaponized medical, media, monetary, and governmental policies that attack our health, our freedom, and our children. What most of us don't seem to understand is how these attacks mirror, and emerge directly from, our daily attacks on the health, freedom, and offspring of the animals we classify as livestock. We are called to explore the deeper, hidden driving forces that propel the situations we find unfolding around us. By making connections that we have been taught not to make, we can rescue ourselves, animals, nature, and our world from the unrecognized harmful repercussions of our food system and its narratives, not just on our physical, environmental, and cultural health, but also on the internal landscape of our attitudes and feelings. This is the empowering adventure that beckons.

It is uniquely challenging to question our daily food choices. Inner resistance is due not only to psychological pressures from lifelong conditioning, such as internalized parental loyalties, acquired taste, convenience, and self-image, but also due to external social pressures from friends, colleagues, and family members. The primary teaching from parents to offspring across all animal species relates directly to food and eating, and consequentially there are deep and intrinsic barriers to questioning our parents' food guidance. In addition, the most powerfully cohesive social forces involve meals.

Questioning and rejecting the foundational foods that characterize our parents' and our culture's meal practices is so socially and psychologically challenging that it is remarkable that some of us are able, nevertheless, to eventually question and change our food choice orientations and eating practices. Because our eating is a product of the communities in which we were raised and in which we live, it is often an alternative community with different meal practices that helps us to catalyze this change. These communities can take many forms, such as health institutes, online groups, educational courses, spiritual centers, intentional communities, animal sanctuaries, restaurants, and local events such as vegfests, monthly potlucks, and gatherings with friends.

In my case, as a young person in college during the Vietnam War in the early 1970s, I struggled with the distress of starting my adult life and beginning to negotiate a societal maze that seemed to be filled with inordinate amounts of injustice, corruption, and triviality. Fortunately, at the same time, I discovered the writings of the 19th century Transcendentalists of Concord, Massachusetts, especially Emerson and Thoreau. Having been born in Concord, in Emerson Hospital, and having learned to swim in Walden Pond, I felt a poignant kinship with their still-relevant emphasis on self-reliance, spiritual exertion, civil disobedience, and respect for the wisdom of the world's spiritual sages, both Western and non-Western. This led to a searing realization that life is precious in its transiency, and that if I failed to start immediately and proactively to seek spiritual awakening and a positive transformation of my consciousness, my life would be hijacked by the deceptive distractions of worldly obligations and social conditioning. I dreaded ending up, in the final years of my life, like many I saw around me: disempowered, frustrated, and still under the spell of consumerist delusions, exploited as mere fodder for a massive and ravenous industrial-financial-medical machine that benefitted none but a privileged few.

I was heartened to discover that my younger brother Ed shared my sentiments, and we left home a few months after my college graduation in 1975 to embark on a spiritual pilgrimage to attain enlightenment. With our parents' blessing, we bade farewell and walked down the driveway, heading from eastern Massachusetts for California, without money and with minimal backpacks. We were emulating the ardent truth-seekers from many times and traditions, about whom we had read, whose only goal was to fulfill their devotion to their spiritual calling. Every day was an open-ended adventure as we walked into the unknown, with our focus more acutely on the inner journey we were also undertaking. We gave first priority to our daily meditations and spiritual readings, and this gave our outer journey a significant sense of meaning and purpose. Minor miracles and synchronicities ensued, and I felt like a living sponge, soaking up events and insights from the many people and situations we encountered every day.

After walking west for several weeks and reaching the Buffalo area in early October, we felt drawn to head south to keep ahead of the approaching winter cold. We ended up walking south, about fifteen to twenty miles a day, on small back-country roads through upstate New York, down through Pennsylvania and West Virginia, and then across Kentucky into Tennessee, and eventually all the way to Huntsville, Alabama, taking up residence in a Zen center there. On our walk we spent nights mainly on the floors of small-town churches, and also in forests, rescue missions, county jails, and in homes of people we met. When we were walking through Tennessee, we stayed for several weeks at The Farm in Summertown, in the rural countryside south of Nashville. At the time, it was the largest hippie commune in the world with about 900 residents.[1] They were mostly from California, which seemed poetically aligned with our original intention.

The Farm was set up as an intentional religious community, and the community members practiced what they called vegetarian living, which nowadays we would call vegan, because they ate no animal flesh, dairy products, eggs, or even honey. They told me that it was for two primary ethical reasons, the first of which was to reduce human suffering by eating lower on the food chain to minimize food waste, and diminish hunger, starvation, and war. The other reason was to reduce the killing and abuse of animals, which is unavoidable in animal-sourced foods. We found the people at The Farm to be upbeat, friendly, and thriving, including about 200 children, many of whom were vegan from birth. Though I had been eating animal foods my entire life, due to the communities in which I was raised, my experience at The Farm changed that forever, and I have never eaten meat in my life since the day in late 1975 when people at The Farm explained to me the reasons for their dietary choices. Many years later, when I met my future wife Madeleine, we discovered that it was in the same month and year that she also stopped eating animal flesh in her home in Switzerland.

When Ed and I left The Farm and walked on further to Huntsville, we took up residence in a local Zen Buddhist center where we undertook more training in meditation, and in the Five Precepts: to refrain from killing, stealing, sexual misconduct, lying, and using (or causing others to use) alcohol or drugs. Interest in money, status, romance, and worldly success had effortlessly faded from my awareness during the pilgrimage, and the focus was on sitting in meditation, inquiring into the nature of mind and consciousness, usually for over eight hours daily. What am I, actually? What is my true nature, beyond all the stories told by memories, education, books, media, parents, and teachers? What is this mind, and what is its source? How can I directly experience the deeper truth of being?

By 1980 I was living in northern California, and had been living in Zen and Tibetan Buddhist meditation centers most of the time since leaving home in Concord. Now more clearly understanding the connections with dairy, eggs, leather, and other products, I committed to living as a vegan to further minimize abuse to animals, and have practiced this way of living ever since. A few years later, in 1984, I shaved my head and went to South Korea to live as a Zen Buddhist monk, and entered a monastic community, Songgwangsa, that had been practicing vegan living for about 750 years, since the beginning of the 13th century. Through thousands of hours of sitting meditation practice, cultivating awareness of the source of my thoughts and feelings, I discovered more freedom from a lifetime of mental conditioning, and realized at a deeper level that what we call vegan living is not a food option, but is an expression of our true nature.

It became clear that, like all of us, my mind had been colonized from birth by a cultural program organized around dominating and unnecessarily abusing other sentient beings, and that like all of us, my true nature would never have chosen this of its own accord. It is eternally free, like the boundless sky. Aware of its unity with all forms of life, it naturally emanates compassion for others. This innate sky of awareness and inner freedom can certainly be hidden from view, but it can ultimately never be harmed, stained, or limited by the coming and going of the clouds of conditioned living. It became clear that joy and understanding are ever-present in the sky-like radiant awareness of mind.

The Unrecognized Core of Our Culture

When we liberate our consciousness from the unrecognized prisons of habituated thinking and addiction to comfort and self-oriented awareness, we become a field of freedom not only for ourselves, but for others as well. Addiction to comfort is a particularly egregious affliction in our world today, with our technology attempting to grant us unprecedented levels of freedom from environmental and bodily discomfort. More nefarious is the attachment to psychological comfort. Refusing to take risks and step out of our comfort zone to explore new perspectives and question internalized orthodoxies leads to inner contraction, and the urge to escape into numbness, distraction, and further addiction. Taking risks, questioning pretenses, developing the capacity to tolerate ambiguity, and stepping outside internalized comfort zones can open unrecognized doorways to more aliveness, understanding, and creativity.

In order to understand ourselves, it is essential to understand our culture, because as children we soak up and incorporate all the nuances of the attitudes, beliefs, and behaviors in which our lives are embedded. We live in a culture, and it, likewise, lives in us, and functions through us. Without making the effort to awaken awareness and mindfulness, we tend to become merely culturally-programmed entities, following directives deposited into our consciousness by parents, relatives, neighbors, authorities, and media from before we can remember. Because the living and essential core of our culture is animal agriculture, much of our social conditioning is not in our best interest. It is rooted in materialism, exploitation, and suppression of spiritual awareness.

For example, it has been well understood and documented for decades that serial killers always practice on animals first, abusing and slaying them before carrying out their destruction of fellow human beings. As a society, every day we similarly practice on animals, mistreating and slaughtering millions for food, medicines, and other products. As a consequence of this, we see that we directly and indirectly kill each other by the millions in unnecessary wars, conflicts, injustices, and indifferences. Pythagoras summed the essential principle over 2,500 years ago, but we ironically fail to teach our children this Pythagorean theorem: "As long as men massacre animals, they will kill each other. Indeed, he who sows the seeds of murder and pain cannot reap joy and love."

Our culture suppresses the liberating awareness that our ongoing violence toward animals is completely unnecessary and obsolete, because all the nutrients we require to thrive are provided by plants, and any nutrients in animal-sourced foods came originally from plants, which we can eat directly. However, with ten thousand years of momentum, animal agriculture has long captured our minds, habits, and every cultural institution and narrative. This makes questioning it a daunting task indeed. We find, nevertheless, that we inevitably harvest according to our practices and actions. Our monumental mistreatment of animals, typically hidden and glossed over, boomerangs relentlessly, though we generally fail to see or make the relevant connections. By the millions daily, we have been enslaving and sexually abusing them, stealing their offspring, and force-medicating and digitally tracking them. We hopefully protest and fight against these same things happening to us and to our children. But are we looking deeply enough into the underlying causes of our problems?

While it is helpful to critique and illuminate the existing systems that devastate the Earth and destroy our health, freedom, and peace, it is even more helpful to offer an alternative that each of us can immediately explore and practice. This ever-present alternative provides positive results that bring restoration and rejuvenation to our health, to ecosystems, to animals, and to our society. As someone who has eaten no animal-sourced foods for over forty years, I am but one of millions of people doing so on a long-term basis. It is clear that growing grains, vegetables, and other plant-sourced foods directly for human consumption is vastly more efficient than growing grains and legumes to feed animals who are then killed so we can consume the nutrients they got from plants. When we eat plants directly, we open to the beckoning vision of a world of abundance and harmony, because we can feed our entire population on a fraction of the land, water, and petroleum resources now being used, and allow rivers, oceans, aquifers, prairies, and forests to heal, and wildlife habitat to revive. Our physical bodies are also naturally healthier and freer of toxins, and our mental, emotional, and spiritual lives are regenerated because we can free our minds and bodies from the harmful culturally-mandated attitudes and actions required by animal agriculture.

Those of us with companion animals are keenly aware that they are capable of suffering, and that they have personalities and interests. Animals exploited for food and other uses are clearly similar. We are called to love all our neighbors, and to do our best to liberate and respect all beings if we would like to be free and healthy ourselves. This is not just a culpability and a challenge that we face; it is also an enticing opportunity that invites us into an awakening and into a new cultural story, and into healthier ways of living. These are based, ironically and as indeed they must be, on ancient wisdom teachings that have been lost in our frantic and ineffective chase after modern technological fixes for what are essentially spiritual issues.

The power of these ancient teachings is not just that they promote peace, health, freedom, justice, and inclusiveness. Their power lies more essentially in their alignment with universal truths that are not normally visible or discussed. We are called to do our best to discover and serve these truths, no matter the consequences. This calling may bring us into conflict not just with authorities, but with friends and family, and with our own indoctrinated beliefs and attitudes. Plato addressed this over two thousand years ago, writing, "No one is hated more than one who speaks the truth," as did George Orwell: "The further a society drifts from the truth, the more it will hate those who speak it." Nevertheless, we also find that this is the inescapable way to reclaim our health, freedom, and spiritual wisdom.

While the animal liberation and vegan movements contribute many important seeds of truth, it is essential to realize that any movement can become deluded and divisive, and like the peace, environmental, labor, and other justice movements, it can be infiltrated and co-opted as well, as we shall discuss. Ultimately, effective social transformation requires authentic personal transformation. Eliminating animal foods and products from our diets and shopping lists is an essential step in our progress toward freedom for both animals and for ourselves, but these transformations require us to go further. We are called as individuals to engage in the inner efforts that free us from our gullibility, and our vulnerability to the military-grade deception campaigns being unleashed globally in this new era of pandemics, lockdowns, trans-humanism, and the Great Reset. We are being systematically poisoned, both physically through toxins delivered through our food, water, and air, as well as mentally, emotionally, and spiritually, through elaborate media campaigns spewing fear and deliberately deceptive narratives.

The underlying understanding is that our routine abuse of animals, primarily for food, boomerangs back toward us in a mirror image, as similar abuse that we experience at the hands of mighty governments, corporations, and financial institutions that are unfurling an agenda of increasing human oppression. We live in a reciprocating universe. Liberating animals—the essential first step to creating a human world of freedom, health, justice, and peace—requires both outer and inner work, and more than we typically realize. Just as our outer practice of imprisoning animals for food erodes our outer freedom and health, the inner attitudes and mental conditioning required to exploit and kill them harm our inner freedom and health. The real prison from which we are called to free ourselves is the prison of misunderstanding created by our conformity to the culturally-ingrained conviction that we are material objects, essentially separate from nature and the world around us. This imprisoning delusion derives directly from our relentless reduction of farmed animals and nature to mere commodities, and leads to the inescapable sense of unsatisfactoriness which, however subtle it may be, compels us into aggressions, ambitions, and addictions that further ensnare us in delusion.

Fortunately, the ancient wisdom traditions, both Eastern and Western, provide guidance and inspiring examples that illuminate the path to spiritual liberation, harmony, and the unfettered joy of realizing the truth of our self-nature.[2] The Golden Rule is an essential teaching of all these wisdom traditions, and by including all beings who are capable of suffering at our hands in our daily practice of The Golden Rule, we can positively transform our lives, and contribute to the healing so needed during these challenging times. As we awaken from socially-inculcated materialism and separatism, we free ourselves, and we naturally help to free others as well. Liberating animals is the essential foundation and the necessary but not sufficient cause for our own liberation.

Understanding clearly how our violence toward animals harms us, we should also understand that our motivation to stop our mistreatment of them should not be merely so that our lives will be better, but so that *their* lives will be better. Self-benefitting motivation is not the same as authentic compassion, but with awareness, it can open our minds to make important connections, which is the goal of this book. Empathy for others, free of self-centered motivation, is the most lasting foundation for rescuing our world from the disease, injustice, and other harms of animal agriculture. A somewhat humorous paradox is that when we act with kindness and generosity to others, this is also selfish because it guarantees more joy, love, abundance, and freedom for us in the long run. Similarly, abusing, robbing, and deceiving others for our own benefit is sure to guarantee our own misery and suffering. Our actions inevitably reciprocate, especially when we look deeply, and open to seeing the larger picture, beyond the relatively short-term visible event-horizons within which we are conditioned to limit our view of the future.

There can be no higher calling than the quest for truth, and to share our discoveries with each other. We live now in the corrupted age that unavoidably emerges out of ten thousand years of cultural deception organized around the traumatizing violence of reducing animals to mere property objects in order to eat and exploit them. This delusion has caused our culture's spiritual health to deteriorate to the point that it now pompously proclaims that all truths and morals are relative, and that we humans are separate from and inherently superior to nature and animals, and that we can create superior organisms, and superior humans, through our technological cleverness, and that morality, like truth, is malleable.

Three Crises and Freedom from Gullibility

Making an effort to attain a broader and more accurate perspective, we can work to free ourselves from these debilitating narratives. This is difficult because it brings us into several challenging crises. The first is an epistemological crisis. As we awaken, we feel increasingly compelled to question what we believe to be truth, and our trusted sources of truth. Because most of us have been raised to trust authorities, experts, government spokespeople, media outlets, doctors, journalists, and educators, it is distressing in the extreme to face the fact that these people are often completely wrong in what they are telling us, and more difficult still, that they (and their superiors) are lying to us. A typical response to this cognitive dissonance is known as the Semmelweis reflex, which impels us to simply and immediately reject anything that threatens our trust in official narratives. Unfortunately, this can be disastrous, because it leads to toxic gullibility, shutting down our inherent wisdom. This gullibility can spread like a contagious disease, as it reinforces the same in others, wreaking havoc on our social immune system, which protects society from being invaded by tyrannical forces that use deception to dominate and oppress the population. Unquestioning, compliant behavior leads to ever-increasing despotism.

If we can successfully meet the epistemological crisis, and begin to trust our inner guarantor of validity—our ability to think critically, discern skillfully, and intuitively make connections— we taste the freedom of self-reliance and begin to be part of the solution to the problems facing society, instead of exacerbating them. This brings us to the next crisis, a teleological crisis. We now find ourselves stepping out of the mainstream consensus trance that gives meaning to the general population, and we are compelled to grapple with the teleology of our society, and of our life itself. What is the purpose of our human species and of our culture and civilization? What is our individual purpose for this lifetime, if we are no longer in alignment with the official narratives, and no longer believe the official truths? With effort, we can deepen our connection with our purpose, and develop our capacity to shine the light and example of our unique life into our culture, though it may not always be recognized as such.

These two crises merge into a third crisis, an ontological crisis. Ontology, our understanding of ourselves as individual beings, is rooted in the cultural assumptions we have internalized from infancy. When we question and reject inner and outer authorities, truths, and our acculturated sense of purpose, we are faced with a crisis of being, and how we shall live and relate with those around us, who are typically operating under assumptions we no longer see as valid or relevant. It can be profoundly challenging, as well as liberating, to reconnect with our internal guidance system and become more free from conditioned cultural norms and from the prison of social conformity. In many ways, these three crises are necessary phases in a healthy process of spiritual, emotional, and intellectual awakening, providing a foundation for us to bring more light into the world.

They are interconnected and reinforce each other simultaneously, but are undermined by self-oriented fears and the urge to cling to approval for validation. Emerson expressed this situation and process in the language of his day 150 years ago: "Whoso would be a man must be a nonconformist." The approval we crave may come from outside—from friends, authorities, and family—or from inside, from our self-image and our sense of obligation to internalized authority figures. In any case, avoiding the challenge presented by these three crises, we remain in a comfort zone that becomes increasingly insidious, and generates what could be called toxic gullibility.

Gullibility is harmful because it increases the violence in the world. It enables and promotes deception, and deception is a treacherous form of violence. In stressful situations, gullibility can become toxic if it becomes aggressive and lashes out at others who refuse to comply with the narratives and mandates we have been seduced to internalize. While it is well understood that deliberate deception is unethical and harmful to others, it's important to understand that gullibility is also unethical and harmful to others. There is significant truth in the old saying, "You cannot fool an honest person." Gullibility doesn't just allow deception; it spurs it on. We tend to think of the easily-deceived person as being an innocent victim, but there is something nefarious and irresponsible in allowing ourselves to be victimized by deception. When we are honest and aware, we are not easily fooled. Being easily fooled does tremendous damage not only to ourselves but to everyone around us, and the contagion of foolishness and rampant deception it creates is difficult to heal or stop, because it is unconscious and hypnotic. It is impervious to reason because it is based on fear and self-clinging, and because it is based on identification with a particular in-group to which we are unquestioningly allegiant. We are taught that trusting authorities is a virtue, when in truth it is more accurately a pernicious vice that reflects a fear of discomfort, and a mistrust of our inner wisdom and potential. It often reflects a craving for acceptance, a fear of self-responsibility, and a dread of losing face or of being shunned or criticized by authority figures or by our in-group.

It is also important to keep our minds and hearts open and to reject feelings and notions of superiority when judging what appears to be gullibility in others. Virtually all of us are potentially deceivable, and the powers that would deceive us are shrewd. There are typically a variety of perspectives available for every situation, and with efforts, we can raise our awareness and grow into larger perspectives and deeper understanding. Through the dedicated practice of questioning approved narratives, we can free ourselves from the cult-like thralldom that spreads like a contagion, and gain liberating insights into health, freedom, and our true nature. Each of us can help liberate humanity from the seemingly insoluble quandaries we are generating. New vistas of awareness and vitality invite us to abandon our inherited food and lifestyle paradigms. We are called to co-create a more conscious world that reflects our inherent empathy and sovereignty.

Giordano Bruno presciently observed that, "If the first button of one's coat is wrongly buttoned, all the rest will be crooked." So too, if our most basic assumptions about food and reality are erroneous, our entire culture and all of us are unknowingly mistaken about virtually everything we think is true. The more we think we are making progress with our science and technology, the more deluded and miserable we become. World freedom is only possible as we mature to the point that we understand clearly the inner and outer consequences of our routine enslavement of animals, and authentically liberate them from human exploitation. Governments and institutions can never bring world peace or world freedom into our lives. It is up to us individually and collectively at the grass-roots level to re-awaken our understanding, transform our behavior, and co-create the positive future that is insistingly beckoning to us on this abundant Earth.

To best provide both critical analysis and practical solutions, this book is divided into two sections. Part One, "Our Banquet of Consequences," provides the foundational ideas. Part Two, "The Two Futures: The Path of Technology and the Path of Spirituality," provides a deeper exploration into our situation and into the devastating impact of official narratives, in order to illuminate and help guide us individually and collectively to a positive shared future. Our short companion book, *The World Peace Way: Six Keys to Health and Harmony for All,* offers a broad range of practical tools and suggestions for positive personal transformation.

For a better comprehension of the ideas in this book, familiarity with our earlier book, *The World Peace Diet,* is recommended. *The World Peace Diet* provides a thorough presentation of the historical, social, and psychological factors that illuminate how animal agriculture is intricately bound up in our current dilemmas. It explores and reveals the often-hidden consequences arising from our culture's routine mistreatment of animals, and how spiritual health and social harmony arise to the degree that we treat animals with respect and kindness. For readers who have not yet read *The World Peace Diet,* this book, *Food for Freedom,* provides some of the most salient background understandings, and expands on the vision and ideas presented in *The World Peace Diet.* Our ongoing failure to question our culture's inherited mealtime violence has necessitated a further elaboration of these principles, and thus the birth of this book.

This book is intended to shine light on the connections between food and freedom, and to illuminate what food for freedom actually is. Further, this book is intended to be, itself, literally, food for freedom.

May our cooperative efforts to question delusory narratives, both externally and internally, illuminate the path to a more conscious, responsible, and harmonious way of living on this Earth, for the benefit of all.

PART ONE

OUR BANQUET
OF CONSEQUENCES

CHAPTER ONE

HEALTH AND FREEDOM FOR ALL

> "Disobedience is the true foundation of liberty.
> The obedient must be slaves."
> —HENRY DAVID THOREAU

> "The welfare of humanity is always the alibi of tyrants."
> —ALBERT CAMUS

> "Medical science is making such remarkable progress that
> soon none of us will be well."
> —ALDOUS HUXLEY

Freedom and Health

Freedom and health: how are they related to each other? How are they related to our food system? How are they connected to spirituality and to our relationship with nature and animals? These are pressing questions for our time, and how deeply we inquire, and how intelligently we make connections, will determine how effectively we are able to respond to the remarkable challenges we face today. If our health is taken from us, our freedom is also taken. Without freedom, our health deteriorates, and there is little purpose for which to be healthy.

When we think of health, we typically think of our personal physical health, which is critical to our ability to function optimally and to learn, grow, and contribute our talents and abilities, and to experience joy and fulfillment in our lives. It is important to understand that our physical health is interconnected with four other dimensions of health and that all five of these aspects of health impact one another in a myriad of complex ways. Three of the five dimensions of health are external: environmental, cultural, and bodily health. Two of them are internal: psychological and spiritual/ethical health.

There are five corresponding aspects of freedom, and we are called to make an effort to understand them as well, and how they interconnect with one another and with our health and the health of the overall systems in which we live. They are environmental, cultural, and personal physical freedom, as well as psychological and spiritual freedom, and whatever nourishes or harms one, nourishes or harms all the others. What we mean by freedom throughout this book is the healthy individual sovereignty that is based on taking responsibility for our lives and choices, and respecting the freedom and sovereignty of others. It is not the faux freedom that self-aggrandizing actors and corporations invoke to rationalize externalizing costs onto others, and harming others for one's own benefit. This is merely toxic self-centered license and is diametrically opposed to and undermines authentic freedom and sovereignty.

Proactively taking responsibility for the health of our physical body is valuable in our personal daily life adventure, and is helpful to everyone around us as well. When we radiate wellness, energy, and vitality, we naturally benefit others. When we are chronically ill, we typically suffer with pain, low energy levels, and limited physical capacities, and this often harms those around us in a variety of ways. For example, we may buy and ingest pharmaceuticals, which are formulated of toxic chemicals that pass through us and pollute the water and environment, harming ecosystems, animals, insects, and other people.[1] This also contributes to the suffering of animals because medications are always tested on animals who are abused and killed in the process, and medications usually contain ingredients derived from the bodies of mistreated animals. Drugs and procedures not only produce toxic medical waste, but are expensive, and insurance to cover the ongoing medical expenses of employees and citizens are passed along as higher prices and taxes for everyone.

Besides these burdens imposed by ill people on healthy people, there's the direct burden of their needing to be looked after and assisted. As the number of people with chronic disease increases, now to heights never seen in history—typically due to higher levels of environmental toxins, drugs, vaccines, stress, electromagnetic frequency fields, and other factors—the wealth and consequent power of the chemical-pharmaceutical-medical complex also increases. It has reached the point that this complex's mighty power has fully captured both mainstream and many alternative media sources, as well as internet platforms, search engines, regulatory agencies, philanthropic organizations, professional associations, medical schools, and academia. Without obstruction, it continually escalates the levels of drugs and chemicals profitably brought to market. This further erodes public health, creating ever more profits, control, and disease.

Maintaining a high level of physical health during these times is unusually challenging. Wealth and power control institutions, narratives, and policies, and healthy people pose a direct threat to these narratives and their captured institutions. It is also difficult to maintain a high level of individual freedom. This freedom requires taking responsibility for our lives, and for our food and health choices, questioning authorities, and speaking up and standing for what we feel is right. Health and freedom feed each other, and when one is eroded, so is the other. For example, the ever-increasing proliferation of toxic chemicals—in processed and non-organic food, in the water and beverages we drink, the air we breathe, the clothes we wear, and the personal care products we rub onto our skin—sabotages our health, reducing our vitality, creativity, and effectiveness. This robs us of our time and resources and, ultimately, our freedom. As another example, dairy products are deliberately forced upon school children, many of whom are lactose intolerant, leading to chronic digestive issues, and sapping both the health and freedom of these children. As a further example, by slaughtering the buffalo, and in a myriad of other ways taking away native Americans' access to their traditional foods, the U.S. government and 18th- and 19th-century settlers were able to undermine the Indians' health, confine them in reservations, and destroy their freedom.[2] There are countless similar examples. When our health is compromised, our freedom deteriorates, and protecting our freedom safeguards our health.

Freedom and health are intertwined and both depend on being self-reliant. If we abandon self-reliance and depend on the medical industry to protect our health, our health will deteriorate quickly. The same is true for our freedom. If we depend on governmental systems to safeguard our freedom, our freedom will disappear. We are now realizing that governmental, educational, media, medical, and corporate institutions that we have been taught to trust have increasingly become parasitic. They profit from and promote our weaknesses, and have even become predatory, as illness increasingly becomes a primary source of both direct and indirect profits, and also of control. Sick, weak, misinformed, distracted, compliant people are much more easily managed and exploited than robust, confident, informed, focused, healthy, freedom-loving people.

Proactively cultivating a high level of physical health benefits not just ourselves and our loved ones, but also the boundless web of relations in which we are embedded. Being chronically ill is more harmful than we may realize. This is of course not to cast any aspersions on those who feel the need for pharmaceuticals or procedures, but the idea is to consciously question established narratives and strive for and practice a way of being and living where we make an effort to understand and take responsibility for the quality of our health, and free ourselves from the need for pharmaceuticals and medical procedures that dissipate our freedom and are harmful to others and ourselves on many levels.

It is also important to recognize that our body is a remarkably intelligent self-cleansing system, and that the symptoms that we are taught to interpret as illness are actually not bad news but good news, because they signal that our body is cleansing. Sore throats, runny noses, headaches, diarrhea, rashes, vomiting, and so forth, are all ways that our miraculous body cleanses itself of toxins. In our world today, we face unprecedented levels of chemical and electromagnetic poisons.

Quite a few times over the years, for example, if I went to an Asian restaurant and specified "No MSG," I would be able to tell later if there actually had been MSG in the food by a specific type of headache that would develop several hours afterward as my body cleansed the toxic chemical. The headache, though interpreted as "bad," was actually "good" because it was a manifestation of the body's cleansing and healing effort. Attempting to interfere with this effort by running to a doctor or pharmacy and using chemical drugs to suppress the unpleasant symptoms might have relieved the pain, but would also have most likely impeded the restorative process and added more toxins, possibly sowing seeds for more serious disease. By thus routinely overwhelming our body with chemical drugs that are harmful, we generate conditions that increase risk for chronic issues, such as cancer, obesity, arthritis, liver disease, autoimmune diseases, and heart disease, as our body is forced to heroically isolate the toxins and repair damages as best it can. This drains our vitality and erodes our capacities and our freedom, all to our detriment and to the detriment of society.

A healthy body functions harmoniously so that we, as the spiritual being for whom this bodily vehicle exists, can freely, creatively, and effectively fulfill our life purpose. We are not here on this Earth just to be healthy as an end in itself, but so that we can fulfill our mission here. Both health and freedom are essential to this, but powerful forces are at work suppressing our capacities and distracting us from our mission, because health and freedom are inherently threatening to the plutocratic globalist agenda of authoritarian control that now pervades and directs virtually all our cultural institutions.

Foundational Teachings

Freedom foods are the foods for which we are designed—organic, whole, plant-sourced foods. These are the foods that most efficiently deliver all the nutrition we need to celebrate our lives on this beautiful and abundant Earth. Our inherent food wisdom has been suppressed and hijacked by a ten-thousand-year-old food practice based on enslaving animals. The reason we eat these animal-sourced foods is because we are born into communities that transmit food customs and narratives into us from birth, generation upon generation. Freeing ourselves and our culture from these narratives requires us to question core beliefs, and for this it's particularly helpful to explore three key ideas that are based on ancient teachings. While not complex, they are often difficult to digest because they run contrary to virtually all of our inherited assumptions about nature, disease, animals, humanity, consciousness, and the relationships among all these. Our inherent wisdom, which has been suppressed from infancy, is ever-present in its potential to understand these ideas. This understanding liberates us from the spell that binds us to harmful cultural superstitions, and that blinds us to the joy, authenticity, and harmony which are our birthright.

The first of these essential ideas is conveyed in The Golden Rule, which calls us to live our lives so that we are doing to others what we would like to have done to us, and conversely, that we refrain from doing to others whatever we wouldn't like done to us. To the degree that we are living in alignment with this universal prime directive, we are giving to others what we most like to receive: respect, freedom, kindness, and understanding. The Golden Rule is applicable to our relations with everyone, not just those people we like, or of whom we approve, or with whom we identify, and clearly includes all those capable of suffering at our hands, such as the animals with whom we share this Earth. It is summed in the Sanskrit word *ahimsa*, which translates as nonharmfulness. Ahimsa can also be articulated positively as lovingkindness, and is the wisdom teaching shining at the heart of the world's spiritual traditions, inspiring the universal teaching of The Golden Rule. Our countless collective daily acts of harm toward animals, and their consequent suffering at our hands, vibrate continually into the planetary web of relations, reverberating, rebounding, and escalating into the massive waves of conflict, disease, and deception that threaten our world today.

The second key idea is the teaching of reciprocity. Paul said, "Do not be deceived: God is not mocked, for whatever one sows, that will one also reap."[3] We refer to this in *The World Peace Diet* as the boomerang effect, and we can see it operating all around us, a universal law like gravity. When we pay attention and observe carefully, we can understand this clearly, and yet, as Paul implies, we are often deceived, and we believe cultural narratives telling us we can reap wealth by misleading or using others, reap health by harming others, especially animals, and have freedom while we deny freedom to others. In particular, when it comes to animals, we are taught that we are God-like in our superiority to them. They are completely inferior in our eyes, vulnerable in our almighty hands, and defenseless to the overwhelming force of our technological might. Instead of treating them with kindness as our neighbors, we find ourselves participating in long-established systems that abuse them unnecessarily and relentlessly, stealing their purposes, health, sovereignty, and lives. We insult each other with words like "pig," "chicken," and "turkey," and fail to realize that we are being deceived by cultural norms, and making a mockery of the divine creative power that is the source of all life. John Muir lovingly referred to animals as "our fellow mortals," encouraging us to sow seeds of respect in our treatment of these fellow passengers on Earth, whose interests are as significant to them as ours are to us. We are deceived into ignoring this principle of reciprocity, and part of the mental prison of our cultural indoctrination is materialistically limiting our life to just the few decades between our birth and our death. As consciousness, our lives are far greater than this, as virtually all wisdom traditions emphasize. We certainly reap the fruits of the seeds we sow, in this life and beyond.

The third idea is interconnectedness. Looking deeply, we can see that our health is interconnected with the health of others. It is interconnected with the health of the larger systems in which we live, and our freedom is also interconnected with the freedom of others. Stealing freedom from billions of animals, we find our freedom increasingly evaporating; liberating them is the unrecognized key to our freedom and to world peace and inner peace. These three guiding lights—The Golden Rule, reciprocity, and interconnectedness—though simple and rather obvious, shine a bright light onto the cause of our seemingly insoluble dilemmas, as well as onto the beckoning path to another way of living that leads directly to a more harmonious and creative future.

Freeing Ourselves from Deception

Up to this point, we have been discussing the health of our physical body, and it is important to understand that this bodily health is thoroughly interconnected with the other four dimensions of health—environmental, cultural, psychological and spiritual—as all are with each other. If we buy and eat processed foods produced with pesticides and chemical preservatives, for example, we directly contribute to polluting not just our cells and organs, but ecosystems and neighborhoods as well. Toxins harm birds, fishes, and insects, and trees, forests, and ecosystems, and add to the dissension in our culture through increased physical, mental, and social illness and disharmony.

Unhealthy foods increase illness, contributing not only to pollution and price inflation, but also to the profits of parasitic corporations that use these funds to influence narratives and generate a vicious circle of increased disease, profits, and deception, leading to ever more harmful foods, and ever more deception, disease, and addiction. An essential goal of these corporate and financial parasites, and the governments they control, is to maximize the number of people who are sick, weak, misinformed, and therefore unfree. Maintaining inner and outer health and freedom today requires us to engage in revolutionary, heroic, and demanding efforts to achieve understanding and to protect ourselves from the many varieties of poisons rampant in our world.

A primary obstacle in our quest for health and freedom is deliberate deception, which is reaching epic proportions. Deception is the most insidious of all forms of violence, because if we are beaten, abused, robbed, and so forth, we know we have been harmed, but when we have been deceived, we are typically unaware of it, and the damage that deception can wreak is thus far greater than any other type of violence. It can continually grow, virtually without limits, ever compounding its harm, stealing our health, our resources, and our freedom, and we remain oblivious and continue to be exploited and harmed as long as we continue to be unable to recognize the deception. Part of the problem is that we ourselves may yearn to be deceived, because as Upton Sinclair put it, "It is difficult to get a man to understand something when his salary depends on him not understanding it." It is often paradoxically advantageous to our job security, income, comfort, and social status to allow ourselves to be deceived. This reality seems to permeate our society, and it seems that the higher up on the social ladder we climb, the more willing we are to allow ourselves to be deceived—and thus to deceive and be a vehicle of deception—for the sake of our career, wealth, and self-image.

Niccolo Machiavelli summed it well: "One who deceives will always find those who allow themselves to be deceived." When we allow ourselves to be deceived, we not only harm ourselves, we harm everyone around us. We contribute to creating pandemics of deception and delusion that are invisible to all who have been fooled. The deception of animal agriculture—that we need to imprison and kill animals to be healthy—is the core deception in our society, giving rise to countless other deceptions that further imprison us in misunderstanding. The longer deception continues, the more entrenched gullibility tends to become, both individually and culturally. Thus, it is not only deceptive coercion that is unethical, as 19th-century English philosopher William K. Clifford emphasized: "There is one thing in the world more wicked than the desire to command, and that is the will to obey." Being willfully compliant and gullible is equivalent in many ways to being willfully harmful and abusive, especially during this time when media, medicine, government, and our inherent altruism are all being weaponized against us, and against truth, health, and freedom.

There is a well-known story in the martial arts tradition of a father with three Samurai sons, who, in order to test their fighting skill, invited them into his room, with a trained assailant hiding behind the door. When the youngest son came through the door, he was easily knocked down from behind and injured by the assailant. When the middle son came through the door, he immediately sensed the assailant's attack and with lightning speed, whirled around and blocked the assailant's blow. However, when the eldest son approached the door, he intuitively felt a threatening presence and stopped and stood outside the door, calling in to his father that he felt something was awry, and thus compelling the father to admit that he had hidden an assailant behind the door to test him. Just as the youngest son, because of his lack of training, created the most violence and most harm, those of us who fail to question official narratives cause the most damage. If we can, like the second son, recognize the deception and block it, we create less harm and violence. With more training and insight, we can, like the eldest son, shine the light of truth, reveal and dissipate potential violence, and help to heal the situation. Discriminating awareness and mindfulness tend to minimize harm and abuse, while gullibility and acquiescence tend to foster them.

We have a moral obligation to cultivate discernment and our capacity for independent, critical thinking so that we contribute truthful perspectives to others, and are not inadvertently propagating deceptive propaganda. Truth, the antidote to deception, typically requires significant effort to attain and safeguard. Reading, studying, listening, contemplating, reflecting, actively engaging, seeking alternatives, discussing, and questioning: all demand a substantial investment of time and effort, as well as commitment and determination, and a willingness to let go of self-invested beliefs and social approval. Cultivating our capacity to interrupt conditioned thinking patterns and to listen internally with openness is vital.

The problem is that we are saturated from birth in ongoing pressures to unquestioningly obey authoritarian narratives, especially in schools. We are typically rewarded when we do, and punished when we don't. This tends to condition us into automaton conformity so, for example, among vegans, a relatively small segment of society that is clearly capable of questioning prevailing cultural narratives, most were unable to effectively challenge the authoritarian Covid medical narrative launched against the world in 2020. Like the majority, especially on the political left, they compliantly acquiesced to the official versions of reality that severely harmed the freedom and health of the entire population. This seems surprising, because we would think that vegans would be savvy about the hideous vivisection and violence rampant in the pharmaceutical-medical industry toward animals, as well as its notorious record of criminal deception. This demonstrates the remarkable power of in-group compliance, coupled with censorship and a corrupt and complicit media, and the ploy of weaponizing our empathy, and our desire to conform, against us. These potent tactics can readily seduce and overwhelm those of us who have failed to do the requisite inner work to protect ourselves from deliberately-released contagions of group-think designed to spread havoc throughout society to benefit the ruling class.

Fortunately, the more we authentically discover clarifying truths and make relevant connections, the wider the doorways to freedom, health, and awareness open to our experience, and the more we can be a force for benefitting others. We will definitely never find our way by exposing our minds to television and radio programming, and the manipulated versions of reality supplied by mainstream media, government, and education. Most of our attitudes, beliefs, and opinions have been culturally implanted into our consciousness from infancy without our consent.

How do we respond to this and live our lives from the truest and largest perspective possible? The benevolent revolution that beckons is the profound transformation that will occur when we liberate our consciousness from herderism's social conditioning, do our inner work, and do our best to live in accordance with the three guiding lights discussed earlier: The Golden Rule, reciprocity, and interconnectedness. Otherwise, as a culture, our violence toward the billions of animals we chronically condemn to dystopian futures will continue to boomerang as a looming technocratic totalitarian future that we generate by our daily actions and attitudes toward animals.

Reclaiming Our Capacities

We humans have three inherent capacities that are essential and precious allies in our quests for understanding and happiness: rationality, empathy, and intuition. If any one of these three allies were actually functioning well in our society, we would have long ago abandoned the practice of animal agriculture. Our rationality easily recognizes that animal agriculture is unnecessarily wasteful of land, water, and resources, and that it generates ongoing conflict, deprivation, disease, and suffering, and is counter-productive and obsolete. Our empathy is easily aware of animal agriculture's inherent cruelty and would guide us to refrain from inflicting abuse on others unnecessarily. Our intuitive wisdom also effortlessly perceives that imprisoning and exploiting others runs completely contrary to our spiritual nature. It would immediately rescue us from such unethical and harmful behavior.

However, all three capacities are suppressed by animal agriculture's environment of exploitation into which we are born, and more specifically by the power of tribalism. The yearning for acceptance by the others in our communities seems to easily override both head and heart. Cultivating any one of these three powers would liberate us from the prison of animal agriculture, but so far it has been too difficult for most of us to resist the familial and tribalistic demand that we comply with "community standards" and fit in with those around us. Sacrificing our individual sovereignty as we sacrifice the sovereignty of the animals at our mercy, we also sacrifice authentic spirituality, and allow our consciousness to be submerged in the fettered shallows of social conditioning.

Contributing to this is the fact that we humans learn primarily through stories, and we have all been indoctrinated from infancy by the stories of animal agriculture, and how we are superior to animals and need to eat them and their secretions for protein and other nutrients. It's "how the West was won," and it's "approved" by our science and by our religion. It is also the primary way we bond with our friends and family. We don't have access to alternative stories, and so our predictable reaction, when confronted with facts and feelings that contradict our stories, is the Semmelweis effect: we ignore or discount them. Anything that doesn't fit into the organizing story we have inherited from our family and culture must be strongly and immediately rejected because it threatens our safety, our worldview, our self-image, our relationships, our comfort, our pleasure, and more.

We organize our life experience through the narratives in our minds. These narratives, also known as paradigms, structure and control our awareness, and whoever controls the narratives in our minds controls us. Freeing ourselves from the harmful narratives of animal agriculture requires us also to generate new stories supporting the truth that all necessary nutrients are provided by plants, and that we can liberate animals and thrive individually and collectively without imprisoning animals. Fortunately, these stories are being written by millions of people who are thriving on foods that require no animal abuse, and these new stories are the seeds of a positive future that beckons, and that is completely possible on this abundant Earth.

It is well understood today, as it has been for thousands of years, that it is difficult for our minds to be healthy if our bodies are unhealthy. The reverse, as with the other dimensions of health and freedom, is also true. Negative emotional states and chronic mental stress take a severe toll on our physical health. The Roman poet Juvenal taught the importance of *mens sana in corpore sano*—a sound mind in a sound body—two thousand years ago, and we have to wonder if we have made any significant progress in this direction over the past twenty centuries, with one in four people in the U.S. now taking psychiatric drugs, such as anti-depressants, anti-psychotics, anti-anxiety drugs, or mood stabilizers.[4] Not only do we find that our emotional health is under duress, but also our physical health, as well as our intellectual health. We can begin to glimpse the underlying causes of all this as we illuminate the connections among the five dimensions of health—physical, environmental, cultural, psychological, and spiritual—and understand how many of our assumptions about reality are deceiving us.

Psychological health and psychological freedom support each other, as do intellectual health and freedom. The emotional negativity that harms our health is not the result of discovering truths, even disturbing truths, but is rather the fear, anger, jealousy, anxiety, frustration, and other states that arise from ignorance and delusion regarding the reality of our situation, and of our true nature. Some of us mistakenly believe that understanding and facing difficult and discomforting truths will harm us emotionally, but truth ultimately liberates and heals us. It may make us uncomfortably disillusioned, but this, while perhaps unpleasant, is also positive, as we are literally dis-illusioned and thus freed from our illusions and from deception. Ultimately, it's far better to be discomforted by truths than to be comforted by lies.

By opening to disturbing truths—such as the hideous abuse of the animals we are eating, and the corruption of government agencies, media sources, and celebrities we had trusted—we increasingly cultivate emotional and mental positivity in our consciousness, because our true nature has an all-encompassing awareness and thrives on the light of truth. By hiding from or repressing truths, we perpetuate and spread emotional negativity, disease, and injustice in our own lives, and for others also.

Our spiritual health, like the other four dimensions of health, affects our physical and psychological health, and also the health of our environment and culture. Spiritual health may be the most important because it determines our essential orientation in the world, and our awareness of our life purpose. Our spiritual health not only connects us to our ethical wisdom, but also reveals that we are boundlessly interconnected with all the other manifestations of consciousness we see and experience around us as, for example, the grocery check-out person, the scrub jay flitting about in the trees, and the trees themselves, silently offering their many benedictions. We all have the same source. The healthier we are spiritually, the more we inhabit mental states of peace, joy, gratitude, and lovingkindness that are increasingly immune to the vicissitudes of outer circumstances. This not only supports our physical and psychological health, but enables us to contribute more effectively to the cultural and environmental health that support all of us.

Sowing and Reaping

Looking into our cultural predicament, and the domination of the many by the wealthy few, and the litany of problems that we face, we can see clearly that this predicament is a poignant mirror and product of our mistreatment of animals. The trillions of animals we abuse and kill annually for food are powerless in our hands and cannot retaliate against us, but our violence itself retaliates against us, as we generate forces that exploit us the same way we exploit animals. Animal agriculture, the living core of our culture, creates the template of our experience. Every problem that we experience in our human world is the result of the boomerang effect: what we inflict on others inevitably returns to afflict us. This is not only the ancient wisdom teaching of reciprocity; it is also a reality that we experience in our daily lives. We plant carrot seeds and we get carrots, not broccoli. Sowing seeds of disease, fear, and exploitation in our treatment of billions of animals, how can we expect to reap freedom, health, and justice in our human world?

For example, to unnaturally boost milk and egg production, we force millions of female cows and chickens into bone degradation and osteoporosis through hyper-confinement, hormones, feed, and pharmaceuticals, and we see osteoporosis becoming widespread and unstoppable in our human world. The same is true of obesity: animals used for food are sold by the pound and we have armies of researchers working to maximize their rapid weight gain through pharmaceuticals, breeding, lighting schedules, and enriched feed. Consequently, we suffer from an obesity epidemic that worsens every year.

We force livestock animals to endure toxic environments and chronic stress, leading to cancer and high disease rates, and find ourselves increasingly living in toxic environments, with chronic stress and higher rates of cancer and disease. We block their ability to form friendships, to communicate, and to form viable communities, and we find ourselves being increasingly isolated, our voices suppressed, and our ability to create healthy communities eroding, leading to increasing depression and suicide, even among children and adolescents. We force medicate and digitally track millions of livestock animals every day, breaking up their families and reducing them to mere exploitable units in a ruthless economic system, and we see this increasingly happening to us. We pay people to stab animals so that we can eat them, and then we pay doctors to stab us for heart bypass surgery.

As we sow, we reap, and for virtually every problem and harm that we are experiencing in our human world, if we look carefully, we will see that we are inflicting this same harm onto the animals who are at our mercy, and to whom we show no mercy. We impose disease and abuse on healthy animals in laboratories in order to make and test pharmaceuticals, and we fail to notice that the more we mistreat and vivisect these animals under the guise of medical research to reduce human disease, the more we are confronted by new, dangerous, and deadly diseases that increasingly proliferate and intensify our suffering, while the profits and power of the meat-biomedical-petrochemical complex continually escalates.

Giving a short talk on this subject on the first day of a three-day meditation retreat in 2007, I noticed a woman in the group who seemed, by her fidgeting, to be upset by our discussion of animal agriculture. Then, on the last day of the retreat, she told me that some repressed memories had come up during the retreat. She knew she had been raised in a family in New Orleans that was part of a satanic cult, but had blocked many of the memories. She said she had been plagued by strong feelings of shame and unworthiness for many years, and during the retreat, she remembered some of the satanic rituals in which she had been forced to participate as a child. She said they all had to do with killing animals and then eating the flesh of the animals. She related that when I had spoken of the harm done to cows on dairy operations, she had gotten angry because the overriding thought filling her mind at that moment was that they are only cows and we should be more concerned about human suffering. Now, however, after remembering and facing the trauma of her childhood experiences of killing and eating animals, she told me she was definitely going vegan, and that she felt she would be able to heal her deep sense of guilt and shame and develop more self-respect. She was visibly moved and seemed deeply relieved because she had made these connections and commitments to herself.

It was quite a shock for me to hear her story and to realize that in many ways I had been similarly raised, and forced to eat the flesh and secretions of terrified animals, and that our entire culture is basically modeled in many ways on a satanic cult, and we don't realize it because it's normalized. We have deeply troubling psycho-social issues around self-respect, gender relations, health, and freedom, perhaps because of this conditioning from infancy that is somewhat similar to the trauma endured by children in some satanic rituals. It's certainly true that animal agriculture is aligned with satanism ethically. Both are based on self-centered interests coming first, while trivializing and ignoring the harm caused to others in the process. This sociopathic elevation of the self, while it may look like freedom, is the opposite of authentic freedom, which is self-responsibility that respects others as we would like to be respected. Both animal agriculture and satanism are the antitheses of The Golden Rule, and because we all know in our core that we are all related and come from the same source, we cannot willfully mistreat others without severely damaging ourselves in the process.

Resurrecting Sophia

Though we are born in challenging times, during what seems to be a late-stage animal agriculture dystopian reckoning, where not only cows, pigs, and chickens are exploited as livestock, but most of humanity as well, we can see it also has poignant potentials for opportunity and rebirth. The past ten thousand years of animal agriculture have sown the seeds of domination and exploitation of animals, nature, and each other, and now each one of us, as individuals, can make a conscientious effort to understand this situation and to question official narratives. We can nourish our innate emotional intelligence that feels empathy for other people, including animals, and resurrect Sophia. Sophia, the ancient Greek word for wisdom, represents the indwelling sacred feminine wisdom that yearns to protect life, that vivifies us, and intuitively loves the one life that lives through us all, recognizing all of us as unique expressions of that life. The call that we hear is the call of freedom. Looking into gardens, orchards, food forests, and fields, we see the inherent loving abundance of the

Earth providing nourishing freedom foods that can create the foundation of a world where peace, justice, and radiant health are finally possible, for us and our children.

Understanding and kindness bring freedom, and inspire us to free others, which liberates us. We can see that we live, nevertheless, within massive technological, governmental, and cultural institutions that have evolved in ways that steal freedom from not just animals but from us humans as well, and so the great opportunity for this lifetime lies in the quality of our response to this situation. How do we respond intelligently and effectively? How do we look deeply enough to glimpse the bigger perspectives, and how can we contribute to the positive transformation that we know is calling, rather than merely being part of the problem? Everything that we see arising in the outer world is connected to our way of living in relation to animals and nature, and to the quality of our consciousness. Making an effort to understand the interconnected impacts of animal agriculture on us collectively and individually, we can discover the hidden path to reclaiming our health and rescuing our world.

CHAPTER TWO

THE CONSEQUENCES OF HERDERISM

❧

"For to be free is not merely to cast off one's chains,
but to live in a way that respects & enhances the freedom of others."
—NELSON MANDELA

"The materialistic physicians will be entrusted with the task of
expelling the souls from mankind."
—RUDOLF STEINER, 1917

"The offerings to the deities of meat obtained by killing animate beings
is like offering a mother the flesh of her own child,
and this is a grievous failure."
—GAMPOPA, RENOWNED TIBETAN YOGI, 12TH CENTURY

Animal Agriculture's Effects on Outer Dimensions of Health
Here is a brief overview of the ways that our culture's core orientation, euphemized as animal husbandry, relentlessly erodes, individually and collectively, all five dimensions of health, beginning with the three outer aspects, which are environmental, cultural, and bodily health. In a similar way, it erodes the corresponding aspects of our freedom.

Environmental Health: Animal agriculture is intensely wasteful of land, water, and fossil fuel resources. This is because the millions of animals we kill daily for food, such as cows, pigs, sheep, chickens, turkeys, and farmed fishes, eat enormous quantities of genetically-engineered corn, soy, wheat, alfalfa and other feed grains to grow and fatten up for slaughter. It is ecologically harmful as well, because these imprisoned animals convert most of that feed into toxic sewage, methane, nitrous oxide, and other wastes that cause river and aquifer pollution and eutrophication, oceanic dead zones, and air pollution, as well as soil erosion and water depletion. Additionally, animal agriculture is the primary driving force behind deforestation, habitat loss, and species extinction, due to ongoing burning and clear-cutting of forests to graze livestock, and to grow monocropped livestock feed grains heavily sprayed with glyphosate, which destroys the vitality of soil microbiomes. According to the largest statistical study to date by Oxford University, humanity is currently using about four billion hectares of land to raise food, and if everyone went vegan, we would require only one-quarter of that amount of land, liberating a full three billion hectares, an area the size of the entire continent of Africa, from the devastating pollution and harm of animal agriculture.[1] When we allow and financially encourage large corporations to enslave the land with mono-cropping and chemical pollution, we further our own enslavement.

Humanity's war against nature and animals extends especially into the oceans, where we have been devastating marine ecosystems for decades to the point where many are now in a state of collapse due to overfishing, driftnet and plastic contamination, and water pollution, as outlined in chapter six of *The World Peace Diet*. Transitioning to a whole-foods plant-sourced diet is the single most potent step we can take to reduce our environmental footprint and contribute globally to habitat regeneration. The enormously significant good news inherent in this is that we can feed all of us human beings on a fraction of the land and poisons we are now using for agriculture, and liberate forests, oceans, lakes, prairies, rivers, and aquifers from human exploitation, and allow them to heal and rejuvenate. As we transition away from animal agriculture, wilderness habitats can rebound and once again thrive for wildlife and for indigenous people, and for all of us, for the inspiration and restoration of our spirits. In sum, animal agriculture is the most devastating human practice in terms of deforestation, habitat destruction, soil despoliation, species extinction, and environmental pollution.

Cultural Health: The inherent and damaging wastefulness of animal agriculture also harms our cultural health. It is well understood that food shortages are one of the primary causes of the conflicts in the world, and that there can never be peace without justice. It is not difficult for those of us in the more industrialized nations to drive up the price of grain on the world markets in order to feed most of it to our imprisoned animals who inefficiently convert it to flesh, bones, blood, milk, eggs, and skin. In doing so, we price corn, soy, wheat, and oats out of reach of people in less industrialized nations with less high-powered economies. They are forced into hunger unnecessarily, because we choose to waste most of the grains and legumes we grow, in order to consume the flesh and secretions of fattened animals. Millions of people are also driven off their ancestral farmlands into overcrowded cities because large-scale animal agriculture operations buy up their land to grow feed grains to export, and to fatten and feed livestock for the wealthy. Gandhi summed this situation well: "The world has enough for everyone's need, but not enough for everyone's greed."

The unremitting injustice—of mothers grieving over starving children while the meat- and dairy-eating wealthier populations squander most of our land, water, grain, and petroleum resources on animal agriculture—erodes our cultural health and causes conflict, as well as millions of refugees from hunger and war, which makes matters far worse. Even by conservative estimates, we grow enough food to feed twelve billion people,[2] yet with only eight billion people, we have nearly a billion of our brothers and sisters chronically hungry and starving.[3] Thich Nhat Hanh summed it well, "Every day forty thousand children die in the world for lack of food. We who overeat in the West, who are feeding grains to animals to make meat, are eating the flesh of these children."[4]

Additionally, we compel armies of slaughterhouse and farm-workers to stab, beat, shock, force-impregnate, and mutilate millions of animals daily, propelling them into perpetrator-induced traumatic stress that drives their high rates not just of work-related injuries, but also of suicide, alcoholism, and spousal and child abuse.[5] Animal agriculture is a massive web of trauma inflicted on farmed animals as well as on wildlife, indigenous people, workers, hungry people, habitats, ecosystems, economies, and every aspect of our shared social life. This relentless trauma continually feeds and increases the disease, conflict, and injustice that we are striving to reduce, but on which massive financial institutions thrive.

Physical/Bodily Health: The products of animal agriculture are well understood today to be harmful to our bodily health. Animal agriculture converts grains and greens into misery, toxic sewage, nitrous oxide, hydrogen sulfide, and other pollutants, as well as the three primary constituents of animal foods: saturated fat, cholesterol, and acidifying and inflammatory animal protein. It is well understood that when a person or animal dies, the flesh quickly becomes more acidic, which signals to bacteria in the area that the body is dead, and so they do their natural work of breaking the dead body down.[6] Eating acidifying animal foods turns normally friendly bacteria into apparent enemies who are confused by the unnaturally acidic state of our bodies. While the solution has been a profitable war on bacteria that harms our microbiome and weakens us, a more liberating and empowering approach is to eat a healthier and more alkaline plant-sourced diet.

Because the media are beholden to their largest advertisers—the pharmaceutical, chemical, petroleum, and fast-food industries—we don't easily learn that meat, dairy products, and eggs are not a helpful source of protein, calcium, and other nutrients.

We are not informed that animal-sourced foods are linked with diabetes, osteoporosis, liver disease, kidney disease, obesity, heart disease, strokes, and dementia, as well as breast, prostate, and colon cancer and other debilitating diseases.[7] The problem of course is that handsome profits are generated by disease, war, technology, and environmental pollution, and these four also centralize power and narrative-control in the same few hands, and devitalize us and render us easier to control. As John McDougall, MD, has pointed out, "People like good news about their bad habits," which also reinforces the ongoing flood of media and medical messages profitably proclaiming the health benefits of animal-sourced foods.

The liberating truth, however, is that all the nutrients that find their way into the flesh of animals and their milk and eggs—all the amino acids that make up the proteins, the lipids that make up the fats, and the vitamins and minerals—come originally from plants, either made by them through photosynthesis or extracted by them from the soil. We can cut out the "middle animal" and eat plants directly, reducing the load of toxins and misery we are causing and eating. Animal foods are also devoid of two of the most essential nutrients: complex carbohydrates for energy, and fiber for digestive health.

As discussed more fully in *The World Peace Diet*, we have neither the physiology nor the psychology for eating meat, dairy products, and eggs. From a physiological perspective, our digestive system is designed for plant-sourced foods. We have small and relatively soft and weak teeth without a protruding snout, with saliva that predigests carbohydrate starches, as well as relatively weak stomach acid and a long and convoluted intestinal tract not designed for animal flesh, and that, like our circulatory system, is harmed and clogged by animal fats. Just as we wouldn't be able to rip through skin, fur, and feathers with our small, soft teeth, flat mouths, and clawless fingers, we don't naturally yearn for the sensation of biting into a live rabbit, cat, squirrel, or duck to eat raw organs, flesh, and blood. This is naturally disgusting to us for a reason, but this inherent wisdom is suppressed from infancy by well-meaning parents and relatives who were similarly wounded in infancy. The baby food sections of grocery stores are filled with cute little jars of cooked chicken, turkey, beef, and cheese. As infants and children, we trustingly eat whatever we are given by parents and relatives, so our orientation toward animals and nature is hijacked from the very beginning.

We are certainly not designed for dairy products, which erode our health in many ways, including the fact that we lack rennin, the enzyme with which calves are naturally equipped, to digest casein, the main protein in cow's milk. Cow's milk is also high in saturated fat as well as IGF-1 (Insulin-like Growth Factor) hormone that promotes cancer growth. Additionally, it contains naturally occurring morphine-like substances that encourage the calf to sleep, but which tend to make dairy products physically addictive for many of us. Eggs are also inherently unhealthy with their unusually high cholesterol content. All of these foods concentrate environmental toxins, cause unnecessary suffering, and require the domination and exploitation of animals, especially female and infant animals.

Our physiological wisdom will always do its best to digest and make the best use of whatever substances we ingest, but by forcing inherently toxic foods into our systems, we sow the seeds for our own exploitation. For example, cows are routinely fed enriched feed to unnaturally boost weight gain and milk output. Instead of just eating grass as they are designed by nature, cows are typically fed grains and legumes like corn, soy, and alfalfa that are unhealthy for them and cause disease, but are profitable for their exploiters. But cow feed is typically enriched even more, with added animal-sourced proteins and fats, such as fish meal, slaughterhouse waste, and poultry litter.

Just as the cows are being fed unnaturally rich feed that they are not designed to be eating (we don't see cows catching fish in nature), so that they can be more profitably exploited, anyone who is eating the unnaturally rich conventional diet is being similarly exploited. The ongoing flood of animal-sourced foods, and the flood of sick people with diabetes, obesity, cancer, heart disease, strokes, liver and kidney disease, and the other conditions rampant in our society, brings a flood of wealth to the meat-medical-media-banking complex. These are not foods we would choose naturally. The only reason any of us eats them is because we are following orders compelling us to do so from infancy. The orders come from people we trust, and who generally mean well, and who were similarly deceived from childhood. It is difficult to question these orders because the most important lesson taught by parents to their offspring, across all species, centers on food and eating, which are essential for survival. Just as we unquestioningly learn and speak the language taught us from infancy by our parents and society, we similarly learn and eat their foods as well. We eat animal-sourced foods because of the communities in which we are raised.

Part of the rationalization we are given by our communities for eating this way is that we are superior to animals, and so we should eat like lions and other powerful animals. However, we decidedly do not eat like them. We eat more like vultures. The animal flesh we eat has long been dead, and so we eat like necrovores. It may be euphemized as aged beef, but it concentrates pesticide, chemical, and pharmaceutical residues, as well as inherent toxins, and unavoidable misery, terror, and pain. We eat and act more like parasites than predators, relentlessly stealing the life-energy and purposes of other living beings we have enslaved.

We can rejoice that we all have been given the gift of physical bodies that do not require any animals to suffer or die to get all the nutrients required to celebrate our lives on this magnificent Earth. The historic and ever-growing presence of millions of healthy long-term vegans is making this abundantly clear. We discuss healthy nutrition more fully in our companion volume, *The World Peace Way*.

Animal Agriculture's Effects on Inner Dimensions of Health
Now we turn our focus to the perhaps even more important aspects of our health, the two main inner dimensions of health that

determine not just our well-being, but also our basic purpose in living. Disease and delusion in these inner facets of our lives have significant harmful impacts on all aspects of our outer health, as well as on our basic orientation in this life, our sense of meaning, and our capacity for psychological growth, for spiritual health, and for contributing to the well-being of those around us.

Psychological Health: The first three dimensions of health just discussed—environmental, cultural, and bodily health—are essentially external, and tend to be more obvious. Nevertheless, the devastating impact of our practice of animal agriculture on the outer world still remains mainly unrecognized in our culture, due primarily to its harmful effects on the inner landscape of our consciousness. After all, we live in a herding culture organized around a hubristic narrative that justifies and rationalizes our relentless exploitation of animals and nature, and blinds us to its harmful consequences. Being compelled from infancy to participate in animal-based meal rituals, we are eating not just harmful foods, but are also eating attitudes that destroy our natural capacities for sensitivity, awareness, empathy, intelligence, self-respect, and harmony with nature and with each other.

Ironically, this is induced and enforced primarily by caring people such as our parents, relatives, friends, neighbors, teachers, doctors, and others who have been similarly deceived from infancy about food. Perhaps in the past, animal-sourced foods seemed essential for survival, but this is clearly not true today, and obsolete protein and calcium narratives, and other deceptive superstitions, generate massive waves of violence and disease in the outer world. But it is on the inner dimensions that the abuse inherent in meat, dairy, and eggs most insidiously wounds us. Paradoxically, it is invisible to us, because the wounding, besides deceiving us, also damages our capacity to recognize that we are being deceived, poisoned, and wounded, and it disconnects us from awareness of our original nature as interconnected and sovereign expressions of life. Our acculturated meals establish and feed a spectrum of dysfunctional attitudes and mental orientations that harm our emotional, attitudinal, and intellectual health. We briefly explore seven such attitudes.

First, an obvious one, is the attitude and orientation of *disconnectedness*. We are taught to stay shallow and to avoid making the obvious and necessary connections between what is on our plates and the actual living beings who have been abused to produce it. This has serious consequences because the essential definition of intelligence in individuals (and societies) is our capacity to make relevant connections. Animal agriculture is a direct assault on this capacity of intelligence, because every meal is a practice of disconnecting the food we are consuming from the violent reality required by it. This ongoing daily practice of disconnecting erodes our intelligence individually and collectively, both the cognitive aspect of intelligence, as well as our emotional intelligence, through chronic desensitization and numbing. Eating animals instills in us an incapacity to care about the animals whose bodies and fluids we are consuming, and for whose excruciatingly miserable lives we bear responsibility. This corrodes our emotional and ethical health and stunts our intellectual growth by confining us to the shallow material surfaces of awareness and understanding. We learn to see only a steak and not a bovine being, a wing and not a bird, an ice cream and not a mother, and as we practice this routinely and relentlessly in our daily meals, we become adept at disconnecting.

Cultures transmit their norms and values from generation to generation through language, customs, and especially through rituals. Meals are primary rituals in every culture. Sharing food is intimate and profound, and instills attitudes that hardwire us into a particular way of seeing and acting that is normalized and invisibilized. When it comes to food, it is taboo to look deeply, feel deeply, question deeply, listen deeply, or care deeply, because if we do, we immediately hit the wall of internalized cultural programming injected into us from infancy by caring people we trusted implicitly. Denial crops right up, followed closely by platitudes that justify and legitimize our failure to recognize the reality of our culturally-mandated violence.

This disconnectedness and loss of emotional and cognitive intelligence with regard to animals and food radiates from this central core—eating—into every dimension of our individual and shared lives, but we understandably fail to be aware of it because of the indoctrinated disconnectedness that permeates our society like a contagion. The animals are trapped in prisons built by our culturally-induced conformity, emotional incapacity, and intellectual inadequacy, and we are also trapped as well. The tragic heroes of Greek antiquity were plagued by the twin character defects of hubris and obtuseness. To avoid the inevitable downfall these shortcomings eventuate, we are called more urgently than ever to awaken from the spell of animal agriculture into which we were born, and to heal the wounds it has inflicted on our psyches.

The herding culture imprisons us by compelling us to imprison animals. Eroding our capacity to make relevant connections, it turns us into livestock who lack the capacity to understand the forces at play that are undermining the health of our minds and our society. We can regain our intelligence, and the sovereignty and capacities we have lost, by honoring the sovereignty and capacities of animals and freeing them. This benevolent revolution starts within the heart and mind of each of us.

A second attitude implicit in animal foods and required of all of us in this culture is the attitude of *privilege and elitism.* The subtext of every meal is that certain beings are inherently superior and others are inherently inferior, and that it is perfectly fine for the superior beings to dominate and exploit the inferior ones. This is what we are actually eating and mentally cultivating at the deepest levels with every meal, so we inevitably reap a world of social injustice that defies all attempts at resolution. We are causing abuse and injustice and then literally eating and incorporating these abusive and unjust actions with our meals. The more we oppress animals, the more difficult it is to free ourselves from being oppressed, and from oppressing each other. As our minds and bodies literally and symbolically feed on injustice and elitism, these increasingly manifest in our world.

A third devastating attitude is that of *commodifying life*. Because of the foundational attitude of animal agriculture, everything and everyone has a price, and animals, nature, and humans are all reduced to mere material commodities in a harsh economic system. Animals are literally sold by the pound, millions of times every day, billions of times daily if we include marine animals. The impact of this reductionistic commodification of living beings is inconceivably vast and deep, and it reflects and infects not just our scientific, medical, educational, and other institutions, but also the inner landscape of our consciousness. As we commodify others, we inescapably become commodities, and we now find we are all conditioned by a herding culture that obligates us to sell ourselves as commodities in the labor markets.

A fourth attitude in the spectrum of animal agriculture's unavoidable dysfunctional mentalities is that of *might-makes-right*. Animals suffer at our hands for the basic reason that we have the ability to completely overpower them through brute force and technology, and we see this same mentality pervading our human consciousness, our relationships, and our economic and political systems. With power and wealth, we can control narratives and censor dissent, and can always appear to be right, to the complete disregard of ethics and truth. The saying that those who win wars write the histories applies also to the countless ongoing social, political, and personal struggles that characterize our world. Wealth translates directly into power, and power flows through centralized military, political, financial, and intelligence institutions, as well as through societal narrative-control, and the capacity to dominate by deception and by force.

This leads directly to a fifth attitude instilled by our culture's food system, which is the *predatory mentality* that justifies those with power preying upon and exploiting those with less power. We eat like predators, consuming the flesh of animals, and yet, just as we don't have the physiology of predators or naturally long to rip through fur and skin with our teeth, we don't naturally long to exploit, dominate, and oppress others. However, our culture's core of animal agriculture preys on and kills millions of animals daily. It is an extreme version of canned hunting, and this predatory quality in our food mentality is reflected in all our cultural institutions. The strong prey upon and exploit the weak in a rancorous economic-political system in which we are all compelled to participate. Even more than predatory, though, our modern high-tech animal agriculture system is parasitic. Millions of animals are born into merciless captivity daily, their purposes and dignity crushed and their offspring stolen as we parasitically reduce them to mere monetary-nutrient units, continually bred to be consumed. We find this parasitic mentality pervading our society as well. Our education, government, media, science, and other institutions are controlled by parasitic plutocrats who feed on our time, energy, and resources, mirroring our treatment and consumption of animals.

A sixth mental attitude required by our culture's food orientation is particularly damaging: *materialism.* We now have ten thousand years of practice in reducing beings to physical objects and selling them by their weight, and our consciousness has been poisoned, wounded, and distorted by this to such a degree that we see not just "food animals" as mere matter, but all of nature and ourselves as well. Philosophical materialism now permeates our culture, infiltrating education, science, religion, and every institution, corroding sanctity, dignity, intelligence, morality, and purpose, manically quantifying and reducing everything, and disconnecting us and our children from our spiritual foundations.

Finally, a seventh damaging attitude is the *complete repression and exploitation of the sacred feminine dimension of life and consciousness,* referred to in *The World Peace Diet* as Sophia. Sophia represents our inner feminine wisdom that naturally yearns to protect and nurture children, communities, and our shared life. Animal agriculture is based at its core on repeatedly shackling and raping very young females, stealing and killing their babies, and then killing these mothers, and doing it millions of times daily. How can we have healthy family and gender relations, or respect the feminine dimension of life and consciousness, when our inner Sophia is being crushed by these opposing actions and attitudes that are injected deeply into us on a daily basis through our meals? Sophia is the inner psycho-spiritual force that would naturally rise up, determined and unvanquishable, to protect our children and our communities from exploitation, pollution, pornography, deceit, and corruption. Animal agriculture, by repressing Sophia in all of us from infancy, lays the foundation for totalitarian control, and it is the resurrection of Sophia wisdom that is the essence of healthy living that respects all expressions of life, and that is fueling the efforts for freedom, health, justice, and peace in our world today.

Spiritual/Ethical Health: This fifth dimension of health has to do with our basic sense of purpose and our connection with our true nature as conscious beings capable of living lives of authenticity, creativity, awakening, and fulfillment. Animal agriculture is the antithesis of all these qualities. We force animals to be born into slavery and deprive them of their purposes and their lives. We steal their milk, eggs, autonomy, sovereignty, children, friendships, homes, and meaning. We are ritually indoctrinated by our daily meals to see beings as mere material objects whose value is determined by their material weight. Virtually any cruelty, as long as it is deemed standard practice, can be inflicted on the animals we mentally categorize as "food animals,"[8] without accountability. Can we imagine a system more barbaric and satanic? Disconnected from basic wisdom, ethics, and awareness, animal agriculture lays waste not just our outer world, but reaches to the most intimate depths of our fundamental connection with the source of our life. It poisons and perverts the landscape of our consciousness by colonizing it with a narrative based on normalized abuse, exploitation, fear, and separation.

Environmental, Cultural, Psychological, and Spiritual Freedom

Just as it is essential to understand that our personal bodily health is interconnected with the other four dimensions of health, it is also helpful to understand how our individual freedom is interconnected with the four corresponding dimensions of freedom. Environmental freedom, for example, is damaged when land is enslaved by animal agriculture's deforestation, monocropping, and pesticide usages that destroy bird, animal, plant, and soil microbiome communities, and when oceans are overfished, poisoned, and imprisoned by the over 640,000 tons of nets, lines, pots and traps used in commercial fishing that are dumped and discarded in the sea every year.[9] As lands, waters, and ecosystems lose their integrity and freedom, we all lose our integrity and freedom.

The same is true for cultural freedom as well. To the degree that political, economic, and social institutions become corrupt and serve the interests of parasitic plutocrats, overall cultural freedom collapses, furthering the enslavement not only of ecosystems and human communities, but also destroying our individual freedom as well. Intimately connected to cultural freedom—political, economic, and social—is psychological freedom, which is essential to all aspects of freedom. When narratives, education systems, media outlets, medical institutions, and other social pillars are manipulated and corrupted, our attitudes, perspectives, and interpretations of situations are also manipulated, destroying both psychological and physical freedom. This is why individual and cultural freedoms, such as freedom of speech, of assembly, of bodily autonomy, of travel, of the press, of religion, and so forth, are essential. They promote a healthy environment for psychological freedom, and for the fifth dimension of freedom that underlies all the others: spiritual freedom.

Spiritual freedom is an essential quality of our true nature. It is the existential wisdom from which flow all aspects of freedom and of health. Spiritual freedom is inherent, and can never be granted or taken away. It is founded on the deeper truth that we are essentially non-corporeal and eternal consciousness, functioning temporarily through a physical vehicle. Our integrity and our being, like that of everyone, are inherently inviolable. We have a mission and a purpose, and this ever-present reality of spiritual freedom as the inherent reality within us naturally inspires us to make an ongoing effort to awaken out of delusion. All living beings are sovereign expressions of one life that lives through us all. These five dimensions of freedom and the five dimensions of health reinforce each other, both individually and collectively.

Though we may be wounded by being raised in an industrialized herding culture[10]—and endure various types of environmental, cultural, physical, psychological, and spiritual illness and loss of freedom as a result—we can proactively seek to learn about, understand, and heal the situation into which we are born. We can reclaim our health and freedom, and through this effort and understanding, rescue ourselves and our world from the hidden cultural agendas that harm and deceive us. We can contribute to the benevolent revolution in human consciousness that our future is calling forth now.

The Herding Revolution

A brief historical overview of our culture is helpful in understanding our current plight, and that of the animals we kill by the millions every day. About ten thousand years ago, in the area that is today, roughly, northern Iraq, the greatest revolution in human history took place when people for the first time began to own and to confine animals as property for food, a practice we refer to as herding. This was a long and slow revolution that spanned centuries, but gradually about six major cultural changes and developments occurred because of it.[11]

The first was that our ancestors began to confine and claim ownership of wild, free-living animals. For the first time, wild sheep, and then wild goats, and then about two thousand years later, wild bovines, were claimed as personal property and reduced to being mere commodities. It is well understood that prior to this, animals, though perhaps hunted, were respected co-habitants of the Earth with us, admired for their capacities, and seen as fellow inhabitants of the natural world. But as is always the case with ownership of beings, whether human or animal, the respected status of these animals had to be destroyed in order to relieve the conscience of our ancestors as they inflicted the requisite confinement and physical and sexual abuse on them. We do the same today to assuage our natural sense of guilt and remorse. We all know that calling someone a cow, pig, chicken, or turkey is a serious insult, even though, in the wild, they are magnificent animals with finely-tuned intelligences that have enabled them to learn, communicate, and thrive over millions of years, experiencing their relationships and emotional lives in ways we can barely imagine, and all the while supporting the complex ecosystems in which they live.

The mentality that developed in ancient herding cultures, of dominating and owning animals, led eventually to the same mentality being weaponized toward nature. Land, and the trees and constituents of the natural world, were increasingly similarly reduced to mere material commodities to be bought and sold. It is difficult to overstate the anthropological and psychological significance of this reduction of animals and the natural world to mere commodity objects. From the perspective of animals, the herding revolution turned our forefathers into satanic demons who bred animals into enslavement and "cared" for them only to inflict a brutal death, from which there was no escape. This ongoing and inevitable generational violence, taught and exemplified from parents to progeny, reduced our forebears' inherent empathy and other capacities. It propelled them to try to escape responsibility by writing sacred texts (which we can still read today) in which the deity demanded the sacrifice of animals. This served to metaphysically project their violence and almighty power over animals onto the deity. Enslaving animals forcefully shattered their long-established sense of cooperation with, and support by, the benevolent and nurturing power of the natural world.[12]

Second, this new practice of animal agriculture gradually, over the millennia, gave rise, for the first time, to a wealthy ruling class. These men were the most powerful because they owned the most livestock. In the ancient world, livestock were wealth. Sheep, goats, and cows, besides being breedable wealth commodities, also required land and water resources. By the time the historic period began about four to five thousand years ago with the first writings such as *The Epic of Gilgamesh* and other ancient Sumerian, Levantine, and Hellenistic texts, we can read about the kings who completely dominated their societies because they owned and controlled the most capital. This word, capital, comes from the ancient Latin word *capita* meaning "head," referring to the wealth inherent in the ownership of head of sheep, cows, and other livestock.

Third, this system of herding, coupled with the arising of a ruling class whose wealth was determined by capital, which was livestock, gave rise to large-scale wars for the first time on Earth. A herder-king would see another herder-king with a lot of cows and other capital, and would send an army of men to attack, and if victorious, would enrich himself with more livestock capital, plus the land and water needed to sustain them. The oldest known word for war, the ancient Sanskrit word *gavyaa*, meant literally, "the desire for more cows." As it similarly is today, war was a primary tool used by the ruling class to increase its riches and power.

Fourth, human slavery began. Not only would the animals become the property of the victors, but the people on the losing side would also become their property as well. In all my research into the consequences of animal agriculture, one of the most sobering realizations has been the understanding that whatever we have done to animals, we have eventually also done to each other. It is a relatively small step from breeding, owning, and exploiting animals to doing the same thing to other human beings. In fact, animal and human slavery are among the most profitable economic undertakings, but also the most ethically destructive. These two devastating institutions, war and slavery, which began with the herding revolution, are still with us today, and more profitable and pervasive than ever. Because we have not yet evolved beyond enslaving and warring on animals, we endure rampant human trafficking and physical conflict. Interestingly, the latest iteration of war, called fifth generation warfare, or information warfare, targets the psychological, biological, and socio-economic dimensions of all of us as individuals. Military tacticians now realize that the most effective and long-lasting way to dominate other humans is not through overt physical force, but through controlling information, perspective, narrative, and individual sovereignty: "The basic idea behind this term [fifth generation warfare] is that in the modern era, wars are not fought by armies or guerillas, but in the minds of common citizens."[13] These tactical forces aim to control and corrode our physical, psychological, and cultural health internally and, like the mentality of animal agriculture, imprison us and defeat us without our realizing it.

Fifth, because the living core of animal agriculture is breeding animals, with their offspring born into life-long slavery, herders desecrated the sacred feminine dimension that births and nurtures life, reducing it to an exploitable commodity. By relentlessly practicing the sexual abuse of cows and other animals in breeding them for wealth, power, and food, with time, women's status was also radically reduced, and women began to be seen by male herders as little more than breeders. By the time the historic period emerged, we can read ancient texts that describe how women were bought and sold like mere chattel property. Additionally, breeding animals to increase flesh and milk gave rise to the first science, the proto-science of systematized knowledge that assisted in exploiting and dominating nature and the feminine. To this day, science retains its materialist orientation as a tool to manipulate and control the world around us, based on the herder mentality of superiority, force, reductionism, disconnectedness from nature, and the routine domination of the sacred feminine.

Sixth, boys were abused from infancy by being required to harden their hearts and repress their inherent tenderness and kindness, and become, instead, capable of ruthless violence toward animals and rival herders. Thus, the gradual herding revolution of ten thousand years ago gave rise to warlike, patriarchal societies in the eastern Mediterranean region and these cultures gradually spread to the northern Mediterranean, central Asia, and Europe, and with colonialism, throughout the world.[14]

An exceedingly damaging force on planet Earth is hard, tough, disconnected, and ambitious men vying for dominance and control. It becomes even more dangerously destructive when they are collaborating for dominance and control.

The herding revolution is still spreading today, greatly facilitated by technology, and similar technology is giving rise to the surveillance state. Global herderism is propelled by McDonald's, Kentucky Fried Chicken, Burger-King, Con-Agra, Cargill, Smithfield, Bayer-Monsanto, the World Health Organization, the World Economic Forum, the Trilateral Commission, the Rockefeller, Gates, and other foundations, and the International Monetary Fund, the Bank for International Settlements, the World Bank, BlackRock, Vanguard, and the other large banks and financial institutions in the background. It works well to siphon most of the world's wealth and power into the hands of a tiny predatory and parasitic ruling class, and to exploit and enslave not only animals and ecosystems, but most of humanity as well. We fail to realize that by supporting and participating in this herding of animals, we are destroying our own freedom.

The good news is that animal agriculture is completely obsolete and unnecessary today. Whatever the reason our ancestors ten thousand years ago decided to own animals as property for food (anthropologists are still unsure what the forces were that drove them to this), we can easily see that it has been devastating in its consequences, and is counterproductive on every level, in terms of our environmental, social, physical, psychological, and spiritual health. Through the social and spiritual dynamics of our situation, we see two great movements contributing to the healing of our world. One is the movement for the liberation of animals, and the other is the movement for human freedom and sovereignty, especially for medical and health freedom, which has been under attack for decades. Both are manifestations of our inherent wisdom and compassion, and naturally reinforce each other, liberating animals and humankind from the dire and unrecognized consequences of herderism.

CHAPTER THREE

ANIMAL BETRAYAL:
THE UNYIELDING DILEMMA

"Those who tell the stories rule society."
—PLATO

"We forge the chains we wear in life."
—CHARLES DICKENS

"We accept the proclamations of scientists in their lab coats
with the same faith once reserved for priests."[1]
—KARY MULLIS, INVENTOR OF THE PCR TECHNOLOGY

Common Ground: Individual Sovereignty

The health freedom movement, known also as the medical freedom movement, exploded in response to tyrannical Covid pandemic policies worldwide, and is devoted to protecting our essential freedoms, such as freedom of speech, of the press, of assembly, of religion, of travel, of bodily autonomy, and of informed consent, all of which were undermined and attacked by public health authorities under the guise of protecting us from contagion and from each other. This health freedom movement is naturally congruent with the animal liberation movement. Both movements are based on protecting and defending the sovereignty of individuals being harmed by powerful corporate, governmental, medical, and cultural forces feeding on and legitimizing the exploitation and abuse of individuals—individual humans in one case, and individual animals in the other.

Both movements are based on questioning official narratives emanating from mainstream sources, and on refusing to comply with socially-mandated actions and attitudes that promote harm to individuals. In both cases, health and science narratives are used as primary incentives and rationalizations to exploit and abuse sovereign individuals. In the first instance, the narrative is that we need to track, control, and medicate individual humans to protect public health and to stave off dangerous pathogens. According to the second narrative, which legitimizes animal-sourced food and products, we need to imprison, abuse, and kill individual animals to avoid malnutrition and get the nutrients and products we need to be healthy and comfortable.

Both narratives are based squarely on untruth, fear, and deception, and on coercive pressure being applied to harm individuals, as well as direct and indirect censorship of any contrarian messages, so that the general public can be artificially insulated from any "misinformation" that both health freedom advocates and animal liberation activists tend to be accused of promoting. This pervasive censorship of truthful and empowering information, targeting even respected experts and whistleblowers, is necessary precisely because undefendable falsehoods are propagated by authorities who well understand that their harmful deceptions would shrivel and die if properly exposed to the light of open public discourse. In a supreme irony, science, which is defined as free inquiry from multiple perspectives, is invoked as a kind of scriptural authority, and those who question mainstream narratives, or the packaged scientific-labeled "consensus" are accused of being "anti-science" if they dare to challenge the prevailing orthodoxy. The idea of scientific consensus is a dangerous illusion,[2] and somewhat comically pretends to reduce truth to something that is ascertained by voting. This idea of settled science destroys the spirit of open inquiry and curiosity, and legitimizes accusing anyone—even recognized and respected researchers—of heresy, and de facto excommunicating them from the body of the faithful. The censorship manifests in a spectrum of forms, from direct, heavy-handed, and even violent, to exceedingly subtle and indirect coercion that compels conformity to the status quo mindset.

The key thing to understand is that our human freedom can only be sustained to the degree that we offer freedom to those who are vulnerable in our hands. If we steal freedom, health, and justice from animals, we create the certainty that the same will happen to us. Oppression is a living force that harms the oppressor as much, if not more, than it harms the oppressed, when we see the bigger picture. Ancient wisdom teachings and natural law are ever reminding us: "As above, so below." Though the animals themselves are incapable of retaliation, our violence toward them retaliates against us in a myriad of ways—as physical and mental disease, as trafficking, war, injustice, child sexual abuse, alienation, fear, loss of freedom, and forfeiture of purpose—to name a few. It is becoming increasingly well understood that human social justice and animal justice are intertwined.[3]

The Two Taboos Against Sovereignty

This basic understanding, that freeing animals is the key to human freedom, while liberating on both the individual and collective level, is also taboo to discuss in most situations in our society because it causes cognitive dissonance as well as affective dissonance. We are compelled from infancy to categorize certain species of animals as "food animals" and as insentient property objects. Because this is obsolete, untrue, unhealthy, and also dreadfully abusive to these sensitive beings, we would rather not allow any thinking or discussion about it, and would also rather not allow any feelings about it either. Animal agriculture in today's world is not only anti-rational in its polluting wastefulness and unhealthiness, but also anti-empathic in its severe abuse of imprisoned animals, as well as of wildlife, indigenous and hungry people, and industry workers. Thus, a primary taboo in our culture is the taboo against knowing who we eat, and the consequences of our behavior. We prefer to avoid being made conscious of the realities we are actually causing and consuming.

Besides this taboo against acknowledging uncomfortable truths regarding the innate sovereignty of individual animals, there is a similar taboo regarding the innate sovereignty of us as individual human beings. We are taught to be uncomfortable with this idea, and to feel a sense of fear in contemplating a society of sovereign individuals who cooperate and live respectfully and freely together without imposed rules, hierarchies, and authorities. We are trained to view humans as essentially dangerous and self-centered, and to consider anarchy as repulsive and violent chaos, rather than possibly consisting of equal and respectful people co-operating and creating abundant and celebratory communities without resorting to authoritarian force, censorship, domination, competition, and repression as essential guarantors of sustainable social structures. In fact, newer philosophical perspectives, such as agorism, are evolving to promote and explore this idea of healthy, nonauthoritarian social systems.

It is clear that the foundation of individual sovereignty consists of our innate freedom to act as long as we do not violate the similarly inherent freedom and sovereignty of other humans, and we are called to include animals in this as well. Animals are also sentient and have interests that matter to them. However, as long as we are in a herding culture based on animal agriculture, which is necessarily organized around the "right" of the strong to dominate and exploit the weak, laws and conflict are inevitable and anarchy unthinkable. Perhaps in the future, a world of freedom that honors the sovereignty of both humans and animals will evolve. It is an enticing vision and possibility, and we can work now to plant the seeds for its future fruition.

Ironically, in this emerging globalist era of pandemics and climate emergencies, many of us advocate sovereignty for animals, but find individual human sovereignty to be threatening. Though we may identify as vegans, thus questioning many aspects of society, the government's declared emergencies may cause us to forsake that questioning attitude and espouse trust in official narratives. Acquiescing to authoritarian fear-mongering, we may proclaim our opposition to medical freedom, and to freedom of travel, of speech, of assembly, of religion, and of bodily autonomy so that we can all be "safe." How is it possible that those of us who naturally value these essential freedoms in order to work effectively to liberate animals—and whose work is to publicly and privately question medical and social narratives that harm individual animals—become easily willing to deny these basic freedoms to other people, and relinquish them ourselves, together with our healthy questioning attitude? Why do we then comply with corporate and media authorities we hitherto resisted, and uncritically embrace narratives that destroy human sovereignty, and our freedom, and the effectiveness of the movement that we supposedly hold dear? How do we not see that if we justify censoring someone else for "hate speech" or "dangerous speech" that we don't like, that the same thing will happen to us eventually?

With the Covid crisis in early 2020, the vegan movement clearly had a golden opportunity to champion the rights, freedom, and sovereignty of not just individual animals, but of individual humans as well. This would have been an enormously valuable contribution to the well-being of society during that dark and challenging time. Yet the vegan movement, similar in many ways to the political left, revealed the extent to which it had been infiltrated and captured by the seductive power of wealth and narrative control. Unable to maintain a vital inner connection with the core values of vegan living, many vegans allowed the rampant fear porn gushing from the media, government, and medical authorities to sweep them into unquestioning compliance, and, ironically, into championing the virulently anti-vegan pharmaceutical-medical-chemical complex.

Equally incongruous, many of us demand respect for our own sovereignty, and rightfully organize and work to educate others about the importance of health freedom and of all our inalienable rights, while at the same time destroying the freedom and sovereignty of animals by failing to question prevailing cultural narratives. We blithely purchase and consume the flesh and secretions of terribly abused and enslaved animals who are reduced to mere livestock property status, thereby directly inflicting brutality and tyranny that are much more severe than that against which we are fighting. As health freedom advocates, we justifiably rebel against being viewed as mere exploitable livestock by the globalist plutocrats managing pandemic and climate narratives, and yet we act in a similar manner ourselves with regard to animals, reducing cows, pigs, chickens, and others to mere exploitable property status. How is it possible that we fail to see that by purchasing animal-sourced foods and products, we directly cause the destruction of the sovereignty of others, the very sovereignty we prize so much for ourselves?

It is clear that the animal liberation movement is called to embrace the movement for human freedom, and that this medical-health freedom movement is similarly called to embrace the animal liberation movement. It is the same basic effort, and the ruling class that profits and benefits from the exploitation of animals also benefits from the exploitation of humans. These plutocrats control not only the social, governmental, and media narratives, but also control, through infiltration and predatory philanthropy, what would be the opposing narratives, thus ensuring the ongoing reliable and profitable exploitation of both animals and humans.

For example, the animal agriculture-medical-chemical complex has for decades captured governmental agencies and legislative bodies to the extent that, in the U.S. (and similar scenarios exist in many countries), we have a massive system of government subsidies that drastically and artificially reduces consumer prices for meat, dairy products, and eggs. This promotes the exploitation not only of cows, pigs, chickens, and other livestock animals, but the exploitation of us humans as well, as our physical, psychological, environmental, and cultural health is sabotaged, increasing the profits and control of the same powerful industries, and the bankers and asset managers in the background. While animal-sourced food production in the U.S. receives billions of government dollars annually in subsidies, price supports, income assistance, emergency assistance, commodity loans, direct payments, allotments, tax breaks, rail and feed subsidies, grazing privileges, the dairy export incentive program, and other governmental services, less than one percent of government subsidies goes to the production of health-promoting vegetables and fruits.[4]

This is not accidental. By severely lowering the market price of animal-sourced foods, the ruling class encourages the U.S population to consume over 200 pounds of meat per capita annually, twice the global average and virtually the highest in the world,[5] guaranteeing the U.S. having the world's most expensive (i.e., profitable) medical system, and arguably one of the most disease-ridden populations as well. If we are eating animal-sourced foods, we are being exploited, and all of us are harmed by the toxic poisons and excessive medical costs involved, with medical procedures being the leading cause of bankruptcies. Additionally, these immense government subsidies enable U.S. meat, dairy, egg, and feed grain producers to flood Latin American and other international markets with low-priced products that put local farmers in these other countries out of business, directly driving hunger, displacement, and immigration pressures on U.S. borders, further propelling the plutocratic agenda of cultural expropriation, both at home and abroad.

If we fail to see the interconnected nature of animal and human liberation, we become merely ironic in our quests for freedom. Enslaving animals for food, our health is harmed on every level, inevitably eroding our freedom. Liberating animals, we can rescue our world from the narratives, traditions, and embedded levers used by the ruling class to propel their agenda of unbridled domination.

Looking at our critical cultural situation, how will we be able to successfully awaken the hearts and minds of the masses of people who are sufficiently poisoned and wounded that they care neither for animal freedom nor human freedom, but seem content to eat and exploit animals as livestock, and to allow themselves to be similarly exploited and oppressed? To approach this question effectively, we are called to a deeper understanding both of our culture and of ourselves.

Herderism: Our Culture's Living Foundation

Any of us who has had a companion animal at some point in our lives understands viscerally that animals have interests that are as significant to them as our human interests are to us. They are not mere insentient sacks of flesh and bones, but are sentient and self-aware. They display unique personality characteristics, and have purposes that we violate, and cherished relations that we destroy, because we are culturally programmed to mentally categorize them as morally-insignificant commoditized property objects.

This cultural indoctrination into herderism—the core practice and attitude in our culture of essential separateness from, and superiority over, animals and nature—not only reduces our cognitive, emotional, and spiritual intelligence but also sows the seeds for our inevitably experiencing the same fate that we inflict on them. We are at grave risk of being overpowered by the increasingly boomeranging impact of our relentless violence toward animals, and of being ourselves exploited through the ever-advancing surveillance and control technologies available to ruling forces today. We are ironically consuming the products of similarly-designed animal-exploitation systems that dominate animals for food and other uses.

Thus, as we persist in engineering a dystopian future for billions of beings, we now see the gaping maw of a dystopian future looming for us as well, with mass tracking and surveillance, loss of basic freedoms, coerced injections, lockdowns, mandatory medical intrusions, separation of family members, microchipping, and highly-centralized financial, political, and social control. All these standard factory-farm practices are openly discussed and many are publicly planned by globalist health officials, pharmaceutical representatives, and government agencies. What we relentlessly inflict on farmed animals we see unfolding in our human world, and, ironically, we seem powerless, and strangely uninspired to stop it.

Why is this? Why are many of us unable to see the obvious, and respond decisively and with clarity, vigor, and solidarity to these insidious existential dangers to us and to our children? Why are we immobilized by fear and mesmerized by the voices of authority, unable to connect effectively with others, or with our intuitive wisdom and our ability to think critically about our situation? Why the nearly-blind allegiance to mainstream media narratives and medical-pharmaceutical forces that we should by now have learned to doubt and question? Why are those who dare to speak up and question the dominant narratives relatively rare among us billions?

It is because animal agriculture not only exploits animals, it exploits us. The predicament seems to be that when we dominate others and steal their freedom, we subconsciously begin also to crave to be dominated and controlled. Truly free people would never exploit animals the way we do, or even tolerate living in such a society. Social psychologist Erich Fromm points out in his classic book, *Escape from Freedom*, that most of us—because we are thoroughly indoctrinated from birth into authoritarian and hierarchical power structures that systematically prevent individual freedom—are conditioned to crave both submission and domination, and thus we do whatever we can to escape from freedom, sovereignty, and authentic responsibility for our actions.[6]

Though much of it operates below the threshold of awareness, we are trained to actually crave being told what to do by outside authorities, and being able to obediently follow their orders. As Fromm discusses, the authoritarian personality not only needs and longs for submission to superiors (including, possibly, a projected deity figure), but also craves to similarly dominate inferior others. Animals bear the full brunt of this dynamic. Fromm failed to realize that this authoritarian culture based on hierarchies of domination is a direct result of the attitudes required by living in a herding culture, and routinely oppressing and eating animals. Fortunately, now we can recognize that it is this underlying practice and mentality of animal agriculture that is the unrecognized driving force generating our unyielding dilemmas and suffering. Consciously abandoning it opens up inspiring vistas of new possibilities to co-create authentically free and egalitarian cultures based on respect for animals, nature, and each other. A benevolent revolution is possible and available to us on this abundant Earth. Nothing but our fear and inertia prevent us from responding to and partaking of its beckoning potentials.

What is Humanity's Purpose?

Thus, the problem is not that we humans are inherently flawed and irrational, and innately yearn to abuse and exploit others. The problem is that we are all being poisoned and wounded by being born and raised in a culture organized around the obsolete practice of herding, which requires us to violate our natural inclinations, and instead to engage in relentless and intimate meal rituals of socially-approved violence. This continually suppresses our rational, empathic, and intuitive capacities and intelligence.

As long as we comply with cultural indoctrination and make choices to eat steak, ham, eggs, cheese, fish, and chicken, we will continue paying an awful price, and not even realize what is happening or why. Robert F. Kennedy, Jr., has rather famously said, "No one has ever complied their way out of totalitarianism," and we are now called to understand that this applies not only to totalitarianism inflicted on us by despotic forces, but also to the totalitarianism that we inflict on animals. "We will not comply," properly understood, applies both to refusing to tyrannize others, as well to allowing ourselves to be tyrannized. We force the animals to bear the full fury of our deluded food narratives, and we unwittingly bear a lot of it as well. Because our innate intelligence is damaged by routinely participating in animal-sourced meals, it seems possible that our ongoing violence against animals will drive us to such severe ferocity toward nature and each other that we could perhaps obliterate our species into extinction. The bitter irony is that we will have no idea why this happened.

This is indeed a sobering realization. We are already driving dozens of species into extinction every day, mainly through habitat destruction by our meat and dairy habits that require massive deforestation, pesticide pollution, and overfishing. Humanity's ongoing attack on nature and animals, causing what is now known as the Anthropocene mass extinction event,[7] the largest in 65 million years, and driven by human behavior, may also lead to our own extinction. This is, to some people, especially misanthropes, a comforting thought. If we humans were to somehow disappear without severely damaging ecosystems in the process, what would follow would undoubtedly be the most exuberant and celebratory springing forth of unfettered life here on Earth that we could imagine. Liberated from toxic human pollution, exploitation, and interference, animals and the natural world would be free to heal and regenerate, and the inherent intelligence of ecosystems, without the burden of human obstruction and poisoning, would reestablish a bountiful paradise of harmony and abundance. The exquisite beauty and sagacity of the natural world are immensely inspiring to contemplate, and lead us directly to a most basic question, as we also contemplate the incalculable potential of human beings: what are we, and how shall we live?

What is humanity's purpose on this Earth? Our established practice and cultural core of herderism tells us our purpose is to dominate animals, to exploit the Earth, and to gauge our success by our status in the social tribe. In a more hidden way, we are told our purpose is to consume extravagantly, because the wealthiest among us are the most highly emulated, and to arrange our lives and careers in service to the interests of the plutocrats who model this consumerism, and who also control the narratives and institutions in our culture. When we do as we are told, we are rewarded with our culture's materialistic prizes, finding meaning through consuming, and even better, through consuming conspicuously.

Yet perhaps humanity has a completely different and more noble purpose. Perhaps it is to create beauty and to communicate intuitively with animals, ecosystems, and with each other, and to evolve spiritually, and savor the boundless opportunities for expression, creativity, and learning that are potentially available here, contributing to, and cooperating with the many dimensions of consciousness around and within us. The great celebration of nature and animals that would occur if humanity disappeared would also potentially occur if humanity would successfully mature beyond herderism, and completely liberate animals from human oppression and killing. The oceans as well as vast areas of the Earth's landmass would resurrect and heal, becoming robust habitats and allowing animals to live freely in nature again, as they did for millennia prior to human interference. Imagining a society based on deep veganism, discussed in Chapter Six, is imagining a society so different from ours that in many ways it seems virtually unimaginable.[8] Nevertheless, it is an inspiring exercise. Co-creating an authentically free, just, and sagacious society requires us to liberate not just animals from herderism, but also to liberate the inner landscape of our consciousness from the mentalities mandated by herderism.

The Enlightenment Fallacy

Outer compassion and inner stillness feed each other. Liberating animals in and of itself is not enough to give birth to a harmonious world; our consciousness, molded and poisoned by herderism, must also be cleansed of its programming. Rescuing both animals and our consciousness from the inner and outer prisons imposed by herderism, we can reclaim spiritual health and freedom, but as we know, there are well-entrenched social and psychological forces arrayed against these efforts. Addressing this, there's an old Buddhist saying attributed to Padmasambhava, "Though the view should be as vast as the sky, keep your

conduct as fine as barley flour." This essential teaching emphasizing values of caring and kindness is an important healing
antidote to the damaging delusions common in many spiritually-
oriented people and communities.

We can call these delusions various aspects of "the enlightenment fallacy," because they arise from a false sense of individual
license to do as we like because we believe we are spiritually advanced and superior to animals. This enlightenment fallacy
reinforces and activates the basic sense of entitlement that is in-
serted into all of us as products of a culture organized around the
shared ritual of eating foods sourced from animals. Though this
violence is counter-productive on every level, the enlightenment
fallacy attempts to justify our contribution to violence by "spir-
itualizing" it through propagating what seems to be a more lofty
and enlightened perspective. This often-fashionable perspective
can convince us that our behavior of funding and consuming animal-sourced foods is either not relevant to our spiritual life, or
that it is actually an indication of our spiritual attainments. It can
be employed not only to justify our human exploitation and mistreatment of animals, but also, in political and economic
contexts, of other humans who are not as evolved as we are, and
who thus need to be managed and perhaps even deceived or eliminated for their own good. There are several versions of this
enlightenment fallacy.

One is that because of our spiritual attainment, we are now
free of attachments and judgments. We believe that the phenomenal world is illusory and therefore no animals (or humans) are
really killed, and in fact nothing negative ever actually happens.
The internal narrative is that we are serving a higher power, and
so we can eat our hot dogs with gratitude and understanding, and
no harm is done. This rationalization assures us that we either
transform the negativity with our high vibration, or that we realize that the beings we're harming are illusory, as is all pain and
suffering, so it doesn't matter what we do in the outer world. All
that matters is the quality of our consciousness.

A similar narrative is that we are no longer bound by conventional morality, which is a system of rules that is artificial and imprisons us in delusions of "good" and "evil." Now we are free of this confining dualism, the narrative goes, and we can act as we please. The temptation is to proclaim that morality is relative, and our spirituality frees us from dualism and rules, so we can do as our "heart" tells us, and also eat whatever foods to which our "body" guides us. We may say we love the animals (and other humans) we dominate, that we are helping them to have a better life, or perhaps a better after-life.

Another tactic is to proclaim that life feeds on life, and the strong dominate the weak, and that's just the way it is here on this Earth, and anyone who resists this is vainly trying to put themselves above the wisdom of nature. However, eating animal-sourced foods is not life feeding on life, but on the unnecessary killing and exploitation of sentient beings. Some of us attempt to avoid responsibility for our actions by relinquishing this responsibility to sacred books or emulated spiritual teachers. We remember well how the Bible was used, for example, to defend slavery in the 19th century, and there are instances when we perhaps justify our eating of animal-sourced foods by rationalizing that our admired gurus, yogis, and founders of religious and spiritual traditions supposedly partook of fish or dairy products, so it must be fine for us as well. We perhaps feel we would be disrespecting our teachers if we would seem more consequent in our actions than they were. It's important to remember that times and customs change, that we are here to evolve and to help humanity mature to higher awareness and standards of action, and that it is actually a sign of respect for one's teacher and tradition to honor their example and message to the degree that we raise it to a purer and more complete expression.

Any narratives justifying us harming others for our own benefit are highly suspect, such as those above, as well as Social Darwinism's principle of applying "survival of the fittest" to our human relations, and should set off loud alarm bells whenever we encounter them. As a somewhat similar example, the 17th and 18th century "Age of Enlightenment" gave rise not only to scientism, vivisection, and an escalation in the exploitation of animals and nature by removing Biblical respect for the sacredness of creation, but also gave rise, for example, to the shadowy "Illuminati," who through their wealth and rituals created secret societies that made them feel superior and "illumined" in relation to the rest of humanity. When their agenda of dominating the rest of humanity was exposed in 1784, they were forced into even more secretive ways of meeting to further their aims, but we see that the underlying suggestion of a hidden cabal feeling entitled to rule humanity continues to this day. It is important to guard against the sense of superiority that often arises in false spirituality, where we develop an inflated sense of ourselves, especially in regard to animals, or to other people who can be deemed inferior. Our herding culture conditions us relentlessly into these kinds of harmful attitudes, and with spiritual practice and awareness, we can free ourselves from them, and reconnect with our inherent compassion for others.

Padmasambhava's wisdom (and there are other examples of this in ancient teachings) specifically addresses the fallacies in these various narratives. When our view is as vast, deep, bright, and all-encompassing as the sky, then we are blessed with the humility to keep our conduct as fine as flour. It's precisely because our view is wide and deep that we are more sensitive to the consequences of actions, and take them seriously. Our heart is naturally filled with a sense of kinship with others, even as we see they are not "others," in the sense that we see that we share the same source. This realization is the foundation of authentic morality, kindness, and spiritual awakening. We inherently delight in helping others as best we can, and recoil from actions that dominate or abuse others for our own advantage, or with the rationalization that ends justify means.

There are many aspects to the enlightenment fallacy, and the various narratives are all the more insidious because of the armor they bestow, hardening our hearts and conveying a pseudo-spirituality that harms not just animals and vulnerable people but all of us. It may certainly be helpful and healing to practice viewing the pain and loss that we personally experience as transient and illusory, but it is the height of delusion and immorality to trivialize the pain and loss we inflict on others by rationalizing it as being transient and illusory. We may often add further layers to the narrative, for example, that our actions are just for their own good, or it's just their karma, or that we're just not attached to outer forms, or that we're just reflecting back to them their own violence, or we are just helping them evolve by using them, or we just have to use them for needed nutrients or benefits, or we are just following our traditions. The "just" in all these narrative excuses reveals our underlying desperate attempt to justify our actions.

How Do We Respond to the Current Situation?

Our human maltreatment of animals is several orders of magnitude more intensely painful and extreme than anything we can easily imagine, far beyond the loss of our privacy and our rights to travel, speak, petition, assemble, and so forth. Our current mistreatment of animals is soberingly instructional. It shows what we are capable of when we become unconscious, and surrender our responsibility to technologies driven by profit and control. Carl Jung summed it well: "Much of the evil in the world is due to the fact that man is hopelessly unconscious."[9] It also shows the direction that the loss of our freedoms could be heading. It is excruciating to ponder what our life would be like if we were to be born as a cow, pig, chicken, goose, fish, rabbit, rat, monkey, or other animal in any animal agriculture or medical experimental operation in the world today.

For example, how do we tolerate the presence in our world of the horrors that we routinely inflict upon millions of pigs, who are force-medicated and mutilated, repeatedly impregnated on rape racks, hyper-confined in iron cages so intensely that they can never turn around, and are literally driven into insanity, often reduced to repeatedly banging their heads against the bars of their enclosures?

How do we countenance a society that imprisons millions of hens in wire cages, packing five birds so tightly they can never raise their wings, chopping off their beaks so they don't cannibalize each other from extreme frustration and pain, filling their bodies with toxic drugs and chemicals to maximize egg production, force-molting them through intentional deprivation of water and food, and then brutally killing them? How do we respond to living in a culture that slaughters several trillion fish and aquatic animals every year, over half of them in toxic aquaculture prisons where they are forced to live in water polluted by their own excrement, as well as by dozens of drugs and chemicals, before being killed by electrocution, suffocation, crushing, or being sliced open?

These examples offer a small glimpse into the tip of a massive iceberg of appalling violence that we routinely inflict on untold billions of our fellow passengers on this beautiful and abundant Earth. While it's mainly for food, there are also millions of animals born to be abused and killed in the heinous medical experiments preceding surgical procedures, drugs, and injections, as well as their suffering at rodeos, circuses, horse and dog races, and bullfights, in the name of entertainment. The mistreatment is inconceivably vast, macabre, and revolting, and it is unnecessary. We are born into it, support it, and consume it, and we also hide it from ourselves, all to our detriment. With awareness, we can see and begin to understand the actual driving force behind our disempowerment, and the undeniable woundedness that masks us, distances us, locks us down, and injects us with toxic fear and disease. Instead of hating humanity or proclaiming us to be incapable of harmony, we can look from another perspective and see that we have been deceived and wounded from birth, and for several hundred generations, by the herding culture's inescapable scourge of inner and outer fear and violence. When people are wounded, we don't blame and curse them, but with loving understanding we do our best to be agents of compassion and healing. This is the way forward for us now.

To illustrate, many of us in the health freedom movement are rightly concerned about the importance of food self-sufficiency, and because we live in a herding culture, the natural assumption is that we should get some land and raise some chickens for eggs and meat, and perhaps also some goats for milk and meat, and some rabbits, fish, or other animals for food. We would then be required to care for, breed, and feed them, and then one day, to betray and kill them. We practice this way of farming because of our upbringing and the pervasive cultural narrative. Plant-based, or veganic, permaculture is another approach, which liberates animals and ourselves from this violence. We may think that it's not practical to refrain from keeping animals, that it is too difficult. How do we know if that's true? Plantation owners in the antebellum South believed it was too difficult to operate farms without slaves, and resisted strenuously, but we can see now that it was possible after all.

It's helpful to note that there are two types of farming: plant and animal. Plant agriculture was originally done by both women and men, and entails working with the natural abundance of life, where we plant one seed and get hundreds or thousands of seeds. Trees, bushes, and plants give fruits, nuts, berries, and seeds, and we feel a sense of gratitude for and cooperation with the plants whose seeds and lives we are cultivating and who miraculously transform earth, water, and sun into delicious and healthy edible nutrition, as we collaborate with the natural cycles of the sun, moon, and seasons. Animal agriculture, in contrast, was exclusively men's work, and required imprisoning and sexually manipulating animals, and betraying and killing them, and though the animals resisted strenuously, overpowering them with superior force and technology. Animal faming is work of domination and tends to bring out the worst in us, and for the past ten thousand years, it is the living core of our culture, and is profitable and advantageous for the ruling class.

Because the mentality of animal agriculture pervades our society, we now engage in plant agriculture in basically the same way we do animal agriculture, and dominate nature using petroleum-based fertilizers and pesticides, genetic engineering, monocropping, and mechanized methods that destroy soil health and wreak havoc on ecosystems. We are called now to reconnect with an agronomy based more on partnership with ecosystems, rather than violent domination of them, using smaller-scale and more local approaches to organic plant agriculture so that we can thrive in harmony with animals and nature. This means reconnecting with traditional practices like crop rotation and less mechanized ways of farming, building up the health of the soil, which in the long run assures more vitality and sustainability. It is well understood that this kind of small-scale agriculture is capable of producing vastly more food with much less space. It is not uncommon, for example, for savvy and motivated suburban gardeners to get several thousand pounds of food from just one-tenth of an acre.[10] We can also rediscover lost secrets to growing fruits, vegetables, herbs, nuts, and other foods that fill them with healing power.[11] Farming, which is now typically viewed as a low-status job in our society, can be seen as one of the most honorable and essential livelihoods, requiring skill, diligence, intuition, experience, and love. Providing healthy plant-sourced foods is foundational to a healthy society and one of the most valuable contributions to freedom and peace that anyone can make.

In order to understand our situation more deeply, it's essential to look more closely into the philosophical materialism that forms the foundation of our behavior and attitudes, and that undergirds our herding culture, in order to liberate ourselves from its devastating consequences.

CHAPTER FOUR

AWAKENING FROM MATERIALISM

⌒⌒

"The day science begins to study non-physical phenomena, it will make
more progress in one decade than in all the previous centuries
of its existence."
—NIKOLA TESLA

"Materialistic science knows nothing about nutrition; it has no idea what
is healthy food for humanity. That is precisely the characteristic of
materialism, that it thinks and thinks and thinks
— and knows nothing."
—RUDOLF STEINER[1]

"Diet, injections, and injunctions will combine, from a very early age, to
produce the sort of character and the sort of beliefs that the authorities
consider desirable, and any serious criticism of the powers that be will
become psychologically impossible. Even if all are miserable, all will
believe themselves happy, because the government will tell them
that they are so."
—BERTRAND RUSSELL[2]

Marketing Beings by the Pound

How can we recognize and treat the hidden roots of the issues that plague our world today, and what role does the deeply-ingrained materialism of our society play in this? How can each of us contribute most effectively to co-creating a society of freedom, respect, and harmony? To meaningfully address these questions, we are called first of all to break the great taboo and pull back the curtain of denial, and clearly recognize the vast web of consequences generated by our participation in the industrialized herding culture into which we are born. Organized at its core around reducing beings to things, it has given rise to materialism, the dominant philosophical ideology of our culture and our science. In a nutshell, materialism is a philosophy for slaves.

Materialism maintains that non-living matter is the only fundamental reality, and that life and even consciousness itself are merely byproducts—epiphenomena—of material interactions. It is not surprising that ten thousand years of relentlessly commodifying animals as mere objects to be sold and eaten has so reduced our capacities and intelligence that we find ourselves prisoners of this materialist delusion, into which all of us have been indoctrinated from infancy.

Herderism, the unrecognized source of our culture's pervasive materialism, relentlessly requires us to mentally reduce sentient beings to nothing more than insensate matter. Animal agriculture is the hidden well from which this toxic materialism springs and flows into every institution in our culture, and from which it insinuates itself into our thoughts, feelings, dreams, attitudes, and relationships. Billions of animals are continually mistreated as mere material objects, and we are compelled to literally eat this philosophical materialism from infancy. We are all ritually trained to view farmed animals as unfeeling commodities that have no other purpose than to be imprisoned, fed, impregnated, used, and killed by us through a hauntingly unquestioned food system that is utterly obsolete.

The grossest form of materialism imaginable—to sell and buy individual beings by bodily weight—betrays such severe disconnectedness from our basic wisdom and decency that we are collectively

forced into a deplorable state of unawareness of which we are ironically unaware. The only way we can tolerate participating in such an
unconscious culture—by far the most materialistic culture the world
has ever seen—is to reduce our awareness and stay shallow. But this
is not easily tolerated, and the existential meaninglessness of our lives
calls out for relief in all sorts of ways, such as escaping into the abuse
of, and addiction to, all manner of harmful substances and dysfunctional actions.

Thus, our culture's ongoing meal rituals train us from infancy
not just to physically eat foods from abused animals, but to mentally eat and embody the materialism of this herding culture as
well. Though the indoctrination is invisible, like the air we
breathe, we are severely poisoned by it nonetheless, and understanding this clearly is vital to healing and to creating a freer and
healthier society.

Herderism and Materialism

Animal foods are harmful to us and others in a spectrum of ways,
and the attitudes they require of us are unhealthy and destructive.
The legitimization of these foods and attitudes benefits the power
and profitability agendas of the globalist plutocrats controlling the
military-industrial-meat-medical-pharmaceutical-media-banking-
technology complex. Anthropologists understand that, cross-cul-
turally, when we participate in meals, we are engaging in potent
rituals, and partaking of, embodying, and affirming our culture's
underlying and often invisible constellation of attitudes about our
relationship to nature, animals, each other, and the cosmos. To understand ourselves, we are called to understand our culture,
because our culture lives in us at a profound level, and to understand our culture, it's necessary to understand our culture's food
rituals. Meals are the foundational indoctrinating ritual in every
culture,[3] and looking undistractedly into our culture's food program is one of the most revelatory adventures of self-discovery we
can undertake, allowing us to understand ourselves more deeply.
It's daunting to come to terms with the violence inherent in

something that is so personal and yet also universal, and to also overcome the strong cultural discouragement of doing so. Relatively few of us dare undertake this journey to its conclusion, but the rewards are enormous, if we persevere.

Animal agriculture is essential to the agenda of those who exploit humanity, because we reap the seeds we sow. By indoctrinating us into complying with and participating in a foundational cultural system that compels all of us to purchase and eat animal-sourced foods, and heartlessly reduce animals to mere commodities, we relentlessly reinforce our own status as obtuse exploitive commodities who are similarly born to be milked and fleeced by those who control the institutions of power, and who manage the narratives that keep everything in place. By consenting to exploit animals, we are consenting to our own exploitation. Our pervasive mistreatment of animals used for food and other products destroys the animals' freedom and well-being, and erodes our own as well.

It is not our fault, in that we are indoctrinated into this from infancy, and compelled to adopt a set of mutually reinforcing mentalities in order to participate in the defining activity of our culture. These mentalities include disconnectedness, desensitization, denial, exclusivism, elitism, domination of the feminine, commodification of living beings, predatory competitiveness, parasitic exploitiveness, reductionism, obtuse gullibility, and the over-arching mentality that supports all of these, which is materialism.[4] According to materialism, only that which can be physically sensed, measured, and quantified is real. Reductionism is materialism in action.

Being coerced into adopting these materialistic attitudes, and into living and functioning within such a societal framework, poisons our consciousness on many levels. However, much of this wounding is hidden and, like the violence, is mostly invisible because it is pervasive, all-encompassing, and normalized. It can only be fully understood when we are able to extricate ourselves from both the outer behavior and the many layers of inner conditioning. This is the liberating pathway that beckons, revealing that our culture's materialism disconnects us from awareness of our true nature and our inherent potentials for creativity, empathy, and freedom. Fortunately, each of us can make an effort to understand this, and we can each, perhaps with help and inspiration from others, undertake an adventure of remembering and healing. Externally, we can free ourselves from the behavior of eating, purchasing, and causing unnecessary suffering to others. Beyond this, we can make an effort that most do not make, which is to free ourselves from the underlying attitude of materialism that legitimizes reducing beings to mere commodities. While the most obvious effect of materialism is the direct suffering of animals, it also inflicts harm on ecosystems, other people, and ourselves.

The Two-Part Journey of Ahimsa

This journey of healing and awakening could be called the journey of *ahimsa* (nonviolence) or the journey of deep veganism. It is an essential gift we can give to ourselves and to our world, and it is becoming increasingly obvious that if we don't, as a culture, take this healing journey to a more conscious and non-exploitive way of living, our industrialized violence will destroy the possibilities of a viable future for all of us.

It is a two-part journey. The first part, freeing ourselves from the abusive behavior of purchasing and consuming animal-sourced foods and products, is relatively straightforward. The second part, freeing ourselves from the sticky web of interrelated attitudes injected into us by our herding culture, tends to be more complex and difficult.

For the first part, the outer vegan journey, we are called to transition to a way of living that minimizes harm, and a way of eating that is comprised entirely of plant-sourced foods. The good news is that this is nutritious and delicious, though it may be less convenient and socially-supported due to the pervasiveness of animal foods in our society. The vegetables, fruits, nuts, seeds, grains, herbs, legumes, tubers, and mushrooms we are eating should be organically grown (preferably without animal inputs) because pesticides, herbicides, and chemical fertilizers are environmentally toxic and sicken and kill birds, fish, insects, and others, and also are harmful to us as consumers. Organically grown foods are more nutrient-rich as well. Better than organic agriculture is veganic agriculture, also called stock-free agriculture, which is completely plant-based. Instead of using bone-meal, blood-meal, fish-meal, manure, and other animal-sourced inputs, it relies on plant-based compost, crop rotation with nitrogen-fixing legumes, soil mineralization with rock dust, building healthy soil with effective microorganisms, and other animal-free and chemical-free inputs. This veganic agriculture is growing in popularity worldwide, providing an alternative to the biodiversity loss and violence connected with animal agriculture, and it is increasingly clear that plant-based organic farming is possible without any losses in yield.[5]

Foods should also be whole and unprocessed or minimally processed, because refined and processed foods tend to include harmful chemical flavorings, additives, preservatives, and processing methods, and also pollute and damage nature and wildlife. In addition to refusing to comply with cultural mandates that exploit animals for food, as vegans we also extend this justice and compassion as far as possible to every area of our lives. Thus, we refrain from purchasing any items with leather, wool, down, silk, beeswax, and other animal-sourced inputs, or that are tested on animals, or require animals to suffer in laboratories or for entertainment, or for our use in any way. This is the outer journey of veganism. It is basically mindfully living our lives to minimize the amount of suffering we cause to animals, and also to fellow humans. We boycott food, clothes, and products involving human exploitation, such as those chocolates, clothing, and other products that use slavery or child slavery, and do our best to be consequent, and as conscious as possible of the ripples that radiate from our actions into the vast web of relations.

This outer aspect of the deep vegan journey lays the foundation for the second aspect, which is the effort to consciously liberate ourselves from the harmful cultural attitudes that still live within us, many of which tend to be relatively untouched by the positive outer changes we are making. This second step, the inner journey of ahimsa, transforms veganism into holistic deep veganism, and is essential because without it, mere veganism or plant-based living tends to be unstable. Many of us go vegan and five or ten years later are no longer vegan because we haven't been able to undo and transform the inner conditioning of materialism, or we are still vegan but fall prey to the materialistic narratives that undermine health and freedom. This inner path calls us to question every aspect of the prevailing narrative, both in the outer world as well as in our internalized beliefs, ambitions, and stories.

As a culture, we have been herding animals now for about ten thousand years.[6] This is roughly four hundred generations, and it has become a deeply ingrained bad habit, a toxic superstition that is completely obsolete. Its devastating tentacles penetrate not only into every dimension of our planetary ecosystems and into our culture, economy, and social institutions, but also into our bodies, minds, feelings, and consciousness. Everything these tentacles touch, they damage, pervert, and destroy.

Being born into a herding culture, and into the exploitive structures of centralized corporate capitalism and socialism that herderism has inevitably generated,[7] injures us all from infancy. The only reason any of us eats animal-sourced foods is because we are following orders that have been imposed on us from infancy by our parents and families, and by every institution and tradition in our society. It is anything but a free choice. Though these orders are not in our best interest, they are exceedingly difficult for us to question because food and meals are our most intimate connection with our culture and relationships, as well as with the natural world, and with our self-image. Additionally, the main goal of our education system, when we look realistically, is to transform us into compliant and obedient order-followers dedicated to pleasing authority figures. This further reduces our capacity to authentically question and put an end to the core violence that we as a society are causing and eating on a daily basis.

The Delusions of Herderism

With ten millennia of practice in the attitudes required to herd and exploit animals, we have now unfortunately incorporated the misperceptions of herderism thoroughly into our worldview, and we have obediently passed these traditional delusions from generation to generation. In doing so, we have passed on herderism's necessarily accompanying materialistic furies as well: war, slavery, exploitation of the feminine, the macho male role-model for boys, a wealthy ruling class, speciesism, social inequity and injustice, and our existential disconnectedness from nature and animals. These are but the many guises through which materialism operates. If we continue to eat animal foods and to parasitically prey upon imprisoned animals, it's unavoidable that we will be similarly preyed upon by a parasitic ruling class.

The sprawling and traumatizing delusion of herderism, summed in one word, materialism, is the defining educational practice of our culture. It relentlessly teaches us from infancy to harden our gaze, to disconnect, and to see certain living beings as nothing more than inconsequential property objects, like concrete blocks. All of us, whatever our race, gender, orientation, religion, or class happen to be, are ritually abused by our culture's food indoctrinations that compel us to mentally transform someones into somethings.[8] We are deceived, and compelled to act on a daily basis, as if living beings are nothing more than insentient matter whose value is determined by the mass of the flesh comprising their physical bodies, and by the secretions and offspring they can produce.

Materialism is an enslaving philosophy, confining us not just physically but spiritually in delusion. Voltaire famously said, "If we believe absurdities, we will commit atrocities," and as a result of our beliefs, animals abused for food, products, research, and other uses have little protection, because they are legally, culturally, and mentally reduced to the status of material property objects. Our ability to make connections, the foundation of cognitive and emotional intelligence,[9] is eroded with every animal-sourced product we consume.

Practicing the extreme form of reductionistic mistreatment that is animal agriculture for ten thousand years, generation upon generation, we have drifted far from the basic wisdom of connecting with and respecting life—both our own and that of others. We have become a thoroughly materialistic and parasitic culture, and with our meals as the template, we see ourselves and each other, and all life, and the very cosmos, in this materialist way as well. Materialism destroys our inherent sense of the sacred, and reductionist science, the reigning repository and faith-based authority of materialism in our world today, has become an abusive control system, well-suited to exploit and oppress our children and all of us, as it is similarly used to exploit nature and animals.

We are indoctrinated from infancy into the mythos of scientism, to see ourselves as mere physical bodies born into a random and essentially meaningless universe. This creates an existential anxiety that disempowers us and undermines our self-confidence and makes us naïve and easily controlled. This anxiety also fuels consumerism, which is our culture's shallow and pathetic surrogate proxy to genuine authenticity and meaning. Invidious consumption is the primary way for us to prove and display our self-worth to others and ourselves, and is the main path offered to find meaning in our lives. This of course ensures our willing subjection to the industrial-medical complex whose products offer us the only approved avenue to validate our self-worth, find success and fulfillment, and protect ourselves from the ever-expanding threats of disease, depression, and absurdity. This delusion of materialism pervades and corrupts our economic system, as well as our reductionist science, medicine, religion, education, and all our institutions. It devastates not just animals and ecosystems, but also our inherent wisdom, compassion, and well-being. The materialism of herderism imprisons us in invisible cages, out of which many of us try to escape through addictions and abusing ourselves and others in various ways. This tends to make us even more miserable, harmful, and confused, which further aids the domination agenda of the parasitic ruling class.

Alternatives to Materialism

The extreme materialism of our contemporary culture is unprecedented, and we are taught to trust materialistic science and to be proud of its technological achievements that afford unparalleled comfort and convenience, and to view less "developed" cultures with paternalistic disdain. And yet, it is obvious that our materialistic approach that relies on technology is destroying the web of life on this Earth, as well as our basic cultural harmony and our physical and mental well-being as individuals. We are causing a remarkably severe extinction of other species, with nuclear annihilation looming amidst chronic global conflicts and unprecedented levels of environmental devastation, economic inequities, social divisions and alienation, human trafficking, child abuse, suicide, drug addiction, pandemics, disease, hunger, and a global mass formation epidemic of fear that has propelled entire societies into devastating medical tyranny. With an increasingly conflicted population, a large percentage of which seems to crave being controlled by an unelected technocracy, we are witnessing animal agriculture's projected materialism in all its demonic ugliness and dysfunctionality.

We ask, what are the alternatives? There are and have been many. Religions and spiritual wisdom traditions are found in every culture, and they traditionally furnished the overarching narratives providing both meaning as well as moral guidance to individuals. They also facilitated social cohesion and opportunities for introspection and reflection. Over the past two centuries, religious institutions and their teachings have been ever-increasingly attacked by education, media, "science," and government narratives and policies. They lie wounded and in tatters today, unable to avoid being shut down by government fiat and casually dismissed as "non-essential." Though the globalist cabal[10] controlling commerce, medicine, government, and other cultural institutions works hard to discredit, ignore, and trivialize the wisdom teachings offered by religious traditions, these traditions continue to potentially bring guidance, empowerment, and healing as they have for thousands of years.

The Golden Rule

One of the first things we notice when we study the world's major religions is that all of them basically agree in their fundamental teachings, and that the core teaching of every religion is articulated similarly. When we lectured in Qufu, the city in northeastern China where Confucius lived about 2,500 years ago, Madeleine and I explored the ancient temple complex there where the core Confucian teaching is worded thus: "Whatever you would not want done to you, do not do to others." This basic teaching of The Golden Rule is foundational moral teaching, and is specifically promulgated as such in Christianity, Islam, Buddhism, Jainism, Hinduism, Judaism, and Taoism as well. These religious traditions carry the potential to bring the light of wisdom and compassion into the minds and hearts of many billions of people worldwide, who profess to follow the core teachings of these religions. Universal principles like The Golden Rule can be practiced and can enrich the lives of non-religious people also. They remind us of a higher standard of being and living, and inspire us to question and oppose systems of exploitation, violence, and injustice.

This essential teaching of the world religions can be summed as, "Whatever you most want for yourself, give that to others. To be loved, be loving. To be free, liberate others. To experience gratitude, joy, and abundance, be generous." When we hear and contemplate this wisdom of The Golden Rule, we realize that it resonates in every cell of our being as profound truth. It reflects and supports another universal wisdom teaching, which is the teaching of the interconnectedness and essential unity of all life. Deeply related to these two spiritual principles is the third universal teaching found in all religions, which is that whatever seeds we sow in our actions, speech, and thought, we will inevitably reap the results.

The Pseudo-Religion of Scientism

These wisdom teachings are completely contrary to the practice of animal agriculture, and the war and exploitation that are so profitable to the plutocratic ruling class, so of course these teachings have to be suppressed and corrupted, and the religions themselves attacked, ignored, and trivialized. The goal is to replace them with less threatening versions, and even better, by materialist science, which is completely value-free and offers no moral guidance, contributes no ethical challenge or inspiration, and provides no foundation for resistance to injustice. In fact, science is easily used to legitimize the domination of the weak by the strong through its inherent moral relativism, and theories such as natural selection, leading to Social Darwinism, which sanction the exploitation of the vulnerable. All manner of scientific narratives can be easily concocted, or perverted, to serve the agendas of the wealthy ruling class.

Because of this, we have witnessed the virtually complete corruption of science, so that it can be elevated to the status of our culture's primary faith-based religion, which must be followed without question. What is typically referred to as science in our world today is not science at all, but is *scientism*. Authentic science is virtually non-existent, because it is the free and open inquiry into the nature of reality, based on observation and the willingness to consider all possible explanations, and free and honest communication of hypotheses, findings, and ideas. In today's world, materialism has captured science, and no scientist is allowed to hypothesize non-material causes, forces, or entities. Science, now reduced to scientism, has become an indoctrinated belief system with rigid boundaries of inquiry.

This scientism has also been further corrupted by money, politics, and power, so that only specific dogmas and findings can be recognized and published, which support approved narratives. As Thomas Kuhn demonstrated in his classic book, *The Structure of Scientific Revolutions*, rigid paradigms (the conditioned internal patterns our minds use to interpret reality) clearly tend to hinder the scientific method, and it is exceedingly difficult to change these paradigms, or even to be aware of them. Thus, innovative so-called progress in science is typically only achieved by the contributions of outside researchers who are freer to think outside the boxes that academia and scientism impose on mainstream researchers.

We are told that we must trust the science, not to do our own research, and also to trust the consensus of scientists about the nature of reality. This so-called science is easily manipulated by those who control funding, educational doctrines, and the media. The idea of consensus as a guarantor of truth would be humorous in its absurdity if it were not so utterly destructive to freedom, rationality, and wisdom. Authentic science, like truth itself, has nothing to do with what a majority of indoctrinated humans may believe; they may all be completely misguided, deluded, or controlled. When alternative voices can easily be censored and ignored, we have but the illusion of scientific consensus, especially when the media is dominated by a small handful of narrative controllers.

It is essential to completely disabuse ourselves of the scientism that is paraded in academia and the media, and into which we are forcibly initiated by the herding culture's rulers. Scientism and the scientific swamp are enthroned, not allowing us to ever question the core of our culture, which is turning not just animals but also humans into exploitable livestock. The power that liberates us from all this delusion and violence is spirituality.

Spirituality

Spirituality is the essence of truth, freedom, joy, and wisdom. It arises within us spontaneously when our mind is quiet and open and we perceive directly that we are not this physical body and its sense-impressions, feelings, and cravings, but are transcendent non-physical awareness that functions through a phenomenal bodily appearance, and that makes this appearance possible. Just as we recognize that a footprint in the sand is not the being who made the footprint, spirituality realizes that this body is, meta-phorically, a footprint, and recognizes the incorporeal being that manifests the outer appearance. When we realize this directly and intuitively, our mind and heart open, and fear dissolves and a sense of peace and joy arises within us, as well as lovingkindness and respect for the many expressions of eternal consciousness that we can see all around us. Spirituality is the foundation of compassion, justice, freedom, wisdom, and peace because it dissolves the delusion of essential separateness, and the fear, greed, and suffering inescapably arising from this delusion.

There is of course a vast spectrum of spirituality, and we are all at different stages of awakening and realization. Our purpose on Earth seems to be to learn and grow authentically, and in our unique way to awaken spiritually, so that we discover our true nature and can contribute creatively to solving the problems here, rather than just making them worse through our indoctrinated misunderstanding and conditioned tribalism. The more spirituality genuinely awakens in us, the more we question internalized programming, and refuse to comply with narratives that legitimize oppression and exploitation. We naturally free ourselves from the imprisoning delusion that reduces beings to exploitable objects, including other humans as well as cows, fishes, and other animals. As spirituality grows in us, our consciousness is cleansed, and what is referred to as a vegan way of living naturally resonates with us and calls to be understood and embraced.

Of course, it is possible to have glimpses of spiritual awareness that are profound and helpful, but nevertheless, in our unique journey, fail to move all the way to a vegan way of living, for various reasons. And it is also possible to respond to the harm inflicted on animals, our Earth, hungry people, and our physical body by our culture's animal-based meal rituals, and adopt a

vegan lifestyle, and only have what seems to be a relatively limited amount of spiritual insight. We are all on our particular paths
and trajectories, and have our unique wounds, purposes, abilities,
and capacities, and there is little benefit in competing or comparing, or in judging or criticizing. The main thing is to understand
the cultural wounding of herderism and how it suppresses authentic spirituality, and do our best to unfold our unique gifts
and purify our consciousness and our actions so that we can help
others through our example and encouragement.

Spirituality clearly reveals to us the underlying unity and interconnectedness of all expressions of life, and awakens within us
the natural yearning to be kind to others and to be a force for
liberation and healing. Without trying to be "good," we find our
behavior naturally harmonizing with The Golden Rule, and our
greatest joy becomes finding ways to help others be free of suffering and the causes of suffering.

Spirituality and Religion

There is an essential difference between spirituality and religion.
The difference is that spirituality's loyalty is undivided. Spirituality is committed to the direct and liberating apprehension of
truth, and cultivating the capacity to live in alignment with this
truth. It flows from realizing that the material world is an arising
in consciousness and that our true nature, and the true nature of
all beings, is infinite and eternal consciousness, which is the
source of our life and of all manifested appearances. Spirituality
can heal every physical, psychological, and cultural wound and
shines compassion and wisdom into our awareness, steadfastly
guiding us to reject the materialistic delusions of fear-based, self-
centered narratives that promote division and oppression.

Religion, in contrast, has a divided loyalty. On the one hand,
it is committed to promoting the authentic spirituality of its
founders and exemplars, but on the other hand, it is a cultural
institution, so it is committed to supporting the primary narratives of whatever culture it is serving. So, in religion there is a

constant tension between the purity of its spiritual wisdom teachings, and the delusions that characterize the culture that the religion is expected to support. Religious corruption of authentic spirituality in practices and teachings is an ever-present problem, calling us to vigilance and increased awareness and inner work.

Basically, it is our authentic spirituality as communities of individuals that guarantees the degree of legitimate spirituality in our religious institutions. We as individuals are responsible for the quality of spirituality in our religious institutions. Yet at the same time, the purity and authenticity of our religions profoundly affect the degree of spirituality we as individuals are likely to attain. As with all cultural dynamics, the core reality is what Thich Nhat Hanh called *interbeing*, the profound interrelatedness of apparently separate entities. A religion both reflects and determines the people, and the people reflect and determine the religion. The same is true at the cultural level as well. As individuals we both create and are created by our society. Which has more power in this dynamic of interbeing, the individual or the society?

Ultimately, it is the individual. Each one of us, as an individual expression of eternal consciousness, has the power to transform our reality and our society. This particular life that each one of us is manifesting is our ongoing opportunity of awakening to the power and potential inherent and latent within us. Our life is meant to be an ongoing discovery, as we learn and overcome challenges so that we can contribute from ever higher levels of understanding. We were not born to be safe, comfortable, and secure, or to try to survive, or to merely pass on our genes, just as a beautiful ship is not created to remain anchored for eighty years in a harbor, trying to be safe and secure. The voices that urge us to be safe are often the demonic fear-based enslaving voices of the culture's toxic herding narrative that steals the purposes of both animals and humans and tries to destroy spirituality and to corrupt religion. We are called to free ourselves from these voices that promote the narratives and conveniences of scientific materialism that despoil not just the living web of beauty and enchantment, but also erode the sacred respect that holds us in harmony with this living web.

Spirituality is the key that unlocks the door to our life as an adventure of exploration, fueling our ability to co-create religious institutions and communities that are healthy, free, and in harmony with the Earth and animals. Every day, we can make progress on our two-part journey of ahimsa and help to rescue our world from deception and materialism.

The tension between spirituality and the overarching culture can be seen especially clearly in the three Abrahamic religions—Christianity, Islam, and Judaism—which emerged in areas of the world where animal agriculture was already most strongly established. While there are many scriptural passages that support spirituality and animal liberation, there are others in these traditions that permit and even seem to encourage human exploitation and killing of animals. "Thou shalt not kill" is typically interpreted to refer only to humans, for example, not to animals exploited for food and other uses, and these traditions clearly reflect the uneasy tension in their societies between authentic spirituality, which would immediately liberate animals, and the established cultural core of herderism, which required religious institutions that would not seriously question the culture's defining practice.

The religious traditions that emerged in areas less devoted to animal agriculture, where people ate a more plant-sourced diet, such as Buddhism, Jainism, Confucianism, Taoism, and many forms of Hinduism, are very explicit that the precept against killing applies not just to humans but to "all sentient beings." Even today, for example, when we travel to Buddhist places like Vietnam, Korea, and China, if someone is a vegetarian or vegan, it is assumed that it is because they are a devoted Buddhist. These non-Western religions tend to be non-theistic in their orientation, focusing more on inner work such as meditation, and on non-violence and on living an ethical life. The theistic religions also have these elements as well, but tend to adopt more of the authoritarian judgmentalism and dualism that are inherent in herderism, with its rigid human supremacist mentality that is required to legitimize its defining practice of reducing animals to livestock.

Countless indigenous spiritual systems also support a wide variety of approaches to spirituality, and all spiritual traditions share the underlying understanding that there is far more to this world than the shallow material veneer. Tragically, we in our herding culture are taught that this thin veneer is all that exists. Most religious traditions teach that we are never mere victims of circumstance. They recognize that we are multi-dimensional beings who are conscious and aware in other manifestations, lifetimes and realms, always sowing and reaping, learning and growing, expressing and contributing.

We are called to make our best efforts to separate the wheat from the chaff, so to speak, and to understand that religious institutions can be corrupted into vehicles of abuse and delusion, and to practice discernment in pondering their teachings. Nevertheless, all of the world's religious traditions provide potentially helpful guidance, and can be enormously beneficial for those who are called to them. They share essential ethical insights, such as The Golden Rule, as well as inspiring metaphysical teachings and opportunities for service and introspection, and practices that provide valuable contexts for reawakening inner resources of wisdom, compassion, creativity, and courage. They can inspire us to make the effort to purify our motivations, pacify our impatience, tame our unruly and obsessive thinking, and harmonize our relationships. These efforts, through whatever tradition we are called to explore and embody, can help us to gain transformational and healing insight into perennial jewels of spiritual wisdom. As we develop our ability to properly discriminate the true from the untrue, we liberate our consciousness and contribute to the healing of our world.

The myriad delusions of materialism sabotage health and harmony, and prime us to be targeted by weaponized financial, governmental, media, and medical systems. This is the current world into which we have been born, rooted in animal agriculture and in the science and technology it has generated. Its paths and trajectories are based on separation and exploitation, and lead us seductively along, ultimately, if we consent, to our own oppression. Animals are the living example of this, and animal liberation is the defining test for us today, both individually and collectively. Freeing animals opens the door to a beckoning path of health and human liberation, leading to an abundant world in which our lives reflect our unity with nature and with all expressions of life.

PART TWO

THE TWO FUTURES:
THE PATH OF TECHNOLOGY
AND THE PATH OF SPIRITUALITY

CHAPTER FIVE

LIBERATING OUR MINDS

～～

"If we could change ourselves, the tendencies in the world would also change. As a man changes his own nature, so does the attitude of the world change towards him. This is the divine mystery supreme. A wonderful thing it is and the source of our happiness. We need not wait to see what others do."
—MOHANDAS GANDHI

"I know of no more encouraging fact than the unquestionable ability of man to elevate his life by a conscious endeavour."
—HENRY DAVID THOREAU, WALDEN

"We must be alert to the danger that public policy could itself become the captive of a scientific, technocratic elite."
—PRESIDENT DWIGHT D. EISENHOWER, FAREWELL ADDRESS, 1960

The Path of Technology and the Path of Spirituality
When we look toward our collective future, even in the short term, we see severe challenges that threaten not only our survival—such as nuclear weapons and our destruction of natural ecosystems—but also our health, freedom, and happiness, such as high-tech

surveillance operations and centralized control of entire societies through digital tracking and Central Bank Digital Currency systems. The essential distinguishing feature of our culture, relentless oppression of animals, is not only aided by science and technology, but it also generates the underlying template of materialism, reductionism, and domination that propels and determines the way science and technology are practiced and developed. Herderism engenders the reductionist narratives and technology that lead directly to the same type of dystopian future that we also inflict on cows, pigs, chickens, and other beings who are reduced to livestock.

It is heartening to see increasing numbers of us discovering that the mainstream narrative with which we've been bombarded from birth—that technology is our savior and will create an abundant and happy future for all—is a grand deceit. We can ask the cows and chickens what it has done for them. Our lives are in many ways defined by our culture's technology. While in some ways our lives are certainly improved by our systems of plumbing, sanitation, transportation, communication, and so forth, technology as it is practiced in our society tends to disconnect us from nature and from each other, as is becoming obvious with social media, for example. It can be deliberately weaponized against us, and high-tech armaments, robotics, chemicals, drugs, and surveillance systems pose a direct threat to our individual freedom, awareness, and wellness. We ironically use similar technologies against animals to facilitate our routine processing and killing of millions of them daily. The roots of modern science and technology, going back thousands of years, lie in our efforts to more effectively breed, confine, and dominate animals.

What we have practiced and developed over the centuries, we increasingly embody in our attitudes and lifestyles, reaping their effects as we do so. Continually devising more efficient and inescapable control systems for the animals we eat, for example, we find now that military technology developed by the Defense Advanced Research Projects Agency (DARPA) is apparently already advanced enough to influence us by planting thoughts and emotions into our minds.[1] Globalist plutocrats are talking about the benefits of being able, with technology, to know what we are thinking and feeling, and thus be able to keep society more safe and secure by arresting us for thought crimes, before any disallowed actions are committed.[2] Technology is undeniably a potent tool of centralization of wealth and power, and of the control of the minds, bodies, and lives of the many by the few.

One primary pillar of the ruling class's agenda of global domination is the relentless poisoning of humanity. Technology affords a wide spectrum of ways to weaken and cull us by deliberately poisoning us physically, mentally, and emotionally. For example, over 80,000 chemicals are registered for use in agriculture, food, commerce, and industry,[3] and many thousands of these are known to cause cancer, birth defects, hormone disruption, digestive issues, nerve damage, and other harms, typically with plausible deniability because they are difficult to isolate and track individually. They are in food, liquids, and the air we breathe, and give rise to chronic disease, which legitimizes even more poisoning through bodily injections and administration of pharmaceutical chemicals. In many countries, including the U.S., public drinking water is deliberately poisoned with fluoride, a known neurotoxin that has been proven to reduce intelligence in human beings.[4] A harmful byproduct of aluminum smelting, fluoride was allegedly used in prison camps because it was discovered to make prisoners docile, lethargic, and easier to control.[5] Fluoride is also known to attack the pineal gland, which in ancient wisdom traditions is understood as a primary conduit of intuition and spiritual awareness.[6]

Another high-tech vector of domination is the ongoing aerial spraying of an estimated 60 to 80 million tons annually of nanoparticulate plumes of aluminum, barium, strontium, graphene, and other harmful substances to allegedly reflect solar radiation to combat global warming.[7] This geoengineering is relentlessly poisoning soil, water, and the air we breathe. As researcher Dane Wigington and others have documented, it is used in conjunction with powerful ionospheric heating arrays such as the High-Frequency Active Auroral Research Program (HAARP) to control weather fronts, creating and manipulating droughts, fires, floods, and hurricanes as part of weather warfare programs, and can be used to directly modify the weather to promote globalist agendas and deceptively advance climate change narratives and fears.[8] Additionally, our entire planet is being blanketed with millions of 5G (fifth-generation) EMF (electromagnetic frequency) emitting stations, as well as tens of thousands of satellites that continually bombard the Earth with electromagnetic radiation, forcing all of us to live in inescapable electromagnetic fields that have been proven to be harmful both physically and psychologically.[9]

This is just a brief and incomplete glimpse into the ongoing poisoning that works to harm and weaken us. Beyond this physical level of chemical, electromagnetic, and nuclear poisoning, we are also poisoned by pervasive media technologies that continuously manage our perception of the world, and implant fear, anxiety, anger, lust, and other negative emotions through carefully-crafted news, music, film, art, advertising, and other programming. Deception itself is a poison to our mental and cultural health, and technology can be easily weaponized in order to engineer our perception of the world. We rely on internet search engines, electronic media and communications, online discussions, and so forth, to form our understanding of reality. These technologically-mediated inputs that condition the minds of the many can easily be manipulated by the few. It's essential to understand that the ruling class relies on technology to implement its agenda of dominating us as "humanstock," and this is one of the main reasons the mainstream media, and front groups like the World Economic Forum and the World Health Organization, constantly promote technology as providing the only solutions to our problems.

In aspiring to a positive future, we do well to question and reject the seductive temptations continually introduced by technology, and the shallow materialism of scientism, and instead to focus on the path of spiritual practice. No amount of technology can ever substitute for the cultivation of our inner resources of discernment, renunciation, integrity, humility, respect for nature and others, hard work, kindness, and authenticity. In many ways, our culture's materialistic science and its technology that we are taught to venerate for bringing us "progress" are actually Trojan Horse forces that continually erode our environmental, cultural, physical, emotional, intellectual, and spiritual health. The price we pay for whatever comfort, convenience, and security that our modern technology supposedly provides is, in many ways, far higher than the benefits conferred. Both animal agriculture, and the materialistic mindset and technologies it fosters, are Faustian bargains that corrode our health and wisdom on every level. We have more pharmaceutical drugs than ever, and more weapons systems, and more surveillance systems, and more pesticides, but are we healthier, more secure, and more in harmony because of them?

When we take time to read the voluminous texts from ancient wisdom traditions, it becomes apparent that people without our technological advantages were in many ways more advanced than we are in their understanding of the subtleties of human consciousness, and of the capacities that we have available to us for co-creating peaceful, rewarding, and abundant lives. However, we are perhaps deceived in our education about the quality of life in less high-tech times and places, with history books conditioning and deceiving us, telling us about how short and miserable their lives must have been compared to ours today. How else do modern day robber barons get us to sit for hours in isolated cubicles staring into computer screens? Are we really freer today with technology's demands? How would we ever know? The disconnectedness from nature that results from our technology is also a disconnection from our aliveness and sense of immediacy and participation in a sacred world filled with intelligent and conscious non-human beings. Besides addicting us to comfort, reducing our vigor and clarity, and insulating us from nature, this disconnectedness deceives us into a state of unawareness concerning the undeveloped capacities that would support us in thriving without modern technology.

As but one small example, when I was living and studying in a Tibetan Buddhist center, I learned about ancient techniques to generate *tummo*, which is "psychic heat," to generate bodily warmth, if necessary, as well as a corresponding practice for cooling the body. These practices gave people more resilience and a sense of bonding with nature, rather than an addicted intolerance for temperature changes and a fear of nature. Making an effort to learn and practice them, we could reduce our dependence on mechanical and resource-intensive heating and air conditioning systems. There were also techniques to project consciousness and engage in mental communication with others, and to be able to see remotely, and also methods of rapidly moving the physical body. Granted, it requires a large investment of time and effort to develop the prodigious mental concentration necessary to attain these and other similar abilities, but this effort would benefit us and others in many ways by purifying, settling, and focusing our minds. This would seem to be more empowering and rewarding than being chained to a job to earn money to buy technological devices with harmful side effects.

Our dependence on technological devices for virtually every aspect of our lives creates an illusion of power, as well as enormous pollution, and besides harming our health and our environment,[10] it throws us out of harmony with nature and with each other. By cultivating inner capacities of sensitivity and focused awareness, we increase our appreciation of nature and others, and potentially open to higher levels of wisdom and understanding that create more harmony for all. We have far greater capacities than our culture acknowledges. However, our education, food, and medical systems, as well as the general social indoctrination we endure from infancy, render us just fit and aware enough to be useful to the exploitive established order, and at the same time, unhealthy, misinformed, and distracted enough to be non-threatening to it.

The technology that permeates our lives is a manifestation of a type of Luciferian hubris that propels us to dominate the natural world, destroying it and "improving" it by violent manipulation. This wounds us all egregiously, without us realizing it. The future it has in store for us cannot be other than one of centralized control, slavery, ugliness, and meaninglessness, no matter how the well-paid narrative-controllers attempt to spin it. When we cultivate the path of deep vegan living, which is respect for nature and for the creative intelligence imbuing every living manifestation, we naturally focus on spiritual evolution, which is our deeper purpose, and which brings love, meaning, joy, and freedom. From this awareness, we may develop what Gandhi referred to as appropriate technology, which is using tools and ways of doing things that don't force us to disconnect, dominate, pollute, and destroy nature, animals, and each other.

Our culture's futuristic narratives in mainstream books, movies, and TV and radio shows—based on the idea that we will have high-tech innovations such as robotics, transhumanism, artificial intelligence, genetic engineering, virtual gadgetry, and SMART (self-monitoring and reporting technology) cars, appliances, and cities—reflect the dominant worldview that is deluded by materialism. Our minds and hearts can never be at peace if we don't have cultural support for self-inquiry, meditation, and empathy for animals, nature, and each other. As a result, we are restless and easily distracted, and our technology reinforces this, and spins futuristic visions that will never bring us inner peace, and in fact are bringing us the opposite.

How does a positive future actually look? This future requires not fancier technology but spiritual depth that savors the sacred beauty and respects the vulnerability of the living beings all around us. This future measures positivity not in terms of consuming and exploiting the natural world, but in terms of contentment, creativity, and freedom from jealousy, greed, anger, lust, and fear. We live on an unimaginably intelligent and abundant planet that we completely misunderstand, and we call our systematized propagation and proliferation of this gross misunderstanding, "science." This so-called science and its technology drag us relentlessly further and further into ignorance and a dystopian future controlled by a privileged few.

As we mature beyond materialism, a positive future emerges. By accessing the innate intuitive wisdom that directly perceives our interconnection with the living web of life, we can co-create decentralized, self-sufficient village-communities based on spiritual principles of cooperation, nonviolence, and interdependence. The first step is liberating animals, and also liberating ourselves from the reductionistic scientism and technology that seek continually to centralize control and dominate our minds and lives. No matter how mainstream narratives proclaim otherwise, we are not matter, and sooner or later, we will awaken to this awareness. We are noncorporeal consciousness and we manifest physical forms. Our inherent wisdom, love, and creative power are like the eternal sky, which is ultimately undamageable and uncontrollable by mere clouds. Each of us can engage in the inner work to understand this more clearly, and cooperate in co-creating the spiritual foundations for the positive future that is our birthright and destiny.

Breaking the Materialistic Spell

In January of 2020, Madeleine and I were on a five-month tour in our RV, promoting vegan living, when we started learning about the Covid-19 "pandemic" and immediately understood it as yet another false flag event designed to scare us all into giving up more of our human freedoms and rights. By the time March rolled around, we were in southern California toward the end of our tour, and though we preferred to finish up presenting the last few events we had scheduled, the local groups canceled them due to public health concerns. It is essential to see that this disturbing pattern of obedient compliance with criminally tyrannical and deceptive narratives and mandates destroys the fabric of our society, and the future of our species. On a worldwide scale, we have been relentlessly enslaving and exploiting billions of animals for food and other purposes, and now we find ourselves increasingly reaping the fruits of the seeds we have sown, and in many cases even eagerly acquiescing to forfeiting our sovereignty, as we have stolen it from the animals we heartlessly oppress. Why have we been so easily fooled and willing to believe the governmental, medical, and media authorities, and accede to their devastating directives, even when they are irrational, anti-scientific, and harm the causes to which we are dedicated?

After all, for many decades it had been universally accepted by public health officials and epidemiologists, and taught in medical schools worldwide, that healthy asymptomatic people do not spread disease. So, how could it be possible to suddenly jettison not only accepted science but basic common sense, and order healthy people to attack their own physical, mental, and societal health, and require them to wear face masks, distance themselves from each other, douse their skin in toxic sanitizers, stick testing sticks far up their nasal cavities into the base of their brains, and even forcibly close down the gyms, yoga studios, restaurants, churches, and stores on which their social, economic, and physical health rely? How would people ever tolerate such blatantly deceitful and draconian anti-scientific and egregiously harmful policies being imposed on them by unelected technocrats? As time went on and these dehumanizing absurdities were imposed on people worldwide, I thought to myself that it was a shame that people in other countries were complying with this harmful nonsense, but felt assured believing that no one would comply with such freedom-crushing medical abuse in the USA. Yet within a few weeks, I was shockingly disappointed to see flocks of dutifully masked and distanced people in the few local stores and businesses allowed to remain open.

Because neither Madeleine nor I ever partake of mainstream media, we had been spared the non-stop fear porn that was driving our fellow citizens to co-create the surreal scenes we saw unfolding around us. In fact, I was focused on alternative news outlets and concerned again to see the relatively few courageous and formerly highly respected doctors, epidemiologists, and journalists who spoke up against the official narratives being attacked and censored, and their messages being completely blocked, distorted, and demeaned in the obviously controlled mainstream and social media. The flagrant propaganda storm and accompanying censorship of truth caused a deep divide in the population and facilitated a devastating attack on societies worldwide that led directly to a massive transfer of wealth and power from the lower and middle classes to the super-rich, as well as sharp increases in rates of suicide, drug overdoses, alcoholism, and violent crime.[11] Next on the agenda came the rollout of experimental gene-altering injections that have killed and seriously injured many millions of people,[12] and irrevocably polluted the human genome with unknown and potentially insidious effects far into the future.[13]

Though we have committed similar atrocities against cows, pigs, and chickens, why did we not resist this brutal power grab more effectively, and why were we so easily deceived? For myself, though it was often somewhat disturbing to realize that I was the only person in a building with my face showing (besides Madeleine if she was with me), it was not a new feeling. Like all long-time vegan activists, I am well acquainted with going against social conventions and refusing to comply with group-think and group-compliant behaviors, especially if they promote injustice and exploitation. So, although we have often endured considerable inconvenience and social coercion to do so, Madeleine and I never complied with any of the degrading and harmful requirements prescribed by the public health authorities. We also endured the anguish of witnessing how easily friends and neighbors could be spooked into acquiescing to forces that were clearly intent on destroying the quality of their lives and stealing their ability to fulfill their purposes. Again, it is similar to the anguish I have felt for decades witnessing people insisting on eating animal-sourced foods that harm their health and abuse animals.

There is significant positive power in learning to say "No." When we understand the deeper situation, it may look to most people, for example, that we deep vegans are always saying no: no to meat, dairy products, eggs, and honey, no to products tested on animals or containing animal-based ingredients, no to circuses and entertainment that exploit animals, no to leather, fur, silk, and down in clothing. Yet all these "Noes" are actually "Yesses." We are saying yes to kindness, yes to justice, yes to sustainability, and yes to radiant health, freedom and equality. It is the same with health freedom. We refuse to comply with authoritarian mandates, and say no to masking, no to social distancing, no to locking down, no to toxic injections, no to censorship. All these "Noes" are similarly "Yesses" to health, solidarity, justice, sovereignty, self-reliance, natural immunity, compassion for children, and the basic freedoms of speech, assembly, religion, movement, and bodily autonomy that are fundamental to our dignity as human beings. By ramping up fear of supposed contagion, plutocrats realize they can not only enslave us, but even enroll many of us in policing their agenda. What is actually contagious is panic and delusion, and when we take responsibility for our health, we have nothing to fear, and we become a force for healing and freedom, rather than credulously spreading fear and mental disease.

Though we vegan advocates should theoretically be aware enough to be immune to the unending deceptions propagated by corporate-controlled mainstream media outlets, especially those serving Big Pharma—the nemesis of animals—it was sobering to see how many of us turned out to be not just susceptible, but aggressively gullible in our attacks on others who refused to comply with the official medical narratives. What I have been saying for many years is now more strongly underlined than ever: animal liberation is the foundation of human liberation, and requires of us not merely an outer change in buying habits, but calls us to undertake an ongoing and thorough transformation of our awareness. It summons us to free ourselves, first, from our violent abuse of animals, and second, from our herding culture's underlying reductionistic and materialistic orientation. This requires inner healing work, introspection, unlearning, and proactively creating a foundation for mental, emotional, and spiritual clarity that is not vulnerable to attacks by fraudulent and coercive outer forces. All of us today are called to make efforts in this direction, and to forge a deeper understanding not only of the hidden power structures in our world, and of the consequences of our violence toward animals, but also of our own true nature as sovereign and creative expressions of infinite consciousness.

The Power of Role Models and Associates

We cannot be free if we don't understand the cultural programming that has shaped our attitudes and paradigms from infancy, including the role models we have been taught to emulate. We virtually always tend to become like those with whom we regularly associate, and we also become like the information sources from which we form our perceptions of the world. It is important to consciously and carefully choose our information sources, as well as our role-models, friends and colleagues. We also serve as role-models to those around us, whether we are aware of it or not. Our actions are contagious, and convey our understanding and attitudes far more potently than do our words.

I feel particularly blessed by my first and primary role models and associates, my father and mother, who conveyed, through their living example, the importance, among other things, of discipline, of creative self-expression, of self-reliance, of holding firmly to one's convictions, and of love for the natural world. My father had intended to become a doctor, and as a young man in the army, served as a medic in France during the Second World War. His experience there caused him to change his mind and seek a different profession, and when I asked him about his time as a medic, he said that one of his main duties was to administer injections to soldiers who would line up for this in long queues, and he said he felt it wasn't good for them at all. His main advice to us three children, which he and my mother also followed, was, "Stay away from doctors." In hindsight, it has been some of the finest advice I've ever received, and I have done my best to follow it ever since.

After the war, he married my mother, a water-color artist, and started his own dance band as the pianist and also began working in newspapers. Right about the time I came along as the first child, he bought a weekly newspaper, *The Beacon*, in the suburbs of Boston. I grew up in the heady journalistic swirl of deadlines, breaking news, and local politics, and learned another lesson besides the one of not trusting the medical establishment: don't trust the media. Being raised in a newspaper family, I know in my bones that the so-called "news" is controlled by advertisers. It was virtually unthinkable to run news articles that major advertisers would find objectionable. I feel blessed by this insight into the media because I now see that few people clearly understand how all media is beholden to advertisers, and how, for example, Big Pharma's billions of dollars in advertising expense in the media is only partly to help sell its products. Pharma's primary motivation in advertising is to buy the absolute certainty that mainstream media will never journalistically challenge it, and will always defend and promote Pharma's narratives and public image, no matter how destructive that may be to the public good.

Money buys influence, allegiance, and narrative control, and there's even more to it than the power of corporate advertisers. Governments, through their so-called intelligence communities as well as military and health agencies, are deeply involved also. The only way to maintain corporate, financial, and military dominance, and an unjust and unequal social system, is through effective media management. As but one example, it is well known that the Central Intelligence Agency (CIA), for example through its Operation Mockingbird,[14] has been working diligently for decades to plant and control journalists, editors, and news managers not only in all major U.S. media outlets and corporations, but worldwide as well.[15] This is greatly facilitated by the consolidation of media ownership into the hands of a few giant conglomerates, whose assets are controlled by a small and wealthy cabal.

My parents virtually never looked at the television, which my father only referred to as "the boob tube," and strongly discouraged us from doing so as well. I feel richly blessed in not watching TV in the last fifty years, and having thus avoided a major source of the pernicious programming and mesmerizing messaging that continually erode the self-reliance of the general population with deceptive and disempowering narratives, and undermine the health of our society, always furthering the agenda of the parasitic ruling class. I have also avoided listening to the radio; virtually all radio programming is similarly destructive and has been captured by the same controlling plutocrats. Though having received a solid parental role-model foundation of healthy distrust for both Big Medica and Big Media, I felt called to extend these principles quite a bit further than they had, and to question and reject medical, media, and cultural narratives that rationalize animal exploitation for food and other purposes. As a vegan advocate since 1980, it has become instinctual to challenge official narratives about virtually everything, even those narratives that are embraced by large swathes of the population, whether of the left or right.

It has been helpful to study the pervasive use of subliminal images and conditioning both in television as well as print media, and I encourage all of us to develop media smarts to defend ourselves from being manipulated, not only by the outward deceptions cascading continually from mainstream media, but also through the pervasive use of stories, subliminals, emotional associations, embedded tribalistic triggers, and image-identifications that are designed to subtly manipulate us into attitudes and actions that are not in our best interests. Billions of dollars are spent on narrative control and on the ongoing effort to manipulate our perceptions, thoughts, and actions, and to control the public mind. Edward Bernays, the nephew of Sigmund Freud, also known as the father of public relations and advertising, articulated the emergent view of the "public mind" and its control back in 1928:

> The conscious and intelligent manipulation of the organized habits and opinions of the masses is an important element in democratic society. Those who manipulate this unseen mechanism of society

constitute an invisible government which is the true ruling power of our country. ...We are governed, our minds are molded, our tastes formed, our ideas suggested, largely by men we have never heard of. In almost every act of our daily lives, whether in the sphere of politics or business, in our social conduct or our ethical thinking, we are dominated by the relatively small number of persons...who understand the mental processes and social patterns of the masses. It is they who pull the wires which control the public mind.[16]

Beyond all this, there is also the reality of mass thought-forms and vibrational fields, which are created by large-scale cultural and media events. When many thousands or millions of people are thinking similar thoughts, or feeling similar emotions, potent thought-forms and resonant fields are created that will tend to draw us into them if our mental and emotional tone is open and receptive to them. This is another reason that meditation, self-inquiry, and internal clarity and self-reliance are essential to our well-being. An effective way to resist the low-vibrational group-think, group-fear, and group-hate that are intended to control the population is to consciously and regularly make an effort to free ourselves from our identification with cultural programs, and to raise our mental and emotional vibratory frequency to higher levels imbued with compassion, gratitude, and inner peace. This confers immunity from the real contagion, which is mental and emotional, not physical.

Though for many years my political views would be considered pretty far to the left, for the last two decades or so I have realized that the old left/right political spectrum model is obsolete because humanity is now being attacked and enslaved by globalist powers that use both left and right to their advantage, especially the left. Like many others, I have seen this coming for decades, with fraudulent false-flag operations like the World Trade Center disaster, the Iraq Weapons of Mass Destruction hoax, Covid, January 6, and many other ruses being orchestrated by the ruling plutocrats as clever and effective ploys to confuse and disempower people in order to forward a clear agenda to reduce humanity to the status of livestock. When asked about the erupting pandemic and the first lockdowns to "flatten the curve" in March of 2020, I typically responded that my concern about getting Covid, on a scale of zero to 100, was zero, but my concern about it being used by the ruling cabal to further exploit humanity was 100.

We become what we practice. With forty years of practice in refusing to comply with cultural mandates that destroy the freedom, happiness, and health of animals and all of us, and often being the only one in a given situation refusing the cheese, egg, or animal flesh, it was also relatively natural to be the only one rejecting toxic nose swabs, hand sanitizers, masking, and social distancing protocols. It was obvious these were all sham theatrics designed to befuddle and exploit our beloved fellow humans. Though it was heart-wrenching to see people obediently complying with such clearly destructive and unhealthy directives, it became quickly apparent that it was a bewildering waste of time to share alternative perspectives with colleagues and acquaintances who believed the official pandemic narratives. They seemed to be immune to reason and logic, and we realized that Covid was in fact primarily a mind-virus, spread mainly by the media, the government, and the medical establishment. This virus of fear was infecting and hypnotizing many people into a cult of hysteria, anxiety and disease, all based on cunning deception. Carl Jung, back in 1957, wrote presciently about the situation,

> Rational argument can be conducted with some prospect of success only so long as the emotionality of a given situation does not exceed a certain critical degree. If the affective temperature rises above this level, the possibility of reason having any effect ceases, and its place is taken by slogans and chimerical wish fantasies. That is to say, a sort of collective possession results, which rapidly develops into a psychic epidemic.[17]

It had all clearly been well planned for many years in advance,[18] and it was fascinating to see how cleverly and successfully the left was especially targeted. In the past, the left was known to be most vehemently opposed to restrictions on freedoms, rights, and transparency, especially by the infamously corrupt and arrogant pharmaceutical cartel, but after years of infiltration and corruption, the left was fragmented, reduced to identity-politics, and completely captured. It became, ironically, the willing well-spring of deception and tyranny. The main message from the authorities was always that we are masking, testing, social distancing, getting jabbed, and going to war not for ourselves but because we care about other people. What self-respecting liberal could ever go against that? The globalist ruling class understands how to weaponize our inherent altruism against us in order to deceive us into relinquishing our freedom and our solidarity. Because those of us who consider ourselves to be on (what calls itself) the left have often marinated longer in the education system, we tend to be more indoctrinated and psychologically wounded by the authority-compliant and reductionistic attitudes that academia relentlessly inculcates.

The Paradox of Education

In 2021, researchers at Carnegie-Mellon University studied Covid vaccine hesitancy as correlated with level of education[19] and found that the highest level of so-called hesitancy was in those with Ph.D. degrees, and the second highest, almost equal to that of the Ph.D.'s, was in those with no college education whatsoever. The highest levels of vaccine compliance were for those with bachelor's degrees, master's degrees (the highest), and professional degrees. When we contemplate our education system, we see that its primary purpose, like all institutions in our society, is to serve the central core of our culture, which is animal agriculture, and the desensitized and disconnected materialism this systemic violence toward animals requires in its population. In alignment with this, our education system promotes reductionism over holism, breaking knowledge up into artificial categories, and training us to submit to authority and trust outside experts rather than developing our inner capacities of rationality, critical thinking, empathy, creativity, and intuition. It rewards those who go through the more advanced educational indoctrination process with more insider status and with more ability to manipulate the system for financial and social benefits. This seems similar to the well-known difference between field slaves in the ante-bellum South, who were wary and skeptical of the slave master, and house slaves, who tended to identify with, support, and benefit by their closer relationship with the master. People with less exposure to government-sponsored formal education may be less devoted to and influenced by its authoritarian narratives, and the reductionistic mentality it demands, and therefore less likely to uncritically trust and identify with medical, media, and government authority figures.[20]

The researchers also found that as medical and governmental authorities applied increasing amounts of social and financial coercion on the general population to get injected with the Covid shots, the less educated people were more likely to succumb to this pressure than were those with Ph.D. degrees, who resisted more staunchly and effectively. In my Ph.D. training at U.C., Berkeley, besides the requisite coursework and research, I took courses in both quantitative and qualitative research methodologies, and became keenly aware of how research is always conditioned by the expectations and goals of the researchers and the funders of the research. In actual practice, science is used to implement and justify agendas, and this becomes clear to those who look behind the curtain of scientific research. Those with professional degrees, like doctors, do not typically get this kind of training or exposure, and so tend to be somewhat naïve about science. They are trained to follow situational protocols only, and are well respected and compensated for this, and rewarded for not asking questions, within the controlled medical framework.

I also studied and taught college courses in epistemology, the branch of philosophy that deals with truth: how do we know that what we think is true is actually true? I have found exploring and questioning the history and foundational assumptions and methodologies of science and of other approaches to knowledge of reality to be profoundly liberating. My Ph.D. focus was the Philosophical Foundations of Education, and my dissertation, "The Role of Intuition in Education,"[21] nominated for the Best Dissertation Award at Berkeley in 1988, addressed intuitive modes of knowing and how these can be educated, primarily in adults. I definitely experienced the enormous academic and social pressures to think like and become like those who were granting the degree and its gatekeepers. But in the prior ten years or so, I had also been fortunate to have spent many thousands of hours in meditation retreats as a Zen monk in Korea and in meditation centers in the U.S., focusing on freeing my consciousness from cultural programming. For this and other reasons, I was perhaps better equipped to somewhat successfully resist these academic pressures. This may have also helped to reduce the wounding that is typically inflicted by yearning for, and identifying with, the seductive advantages that advanced academic degrees often confer.

Responding to Transiency

As individuals we are being tested during these times in demanding ways. What we see unfolding since 2020 is the most sophisticated, expensive, well-organized, and far-reaching psychological, medical, economic, and physical assault on humanity-at-large in the history of the world. The false Covid medical narrative, part of a larger agenda, relentlessly hijacked every branch of government of virtually every country. It was clearly a trans-national operation, with globalist plutocrats functioning primarily through the World Health Organization (WHO) and the United Nations and thereby controlling national health agencies, governments, academia, and media. Children, the elderly, and small business owners were especially targeted, but all of us, with the exception of the wealthiest class, were assaulted and have had our freedoms eroded. Fortunately, there have been resilient pockets of higher awareness, and as the months and years have gone by, increasing numbers of us are awakening to the realities of the pervasive deception.

It is essential to work toward understanding the bigger picture of what we are. What inspired me to leave home and embark on the spiritual pilgrimage in my youth was the realization that there have been remarkable human beings who have awakened from delusion and attained significantly higher levels of consciousness. This seemed to me to be the primary worthwhile and foundational goal in life. Everything else seemed to be but distractions, and because time on this Earth is brief, uncertain, and flies by quickly, it seemed best to "seek first the kingdom of heaven." This metaphor for prioritizing the spiritual quest to uncover the living truth within, which is hidden by mental conceptualization and emotional affliction, was deeply inspiring. The well-known Biblical jewel goes on to say that the consequent result is that, "everything else shall be added..." On our initial walk from Massachusetts to Alabama, Ed and I had found this to be one of our key guiding phrases as we did our best to prioritize our quest for spiritual truth. We experienced it repeatedly and in a myriad of ways: the more we single-mindedly focused on inner realization, and invested our time and attention into that, the more reliably it seemed that food, shelter, and helpful connections synchronistically and effortlessly manifested in the outer world.

These and other universal spiritual teachings, so repressed and neglected in our society today, seemed to radiate their wisdom and peace during my early twenties, living in meditation centers and often rising at three or four in the morning and spending eight or more hours daily in meditation, studying sacred texts, learning about my mind and the power of thought, how attention and breathing are connected, and how emotions rise and fall. Gradually glimpses began arising, leading to profound feelings of joy and peace, and then periods of difficult struggle with longstanding mental tendencies, and then more insights and healings. The exploration of the inner world beckoned to potentialities more vast and more inspiring than the mighty Himalayas.

I began to realize that our mind is like an exquisite grand piano that we have never been taught to tune, understand, or play properly, so on the whole, we tend to make and experience a lot of dissonant noise, instead of the beautiful music that is available as a latent potential. We are taught from infancy by example to bang on the keys and spill drinks into the delicate action, rather than learning to respect our instrument and compose and savor the uplifting and unique harmonies, melodies, and rhythms of which our mind and spirit are fully capable. As time went on, I learned that my mind, understood and watched with awareness and discipline, was my best friend and most useful tool, bringing continuous possibilities of creativity, health, freedom, joy, and insight. Misunderstood and untamed, it could also be the worst possible enemy, creating a torturous prison of delusion, disease, and fear, and harming others as well. Underlying everything, I discovered the inherent tendency toward healing, compassion, and creative expression.

Looking back now from five decades of perspective since leaving home, I have nothing but the deepest gratitude for all the forces that led me as a youth to question the life paths that were being offered. The irresistible impulse to leave home opened a doorway to create an initiatory journey, and the underlying impulse was to forge a life dedicated to spiritual awakening first and foremost. All of us have the potential to connect with our inner wisdom and to leave home, which simply means leaving the indoctrinated tribal mentality that tends to imprison us in the shallows of awareness. My heart extends appreciation to the many teachings, teachers, and fellow seekers who have blessed this brief incarnation. More than learning, it has been about practicing and understanding the importance of unlearning, letting go, dropping, and releasing.

The essential idea is this: without a committed and ongoing inner practice, our minds have been so thoroughly poisoned by herderism's cultural conditioning that, as individuals and as a collective, we lack the strong foundation for effecting a positive transformation in our lives and in our world. It was toward the end of a 90-day meditation retreat that I glimpsed a fuller sense of the extent of the cultural conditioning, and how, from birth, and even before, my mind had been colonized by a harmful and deluded set of cultural narratives and attitudes that had become deeply entrenched in the very core of self-identity. I could see how this conditioning pervaded my thoughts, drove my feelings, ambitions, and self-concept, and that actually liberating my consciousness from its imprisoning structure would require focused dedication, perseverance, and hard work.

Nevertheless, as virtually all spiritual teachers have emphasized, progress is definitely possible when we devote ourselves to cultivating our inner resources. An illuminating image that appeared to me was of being born in a country where the sky is always covered by clouds, with these clouds representing the conditioning that blocks any direct view of the blue sky above. This sky is our true nature: radiant, free, infinite and eternal, and forever undamageable and unhindered by the presence or absence of clouds. After several years of meditation and self-inquiry practice, I began to get the first faint glimpses of this inner sky, and these revelations granted a sense of freedom from the chronic cloud cover that had completely blocked any awareness of the boundless consciousness ever-present beyond the clouds. With time, the metaphoric clouds seemed to thin, and the sky to become more visible and present as the ever-present truth of being. Eventually at one point, in October of 1987 at a meditation retreat in northern California, during the practice of self-inquiry, everything at once seemed to completely fall away, and then the falling away itself fell away, and with it the sense of myself as separate self, and an indescribable luminous joy and freedom filled all awareness. Something deep inside seemed to revive.

This glimpse, like a flash of lightening that briefly illumines a hitherto dark landscape, revealed the outlines of an awareness that we are, essentially, far different from and far beyond the body-and-name identity, with its never-ending collection of feelings, perceptions, thoughts, and memories. My old Zen teacher advised that my work would now be to bring every thought, word, and deed into alignment with the awareness that filled my mind and heart during that glimpse, which though difficult to capture in words, would be that there is but one life living through us all, and we are that life itself, not merely the material forms it emits, like temporary footprints in sand. The eternal sky is ever-present—illuminating, manifesting, and inspiring—and we are connected to inner well-springs of peace and healing that are always available. From this awareness, it is not difficult or unnatural to look beyond outer appearances, and see apparent others with eyes of kindness and respect, and do our best to fulfill our responsibilities in this life. This sense of benevolence also requires that we develop our capacity for agency and for insightful comprehension. Without wisdom, compassion can cause more harm than good, as illustrated by the old Buddhist metaphor of the kind and loving monkey. This monkey, though he meant well, looked down from high up in a tree and saw a fish below him in a river and caringly went down and rescued the fish, bringing the fish with him high up into the safety of the tree.

Elephants and Snakes: From Whence Comes Our Guidance?

At every moment, we are being guided in our words and actions. The question is, are we being guided by our inner wisdom, or are we being guided by the internal dialogue that is conditioned by our cultural programming? There are tremendous forces at work whose only goal is to control our thoughts, attitudes, and feelings, and to manage our perceptions and dictate the stories that we tell ourselves about what is happening to us, and in the world around us. We are discouraged from introspection, meditation, self-inquiry, and silent contemplation. Properly understood and practiced, these are the doorways to insight and freedom. Through them we can discover the bigger picture of what and who we are, and liberate our consciousness from seeking guidance and approval from the tribe around us. This was one of Thoreau's great revelations during his retreat by the pond that he wrote about in *Walden*: that each one of us can, by our own efforts, connect with our inner guidance system and with our purpose, and discover how to live our unique life authentically, and help to positively transform our culture.

Two well-known metaphors from India sum up our situation. The first is of the blind men and the elephant. According to this ancient story, there are five blind men who each have their hands on a different part of an elephant, and they are arguing incessantly and bitterly about the nature of the elephant. The one by the ear says that an elephant is obviously a large and leathery leaf; the one by the leg says no, it's a pillar; for the one by the side of the elephant, it's a wall; for the one by the tail, it's a rope-like object; according to the fifth, who is by the trunk, an elephant is definitely a large and heavy hose.

Like the blind men, each of whom is absolutely correct on one level, yet suffers from an inability to see the bigger picture, we also have had blinders affixed to us that limit our awareness, and so we are divided as a culture and in conflict over our opposing views. If the blind men in the elephant metaphor could take off their blinders and see, they would immediately see the whole elephant, and in a flash of understanding, their angry conflict would dissolve into laughter and a sense of loving camaraderie with their former opponents. They would see that yes, everyone is right and sincere, but unable to see the larger whole, due to their vision being narrowed to a small and disconnected piece of truth. In the same way, we have all, in many ways, had blinders affixed to our mental capacities from infancy. It is essential and profitable for the ruling class that these blinders be not only firmly established and difficult to remove, but also that we are proud of them, and loyal to the views into which we have been indoctrinated. We are strongly discouraged from any knowledge that such blinders could even exist, or any behavior (such as authentic conversations with each other) or insight that would help us remove them. The blinders not only assure that we are kept in a deluded state and fail to understand our true nature and the nature of our society, so we are thus easily controlled, but also that we are divided and in conflict with each other, which facilitates the tiny minority's domination of the vast majority.

Once the scales start falling from our eyes, we are no longer so easily deceived, and we begin to comprehend the true nature of the elephant, and instead of fighting with each other, we turn our attention to the ones who affixed the blinders on us in the first place, and we take action to prevent them from continuing this harmful behavior. It is exceedingly difficult to put blinders on adults, because they naturally resist, just like it is difficult to domesticate free-living adult animals. But with infants, it is another matter, and like animals born into captivity who cannot long for freedom because they've never known it, children born into culturally-imposed blinders and mental confinement have difficulty understanding the extent to which their natural capacities have been violated and reduced. Because children are especially vulnerable in their formative years, it is incumbent on us as parents and adults to protect them and to exemplify to them the value of self-reliance, which is foundational to a healthy society.

Fortunately, there is within each of us a bright guiding star that also inspires and continually nudges us toward awakening, freedom, authenticity, and healing. This force, our true nature, is ultimately unyielding, and like the blind men, our task is to remove the imposed blinders and open to ever-larger and truer perspectives, which confer ever-greater immunity from the fear-based narratives that would deceive us and our children into exploitation and delusion.

The second Indian metaphor is related directly to this. A person is walking home at night and suddenly sees a snake and freezes in terror. As the person continues to gaze at the deadly snake, it becomes apparent that it is actually a coil of rope that has been mistakenly perceived to be a harmful snake. The person's fear evaporates immediately. This applies directly to our situation. Many of our problems are caused by mistakenly believing that a rope is actually a snake. We are taught by our cultural conditioning that there are dangerous snakes everywhere: there are deadly germs and viruses, there are terrorists, there is anthropogenic climate change, there are harmful natural and human forces. With the Covid hoax, infants and children were intensely programmed into baseless and deleterious fears of other people and of so-called contagion by being forced to wear harmful facial coverings, and to view family members and themselves as dangerous disease-spreaders. A whole generation has been psychologically injured. When we mistake a rope for a snake because of our distorted vision or indoctrinated belief system, our body fills with adrenalin, and our knees quiver and palms get sweaty and dis-ease begins to take over our being. When we unlearn our error, admit our mistake, and understand that it's just a rope, our body-mind relaxes and we are at peace—healthy and aware.

The key point is that we do not have to work hard, or pray intensely, or invoke complicated mantras or magical spells to transform the snake into a rope so we can be free and at peace. All we need to do is see the true nature of the situation, and realize that what we were believing was a snake is just a rope. In this regard, it's helpful to remember the wisdom of journalist H. L. Mencken, who pointed out in 1918 that, "The whole aim of practical politics is to keep the populace alarmed (and hence clamorous to be led to safety) by menacing it with an endless series of hobgoblins, all of them imaginary."[22] It may take considerable inner work to attain this realization, however, which can be liberating on many levels.

On the other hand, sometimes what we perceive to be a rope is actually a snake. We have been taught, for example, to trust the pharmaceutical-medical complex to keep us healthy, the media complex to keep us well-informed, the educational system to teach us, the government to protect us, the banking industry to provide fair financial services, the food industry to provide safe and healthy food, and the scientific establishment to provide convenience, freedom, and security. Needless to say, the exact opposite is far truer. Fabricating "emergencies" is a reliable way for the plutocratic class to increase wealth and power. We should by now be fully aware that all these institutions, systems, complexes, and agencies have been infiltrated, that governmental bureaus invariably get captured by the industries they are created to regulate, that sick people are far more profitable than healthy people, that science is being used to surveil, harm, and imprison us, and by creating trillions of dollars out of thin air to "help" us, governments, banks, and corporations are stealing our prosperity with inflation. Immense financial institutions rob our economic freedom to increase our poverty and dependency, giving new meaning to bank robbery.

We are called to cultivate the wisdom of discriminating awareness, a Buddhist term that refers to our inner capacity to combine our faculties of logic, reason, and investigative questioning with our intuitive and spiritual powers of insight to clearly understand what we are perceiving in the world around us. This is an essential aspect of the inner work required to live responsibly and contribute to building a world of harmony and freedom, and it means understanding a rope to be a rope and a snake to be a snake.

If everyone around us is panicking, believing a rope to be a snake, we are simply called to see clearly and trust this clarity; it is only perceptual delusion that is the problem, and our perception is conditioned by internalized cultural narratives. The snake is a misperception, nothing more. If what we are seeing is actually a snake, we can interact with it skillfully, not expecting it to be a harmless and useful rope. Combining discriminating awareness and spiritual intuition, we can take responsibility for the quality of our awareness and for our actions, and reduce the amount that we are deceived. If we are not sure in a particular situation, we keep an open mind, attentively listening, watching, researching, conversing with others, questioning, and making connections. With practice, we learn to increasingly trust our intuitive wisdom and discriminating awareness.

The problem is never actually in the apparent outer world. Clouds can never damage or ultimately restrict the sky of our true nature. Harmful delusions exist only in our perception and in our responses to our perceptions. When we are hypnotized or deceived by others, or by our own thought-habits, or by group behavior, then we misperceive reality and suffer the consequences. Looking carefully, deeply and undistractedly, we can wake up from the cultural spell that is causing us to misperceive snakes and ropes—misperceptions that the cultural spell itself is projecting—and we can smile and be free, understanding the illusion.

Our true nature, like the sky, is free of both ropes and snakes, and of the clouds of misunderstanding. This misunderstanding is often culturally imposed, and misunderstanding tends to breed further misunderstanding. It causes fear and suffering that last as long as the misunderstanding lasts, which can seem excessive, just as darkness remains as long as light is absent—for moments, years, centuries, or millennia—but vanishes instantaneously when light manifests, as if it had never existed. In this light of understanding, the blinders dissolve and we see the whole elephant, far beyond the limitations imposed by our cultural conditioning. In our unique ways, we are each called to awaken to this awareness, perceive the larger wholes that illuminate and sanctify our life, and properly discriminate the ropes and snakes arising in our world. We can reclaim our power and spiritual sovereignty, and help each other realize the true nature of our minds, and of all the arisings in the limitless sky of our awareness.

CHAPTER SIX

THE BENEFITS OF DEEP VEGANISM

~

"Everyone thinks of changing the world,
but no one thinks of changing himself."
—LEO TOLSTOY

"Almost all nations have traditions of a golden age of innocence,
when men abstained from killing animals."
—OVID: THE METAMORPHOSIS

"If the Bill of Rights contains no guarantee that a citizen shall be secure
against lethal poisons distributed either by private individuals or
by public officials, it is surely because our forefathers could
conceive of no such problem."
—RACHEL CARSON

The Liberating Journey: From Outer to Inner

Deep veganism, which could also be called holistic veganism, is
based on the idea that the causal level of our human world is
mental, and that all of the aspects of our lives originate funda-
mentally from mental ideas. True, deep, and holistic liberation is
not merely changing our outer behavior; it includes the second

step of understanding the ideas and the deep mental forces that are at the roots of outer appearances. Everything in our human world that we rely on and use existed first in the non-physical realm of mind, including not only objects like tables, cars, and houses, but also more abstract systems, such as governance, health-care, nutrition, and agriculture. Deep veganism calls us to address, beyond the level of our outer behavior in the world, this larger realm of ideas and attitudes that our enslavement of animals requires, and by which it is supported.

Virtually everything in our human world is connected directly or indirectly to the assumptions at the foundation of our food system of animal oppression. The adventure of understanding that is thus called for by deep veganism is vast in both scope and intricacy. Like an immense mandala of nearly infinite detail, understanding ourselves requires understanding our culture and its food system, and this calls us to explore and uncover connections and insights that intersect in an immense web of social, historical, psychological, spiritual, and physical dimensions.

There seem to be three broad stages on the path of vegan living. The first stage, beginning veganism, is challenging because there are many things to learn and unlearn about nutrition and food preparation in order to reach a way of living that we find is nutritious, convenient, and that works well with our particular tastes, relationships, schedule, and so forth. In addition, there are steep learning and unlearning curves that relate to our interactions with other people, who are perhaps upset that we are changing our dietary regime, or are concerned we aren't getting adequate protein, or that if everyone went vegan it would be a disaster, because cows would take over the world, and so forth. In many ways, vegan living is easy, but it is other people that make it difficult and complicated.

We may stay in this first stage for several months, or for years, learning and doing our best to fit in with the overwhelmingly non-vegan world around us. At some point we may feel called to share these ideas with others, and this typically brings us to the second main stage of veganism, which could be called the "angry vegan" stage. We find out how difficult it is to share the many benefits of vegan living with others, because they often resist and block our efforts, and this may tend to create an undercurrent of anger and even misanthropy in our feelings and philosophy. Some of us avoid these psychologically painful aspects of the second stage by seeking refuge in what we can refer to as the closet vegan stage, where we avoid ever mentioning that we follow a vegan lifestyle, to better ensure that we can get along and fit in. Both the angry vegan and the closet vegan aspects of the second stage are problematic and difficult to maintain, and for these reasons, people in both the first and second stages of vegan living may fail to maintain their vegan lifestyle, and find rationalizations to quietly slip back into mainstream attitudes and practices, perhaps to come back to vegan living again when they are ready.

Fortunately, there is a third stage, which we refer to as deep veganism, which is both empowering and rewarding. It is holistic in the sense that we open to understanding the bigger cultural, psychological, and spiritual picture of what is happening, and also make an effort to transform our mentality and emotions so that we are no longer merely fighting against an obsolete superstition and way of living, but are proactively working to help build a positive alternative. When we reach the stage of deep veganism, there is no going back ever, because our outer behavior is based on a solid foundation of understanding. With the first two stages, we are making positive changes in our behavior, and beginning to question our culture's food narratives, but with deep veganism, we not only develop confidence in our vegan way of living as an action, but also take the essential second step. By making an effort to comprehend the whole constellation of ideas, narratives, and practices that flow from and interconnect with our culture's food narratives, we develop an illuminating awareness of the consequences of these ideas and practices. Through these efforts, we liberate ourselves not just on the physical level of behavior, but on the mental level as well, and with time on the spiritual level. It is a calling to free ourselves from the delusion of materialism, and this requires us to challenge the essential core of our indoctrination. Liberating our awareness is more difficult and involved than simply changing our outer food choices, and this inner work is ultimately essential to rescuing our human world from the devastating effects of animal agriculture.

An encouraging realization is that all the animals we routinely imprison for food—pigs, turkeys, chickens, goats, sheep, rabbits, fishes, and all the rest, with the sole exception of cows—are right now also celebrating their lives in nature as they have done for millions of years. Chickens are thriving in their native jungles of southeast Asia, turkeys in the forests of North America, wild pigs, goats and sheep in Europe, Asia, and the Americas, and so forth, and it is only cows who are now extinct in the wild. One of the last wild bovines (the aurochs, from which most of our domesticated cattle derive) was shot by hunters in Poland relatively recently, in 1627,[1] and as we transition back to plant-sourced diets, we will free up millions of acres of agricultural land to become forest and grassland habitat for free-living bovines and other animals who are now marginalized by our domination of the Earth and our domestication of animals.

It is remarkable to contemplate that before the advent of animal agriculture, we human beings comprised only one-tenth of one percent of the biomass of all land-based mammals, and today, just a mere ten thousand years later, free-living mammals have been reduced from 99.9 percent to just four percent of biomass. We humans, together with the animals we own as property, now comprise 96 percent of biomass.[2] We have stolen indispensable habitat from free-living animals by our relentless craving for animal foods, and are consequently driving unprecedented numbers of both animal and plant species into extinction.

If we would liberate animals from our oppression, we would be able to savor their camaraderie in new and quite unimaginable ways, and relish the grace of their sovereignty and intelligence surging through them as it did for countless centuries before we began to steal their purposes, and to imprison, terrorize, and commodify them. This awakening would help liberate us from our cages as well: the persistent and unrecognized corrals of alienation, anxiety, elitism, injustice, reductionism, and so forth. As we deepen our ability to question our culture's narratives that legitimize abuse, we embark on a liberating journey to overhaul and transform not just our outer behavior, but also our underlying attitudes, assumptions, and way of being, and to become a force for authentically healing our culture's wounds.

Deep, holistic veganism is not so much an accomplishment as it is an ongoing process of questioning, and of recognizing, realizing, remembering, and returning home to the ever-present grace that has been concealed from us. Seeing animals as beings, we can begin to reawaken our sense of respect for nature and ourselves, and to glimpse the deeper truth that our consciousness has been captured and corrupted by a harmful cultural force that hides deeper truths from us and that steals our sovereignty and undermines our capacities. As we begin to understand the harm that these herderism-based delusions are causing us and those around us, we naturally make an effort to liberate our consciousness from them, and to question the narratives that have been injected into us since infancy.

We are called to an in-the-trenches daily practice of reclaiming and reestablishing our natural capacity to treat both animals as well as each other with understanding and respect, and free our consciousness from the preemptive influence of our culture's materialism. It is an ongoing inner endeavor of significant consequence, because striving to live a nonviolent life within a herding culture founded upon violence transforms us, ready or not, and our example naturally encourages others to do the same. Deep veganism is the solid foundation, available to all of us, for co-creating an effective movement for the liberation of both animals and humanity.

The Antidote to Herderism and Materialism

The real issues we face, both as vegans and as pre-vegans, are connected to the physical and mental poisoning that we have endured by being born and raised in a culture that normalizes and legitimizes the often-unrecognized torrents of abuse all around us. Deep veganism has the power to awaken our culture from its thralldom to animal agriculture. Philosophically, it is a praxis comprising both a theoretical dimension and a practical dimension, and as we explore and grasp the essential ideas and incorporate them into our daily lives, we can experience transformational benefits in many areas of health, individually and collectively. Deep veganism addresses not just our food choices but all our relationships, as well as the underlying paradigms that guide our aspirations, thoughts, and feelings. As concrete behavior, deep veganism is an effort to respect the lives and sovereignty of others, so we practice eliminating and minimizing consumption and support of products or services that involve abuse of animals, including other humans. Internally, it is a journey of inquiry and healing, calling us to question internalized narratives, and to endeavor to escape from the brambles of materialism and reductionism. We learn to see holistically and make connections, and to liberate our consciousness so that we can appreciate the beauty and vulnerability of other expressions of life. We realize that our brief time on this Earth is a precious opportunity to learn, and to contribute our unique gifts to the cause.

As our heart and mind both open, we begin to see that, while the outer expression of veganism in our patterns of consuming is certainly important and helpful, there is much more to veganism than boycotting industries and products. Beyond rejecting the internalized delusions of materialism, we are called to realize that all life is a manifestation of consciousness that is essentially benevolent, joyful, and eternal.

The outermost practice is to ever more fully and conscientiously adopt and promote an organic, whole-food, completely plant-sourced way of eating and living for ethical reasons, and to do our best to facilitate justice, compassion, freedom, and health for animals, for hungry people, for workers, for ecosystems, wildlife, indigenous people, and for future generations of all beings. In a world organized around promoting consumerism and the exploitation of animals and nature on a massive scale through animal-based foods and products, and toxic chemical additives and residues in food, water, air, and virtually all products, this in itself is a significant and ever-challenging adventure of discovery and refinement. Doing so, we benefit our communities and ourselves, and the guiding principle is that while we may not have power or control over the outer world situation, we always have power and control over our responses to it. This is a significant power. It is through our responses that we build our life and co-create our future. In every situation, how do we best respond?

As our awareness continues to expand, we realize that the only person we have the power to change and liberate is the person we are, and that the way to be an effective advocate for freedom, truth, and compassion is to strive to ever more deeply understand the person in the mirror. Only we can uproot the materialist and reductionist programmed tendencies that still remain in our consciousness, and that generate our tendency to blame, categorize, exclude, and criticize others, and to see others as the problem.

Deep veganism is an ongoing effort to mature emotionally and existentially beyond our culture's indoctrinated ambition to solve problems by changing or censoring other people. We can recognize that this manipulative effort is a form of violence based in the materialist delusion that we are essentially separate—mere material objects that were born and will die—and that others are as well. This inevitably creates resistance and conflict that are counterproductive. We all know that if someone were to approach us with the object of changing us and making us more like them, that it is a natural and healthy response to resist and question their motives and actions.

With second-stage "angry" veganism, we tend to think that we are right in our way of living, and that non-vegans are wrong and are the cause of the problems in the world, and we feel justified to use practically any means necessary to get them to change and be more like us. This is the herding culture's materialism still alive and unquestioned in us, propelling us to reduce beings to objects, and to see others as disconnected objects whom we are called to convert so that we emerge victorious "for the animals." The problem with our approach at this stage is that it is dualistic, divisive, and generates ill-will. It fails to recognize the power of transforming our consciousness so that there is congruence between our inner and outer worlds. What matters most is not so much what we say or express to others, but how we express it, and who we are as we are expressing it. Emerson summed it well: "Who you are speaks so loudly I can't hear what you're saying." Our being is always unfailingly communicating, and if we have not matured in our understanding so that we are authentically embodying lovingkindness and respect for others—which is what veganism essentially is—then we are not actually spreading the message of ahimsa and vegan living, and we are still part of the problem. Being congruent in our message—words, gestures, intonations, and actions—brings effectiveness, allowing us to plant seeds that inspire positive change in others.

This same unquestioned materialism also pushes us to try to find ways to compellingly market this vegan message to others, as if veganism would be a mere commodity that we are packaging for consumption. Rightly understood, veganism and ahimsa are transformational spiritual practices and understandings that are best relayed through living exemplification and embodiment. With deep veganism, we realize that efforts to manipulate others to change in a way that we want them to, and arguing with or criticizing or blaming them, run contrary to the spirit of inclusiveness and respect that is the essence of vegan living. We realize that we can easily be vegan in the veneer of our outer lifestyle, but internally still be trapped in the shallows of the materialist herder delusion of separateness, exclusiveness, and manipulativeness. Deep veganism, like ahimsa, is a call from our future and more evolved awareness to remember that there is no other way to spread and share love, kindness, and respect—which is what vegan living is all about—than embodying love, kindness and respect for all animals, including all human animals. The path *is* the goal.

People have sometimes asked me what the most effective formulation of this underlying truth might be. For example, if we only have a half-minute or so, what message would convey the essence of healing truth to another person? By letting go of trying to change others, and instead doing our best to embody vegan values of kindness and respect, our words, gestures, and actions become congruent, and we can plant seeds of truth with effectiveness. Congruence is the key, and with it, *satyagraha*, truth-force, works through us.

Remembering the importance of congruence, this, in a nutshell, seems to be the essential message we can do our best to convey and embody:

I am happy and grateful that I discovered that the only reason I was eating animal foods for all the years that I did was because I was just following orders. Fortunately, I realized that those orders were not in my best interest, or in the interest of our world, and so I'm not following them anymore, and it's fantastic.

That's it. When we express this truth, in our own words of course as befits the occasion, we are conveying a simple and basic set of transformative ideas, which is our truth. Usually, it's best not to say a lot more, and to let go and let the seed we have planted germinate and grow organically. Delivered with respect and without any underlying motivation to manipulate others, we plant a potent seed of light, truth, and healing in the consciousness of the person. It will sprout and grow and help them to heal as well, because that is what truth-power does. Basically, our experience is all the same growing up in this herding culture, and our personal truth is also a universal truth.

The only reason any of us eats animal foods is because we're just following orders, and we all know this deep down and also understand that it's not in our best interest. When any of us articulates and embodies this fundamental, world-transforming truth, and then follows up, articulating that it is terrific to be free of this indoctrination, we are essentially opening the door of the prison that keeps human beings deceived into destructive, anti-rational behavior. At our core, none of us wants to be a mere automaton blindly following toxic and destructive orders. We can point out that we have discovered this for ourselves and how liberating it is. We are simply speaking our truth and telling our story in a positive and loving way. This is minimally threatening to others, and beckons them to come forth from the prison into which they, like all of us, have been born.

If we do it well, the person will forget us and the conversation, and yet the seed of truth we planted is alive inside them, growing and encouraging them toward health and freedom. Their innate wisdom and compassion will water the seed, and if and when they go vegan, it will not be because they are being pushed, but because their inner caring has been activated. We have within us the capacity to be instruments of satyagraha, truth-force, and to speak our truth, which is a universal truth, thereby planting seeds that can positively transform our world.

Farming Children

With deep veganism, we become more effective in our advocacy because we begin to understand that under the impact of our culture's unrecognized core of herderism, and through well-meaning but injured parents, relatives, and authorities, we have all been wounded. This understanding gives us the foundation for authentic respect and compassion for others, and helps heal our enculturated tendency to criticize and censor them. We see more clearly that forcing infants and children to eat the flesh and secretions of abused animals is a pervasive and culturally approved form of child abuse that harms everyone on many levels. First of all, it causes us as children tremendous physical suffering in the form of digestive issues, sore throats, earaches, tonsilitis, appendicitis, obesity, diabetes, constipation, and many other conditions. Dairy products are especially effective in generating childhood disease symptoms (and pharmaceutical-medical windfalls). But the abuse we endure runs to much deeper levels than this.

When as children we realize what hot dogs and bacon actually are, a cold darkness slips into our chest. Our natural sense of kindness toward other animals is repressed under the weight of the inescapable and hypnotically ignored cultural practice of heartless and relentless killing and eating. We are taught to be kind to others, but then at the same time we're also compelled to sow the seeds and eat the fruits of exploitation and violence. We are cast out of the garden of innocence and harmony, and our inherent self-esteem is eroded. We know in our bones that our meals are an offense against the natural order, but our cultural indoctrination represses this awareness. Sophia, the inner sacred feminine dimension of consciousness within us that naturally yearns to love and protect life, is repressed by the reality of our daily meals.

We are aware that animals are being brutally mistreated and exploited, and though this is appalling to our inherent empathy, we nevertheless directly cause this suffering by monetarily voting for it and eating it, continually repressing our awareness and our feelings. This is the unyielding dilemma at the core of our society, the open and festering wound poisoning the cultural well from which we all drink, and through which we co-create our shared reality. Understanding how virtually everyone we meet has been wounded and poisoned in these ways by well-meaning caregivers and colleagues from infancy, we find our hearts opening to help and bless, rather than to criticize, blame, and judge.

Our entire culture is, in many ways, modeled on a farm where we, as newborn infants, are treated like calves on a dairy farm, as exploitable commodities in a ruthless economic system. Like the calves, we are typically not allowed to bond with our mothers properly. We have foods, beverages, media messages, and medications imposed on us that are not in our interest but are advantageous to our exploiters, the meat-medical-media-banking complex. We enter a cultural system of intense social and economic competition and authoritarianism where we are seen as objects, and are taught to see ourselves and other people as competitors and as instruments to be manipulated and used. We are taught to trust scientific authorities and follow their orders religiously. We are required to eat foods of embedded toxicity, terror, despair, and anxiety. Our natural sense of kinship with animals, and ultimately with each other, is fractured as we dine on their misery and on the underlying mentality of materialism that reduces living beings to commodified objects.

We are taught that we live in an essentially meaningless and random universe, and are expected to believe in absurdly impossible fairy tales such as the "Big Bang"—the inexplicable and purposeless scientific equivalent of a miracle—that magically birthed our cosmos, which then supposedly evolved the incomprehensibly complex and beautiful flowers, trees, animals, humans, and other life forms through mere random mutation of elements and compounds, and out of this randomness, that consciousness somehow happened to emerge. That anyone actually pretends to believe such comically reductionistic absurdity is a tribute to the dumbing-down power of ten thousand years of herderism, and to the blind, disconnected materialism that this herderism has inflicted on all of us. It offers no account for the manifestation of unfathomably complex and interrelated whole systems such as eyes, ears, and hearts, much less for consciousness, feelings, creativity, and intuitions. As a narrative designed for slaves, it works well and fulfills its mission of keeping us disconnected from nature and from our inner wisdom and power, and fosters a sense of meaningless incongruity that propels us into profitable and addictive consumerism in a vain search for significance and purpose.

The Plague of False Narratives

How does it affect us to live in a society where we are expected to all agree with culturally-mandated stories and explanations that are obviously not true? This has been going on for a long time now; to what degree is it deliberate? Who benefits from this? When we are compelled to accept ideas and policies that are patently ridiculous, and act on them, what does this do to our self-respect, integrity, and willingness to question authority and defend our sovereignty and the sovereignty of others? It seems that our tribal loyalty trumps our intelligence in many cases. For many of us, it seems to be less painful to accept and act on the absurd falsehoods the people around us believe, than to question those falsehoods and be noticeably different, and possibly be rejected by our friends and colleagues. Social psychologist Solomon Asch discovered this in his experiments on group conformity, summing up his findings:

> The tendency to conformity in our society is so strong that reasonably intelligent and well-meaning young people are willing to call white black. This is a matter of concern. It raises questions about our ways of education and about the values that guide our conduct.[3]

The root instance of this again is food: we are taught and act on the mandated belief that we must imprison, kill, and eat animals to build muscle and bone, when all around us are animals, with far stronger bones and muscles than we have, who build them on plants, without resorting to any killing at all. Why do we not question this more seriously, instead of just going along with it? Questioning has consequences, and can be disruptive to our relationships and our lives.

Other narratives are in the realm of religion (including the religion of scientism). We may be taught many supernatural stories that religious authorities have declared that we must believe to be included among the faithful and thus rewarded. What kinds of agendas mandate these narratives? Who benefits from them?

Many false narratives are political in nature. For example, we were told that two flimsy aluminum airplanes hit two massive concrete and steel towers and didn't just break a few windows, but caused these buildings, and a third one nearby that was untouched, to completely disintegrate into fine powder and collapse at free-fall speed into massive piles of dust and streams of molten steel. Just running into a flock of geese is well-known to seriously damage the thin aluminum front end shell of a jet plane. Copious amounts of thermitic material were later found in the fine powder residues of the exploding dust clouds that covered the surrounding area for many blocks.[4] The material, nano-thermate, a high-tech military-grade explosive used to cut and melt steel, as in these controlled demolitions, would only be accessible to military and intelligence agencies.[5] Jet fuel burns at a maximum of 1,800 degrees, and steel will not melt below 2,500 degrees, and yet firemen reported, "molten steel was flowing down the channel rails like in a foundry..."[6] Even many months later, in February 2002, after millions of gallons of water had been sprayed onto the smoking ruin of the twin towers, cleanup crews found still-molten steel at the bottom of the WTC crater.[7] Dr. Judy Wood has pointed out that there has never been a proper investigation into what it was that pulverized thousands of tons of concrete into fine powdery dust.[8] It is remarkable that the blatant absurdity of the official explanation is still generally unrecognized. In the intervening years, hundreds of books, articles, videos, organizations, and websites have been created that demonstrate beyond any doubt that the Twin Towers were brought down by controlled demolition in a false flag attack.[9]

Those who carried out this false flag operation also employed military-grade propaganda and censorship technologies, as well as complete capture of the relevant governmental agencies and investigations.[10] The controlled media immediately proclaimed and established the false Islamic terrorist narrative and successfully fooled millions of (eerily foolable) people in the aftermath. Even after twenty years, we have allowed the power of authoritarian dictates and group peer pressure to keep truth hidden, and also to facilitate a massive ongoing expansion of the surveillance state, under the pre-packaged PATRIOT Act, which was immediately passed because of the "emergency." This new narrative—that dangerous invisible terrorists swarm among us (much like germs and viruses)—was used by the ruling class (perhaps it should be called the fooling class because it keeps fooling us) to dismantle basic freedoms, and, for example, to prohibit us from bringing water or even a container of hummus dip onto any flight. We were told that if we were a terrorist, we could make a bomb out of our hummus, or else with our shoe. We have been forced to believe in and comply with this foolishness, supposedly for our safety and security. There seems to be a method to the apparent madness, because it gradually instills in us a toxic gullibility that renders us pliable, and willing to trust and comply with virtually anything authorities tell us, regardless of its absurdity, and conditions us to reject our innate rationality, sense, and intuition.

Who benefits from these types of mass indoctrination efforts that make a mockery of our intelligence, treating us like docile and uncomprehending simpletons, and what is the agenda behind them? What have been the results of the success of these deceptions? Further and more blatant acts of fraud and treachery, and more confidence that the public will again and always be easily fooled by any officially-sanctioned narrative? How does all this affect us socially and psychologically? Why are we willing to sacrifice precious freedoms, which are difficult to regain once lost, for small and dubious safety benefits? Why do we trust technocratic and bureaucratic authorities and comply with their dictates, even when they defy common sense?

Well-known experiments have been conducted in this area, such as those by Stanley Milgram, Asch, and others, that underline all of this.[11] Milgram's research indicated that about 65% of ordinary people would inflict harm on a likeable person if requested to do so by an external authority.[12] He referred to this as the "agentic shift," in which a person voluntarily relinquishes personal control, judgment, and responsibility to an external agent.[13] We humans seem to be able to jettison our moral agency, and our common sense, in order to be accepted by the surrounding group, and even more so, to be approved by an authority figure. The underlying template is formed by our daily meals, which are like Milgram experiments in which we cause horrific harm to others because we are just following orders from internalized authority figures. Our behavior, like with the Asch perceptual experiments, is driven by the obsession to conform with everyone around us, regardless of the consequences. As Étienne de la Boétie pointed out in 1553, cultural health and authentic freedom call us to refuse to comply with authoritarian mandates and social pressure: "Freedom from servitude comes not from violent action, but from the refusal to comply. Tyrants fall when the people withdraw their support."[14]

Our tendency to obediently follow authoritarian orders, and to compulsively conform to our in-group, is obviously well understood by the ruling cabal. The false narrative pattern that is initiated in many different guises is relatively simple: fabricate a shocking event, declare an emergency, drum up emotional fear-based hysteria, and offer a solution in the form of safety and security, which in reality is not safety and security, but an erosion of sovereignty that generates further submission and subservience. In these situations, it seems many of us are powerless to resist the urge to blindly follow and do whatever authorities dictate, and to police those around us to similarly comply. As Milgram realized, our culture's conditioning tends to pressure us to relinquish our autonomy and to become its agents.

We were told to believe a story of a deadly virus, and that we were sick with it when we tested positive, even though we felt fine. We were told that we must go along with this official narrative by locking down, masking, and social distancing, all of which were completely unverified responses that inflicted significant harm on individuals and communities. We were pressured into taking an experimental injection developed at so-called warp speed that was never properly tested on humans, with the official narrative being that it was safe and effective and would prevent transmission of the so-called disease. Later we found it that it was neither safe nor effective, nor did it prevent transmission of anything. In fact, even the corrupt and captured medical journals have had to eventually admit that the injections caused more harm than benefit.[15] Some have scrubbed evidence that they pushed the mandates.[16]

We should be asking not only about the agenda behind these patently false narratives, and who has benefitted, and how they will be held accountable, but also how it affects us to willingly comply, and why we allow ourselves to be deceived by authorities wielding the baton of the materialist pseudo-religion labelled as "science."[17] Being born into a culture steeped in materialism renders us apprehensive and docile in the hands of the authoritarian forces that propagate, and benefit from, disempowering narratives. Many of us, in our dutiful anxiety, mock those who question official narratives as dangerous science-deniers and conspiracy theorists.

The ironies abound, and as the situation becomes more dire, increasing numbers of us seem to be awakening to the reality of what has been happening. The parasitic plutocratic forces waging this fifth-generation war against humanity weaponize our craving for conformity to humiliate and enslave us, as we do the animals we nonchalantly consume every day. It is time to understand not just the war being waged against us, but also the war we ourselves are waging against animals. The eternal wisdom that shines always in our hearts can never be completely covered over or extinguished, and each of us, like Neo in *The Matrix*, is "the One," and called to fulfill our calling as a unique ambassador of awareness, vital to the larger awakening of humanity. Understanding that our lives are quite brief, and that our true nature is eternal and undamageable, we can inquire diligently and contribute to creating a field of compassion for all life, helping to uplift humanity's consciousness.

Through deep veganism, we not only make an effort to liberate our outer behavior from violence toward animals and other people, but also do the inner work to immunize ourselves against official narratives that spread fear, and that attempt to control us through deception. Making an effort to raise our vibratory level so that we are less easily roped in by fear-based manipulations, we can do our best to disconnect from centralized, controlled sources of information. By cultivating discerning awareness and intuition in order to perceive the underlying patterns, we learn to connect the dots that link the events unfolding around us, and to unlearn the false stories planted in our minds.

It is a supreme challenge to be incarnated in this culture where every day we are expected to ritually consume the flesh and secretions of terrified animals, deepening our alienation from nature and from our true nature, and passing it on to our children, not just in the food rituals, but in virtually all the institutions of our society. To address this challenge, we are called to question everything, especially the reductionism epitomized in scientism. Materialist science has seized undisputed ascendancy as the official epistemological guarantor of truth and reality because it also guarantees the greatest profits and power to the ruling cabal that depends on fear and deception to maintain its control of the masses of humanity.

The god of scientism has established itself as the new planetary monotheism, universally and proudly propagated through all our culture's institutions. White-coated scientists are the ruling priestly technocratic class, and "science" has become a faith-based religion complete with liturgies, ritual implements and costumes, sacred texts, magic potions, invisible evil spirits, blasphemy, unpardonable sins, ecclesiastical hierarchies, clerical superiority and infallibility, sacred shrines, salvation for the faithful, and secret codes understandable only by the highly initiated. The god of scientism is a jealous god, and will have no other gods before him. Cancellation and censorship are meted out to all infidels, heretics, and questioners of the orthodoxy. They are reviled as dangerous and unclean blasphemers, and must be silenced and marginalized to protect the faith of the true believers.

Our Shadow of Fear and Violence

The gross materialism inherent in animal agriculture is the obvious but nevertheless unrecognized driving force behind the ascendancy of scientism and its ongoing damage not just to the outer world, but to our psyches as well. Because our ocean of violence toward animals is virtually invisible to us as the buying and eating perpetrators, and because virtually everyone participates, and it is business-as-usual, it constitutes our culture's largest psychological shadow.

Psychologically, the shadow archetype of repressed awareness has enormous potential power, and the stronger the repression, the more powerfully the shadow pressures us in two directions. One demand of the shadow is that we block our awareness and become literally unconscious about what we are doing. The biggest elephant in the room becomes weirdly invisible, and the bigger it grows, the more invisible it becomes.

Thus, the first demand of the shadow archetype is to blind us to what we are doing to others and to ourselves, and its second demand is to project what we cannot see in ourselves onto others, and see it very clearly in them. We see ourselves as kind, just, caring people who like a good steak and omelette and ice cream, but the masked torrent of violence we are causing and eating is projected in many ways. We perceive and fear dangerous enemies threatening us with violence, leading to our frenetic ongoing creation of weapons capable of destroying the Earth and humanity many times over, and surveillance systems that monitor and track our every purchase and action. We are irresistibly drawn to support the mass cultural fascination with violent films, music, art, and entertainment. We create a science based on a model of conflict, justifying our domination of nature and animals, and our endless battles against inimical forces, such as invisible pathogens that we believe are lurking everywhere, and dangerous weather, and the sun, and carbon, and aging, and time, and boredom, and other people. We co-create a society with rampant trafficking, child sexual abuse, pornography, and injustice, which are the consequential outpicturing of our shadow's ongoing trafficking and sexual abuse of young animals. Because we yearn to avoid facing the underlying cognitive dissonance, and the realities we are causing and eating, the more our outer violence increases, the more we fear quiet introspection, and crave distractions and busy-ness, and do what we can to escape from ourselves, and the generalized sense of anxiety and alienation.

Our enslavement of animals boomerangs as the yearning for our own enslavement. The power of our repressed shadow numbs our feelings and reduces our intelligence so that our resulting gullibility and servile obedience to authority deliver us into the loss of freedom and responsibility that we are subconsciously craving. The power of the shadow to imprison us in fear and delusion grows every day as we sow these seeds with our ongoing mistreatment of animals. As we lose our health, we lose our freedom. This is the price we pay for our food choices, and the irony is that we are only eating animal-sourced foods because we are following orders from childhood, and failing to question them. In many ways, we have been reduced to obedient, order-following children, blindly loyal to a tribal narrative of fear, and propelled to police it and enforce it on others.

The materialism of animal agriculture erodes our basic self-confidence and self-respect, as well as our love and respect for nature, and because we terrorize and destroy animals and the natural world on a massive scale, we are afraid that nature and animals will harm us, and we are especially vulnerable to irrational fears of invisible natural forces, like microscopic "pathogens" and genetic "defects" that we blame for our physical and mental health problems. Under the spell of materialistic science, we allow ourselves to be cast in the false role of being innocent victims, and allow the medical industry to reduce our bodies to battlegrounds that must endure militarized chemical offensives against the dangerous invisible enemies that we are indoctrinated to blame for our problems.

We participate with our consent and with our dollars, empowering these industries to engage in harmful genetic engineering and to concoct tens of thousands of toxic drugs and chemicals to attack supposedly menacing microbes. We are blind to the fact that we are projecting the shadow of animal agriculture, and that our fear-based consciousness is actually creating diseases in our bodies that reflect the dis-ease in our minds. We fail to see the benevolent synergy that interconnects our body and mind with our genetic heritage, and with the living field of trillions of bacteria and decillions of exosomes within which we are embedded, and fail to understand that all work together, benevolently sharing information in intelligent processes that have developed over countless millennia—far beyond the primitive view of materialistic science—and that make our lives possible. Instead, we are like the proverbial fool, furiously cutting off the very tree branch on which we sit, failing to realize and respect the connections that support our lives. We are also blind to the harmful impact of the many chemical and electro-magnetic toxins polluting our bodies and living spaces.[18] It is all highly profitable, and we are taught not to question the experts.

It is especially ironic that we fear invisible forces that we are sure are out to harm and kill us, because this is exactly the projection of our own routine behavior. Every time we go to a store or restaurant and pay for the flesh or secretions of animals, we are, ourselves, invisible killers and abusers. Because of our actions, a sentient animal, with interests like our own, will be imprisoned from birth, mutilated, violently killed, and in many cases sexually abused multiple times as well. We are of course completely invisible to the hapless animals, and to the human workers we are also harming by paying them to do the sadistic dirty work we'd recoil from doing, and of which we'd rather not be aware. Hence, we are especially afraid of invisible killers, because that is exactly what we are.

We are thus easily deluded and reflexively embrace the fear-based germ theory. This convenient theory surrounds us with malevolent invisible forces, a perfect psychological, cultural, and financially profitable fit. In addition to resonating with this germ theory, we may also uphold a perspective that flatly rejects any critique of experts and established science as "negative." Because of the materialistic authoritarianism that underlies our culture, we easily fall prey to these deceptions. Deep veganism embraces truth-seeking, without concern if the truth appears to be negative or positive. Quite often, the most discomforting and painful truths are the most necessary and liberating. What seems negative is positive when it helps open us to the light of truth that brings greater awareness and freedom. Discomforting truths can liberate us from comfortable falsehoods.

When we sow harmful actions and attitudes that feed our shadow, we eventually reap the fear, disease, and violence that we impose on others. We collectively project this drama into our world, and though the whole process is mostly unconscious, we are abused like the animals we abuse, and it all serves the agenda of the globalist ruling class. Our sense of celebrating our lives in an essentially benevolent and loving atmosphere is compromised if not completely shattered.

By practicing the two steps of deep veganism—outer ahimsa and inner introspection and purification—we can develop an empowering understanding of how all of us have been psychologically wounded by being born into this herding culture's way of living, and through this understanding, we can reawaken our compassion not just for animals but also for ourselves and other wounded people. Our tendency to blame and our urge to change others dissolve into a deeper yearning to show them love and respect, and to help them take the journey of healing that we are in the process of taking. A new sense of respect informs our advocacy efforts, and while we are still keenly aware of the misery and abuse inflicted by animal agriculture and by the actions of indoctrinated and wounded people, we are grateful for the many opportunities we have in this lifetime to learn, grow, unlearn, release, and contribute our unique gifts to bring healing to our world.

We can realize that, because we are all wounded by our culture's herderism and pervasive materialistic assumptions, we can cultivate a sense of solidarity with other people and a sense of compassion and understanding for them, even though they may be acting in ways with which we disagree. We see that the perpetrators are also victims. Hurt people hurt others. We all need healing, and healing comes from love. Disrespect cannot heal disrespect; only respect and love can heal. The most effective contribution we make is our effort to reclaim our consciousness, so that we are ever more authentically living the truth of deep veganism, which is kindness and understanding for all beings, including other human beings and ourselves.

CHAPTER SEVEN

DARK INSTITUTIONS, FOOD,
AND FREEDOM

⌖

"No person is your friend who demands your silence,
or denies your right to grow."
—ALICE WALKER

"The medical establishment has become a major threat to health."
—IVAN ILLICH, MEDICAL NEMESIS

"What is the motivation behind the worldwide corruption?
Why is there such an effort to infiltrate every aspect of human society?
The answer is very simple: globalization. Globalization means the
eradication of national sovereignty and personal liberty, and bringing
all of humanity under the control of a small group of people who
determine what happens in our world."
—DAVID SORENSON

The Empire of Lies

We see unfolding around us a rapid acceleration of trends that have
already been well established for many decades in science, medicine,
government, banking, commerce, education, agriculture, and the

media. These trends are twofold: to erode individual sovereignty and other essential human rights, and to concentrate ever-increasing control of power, wealth, narrative-management, and information in the hands of a small and wealthy cabal.

This is accomplished through harnessing technology's power to amass personal data and control access to information, which drives ever-increasing corruption of our basic institutions. While it is noble to genuinely seek truth through scientific inquiry, to trade honestly in commerce, to serve the common interest in government, and so forth, our institutions and social functions have been captured, and have become inverted and deceptive. We do not sufficiently recognize the extent to which this has happened, and the impact it is having on all dimensions of our health. Our language is also corrupted to reflect this, and meanings of words become their opposites in ironic ways. Journalist Chris Hedges illustrates this: "We now live in a nation where doctors destroy health, lawyers destroy justice, universities destroy knowledge, governments destroy freedom, the press destroys information, religion destroys morals, and our banks destroy the economy."[1] We live within what is accurately called, "The Empire of Lies."

The living core of our culture is animal agriculture and the core of this herderism is heartless exploitation of the weak by the strong, which requires deception and relentlessly gives rise to more deception. Our culture's defining core deception is that of the good shepherd who cares for his flock. Although Jesus is recorded as saying, "The good shepherd lays down his life for his sheep," in reality, the shepherd's entire enterprise is based on deceiving these animals, stealing their natural and inherent sovereignty, and exploiting them to death. Though he provides for them and makes sure they can reproduce, like the culture for which he is but an indoctrinated agent, he does not care for them as individuals. The underlying purpose is to cut their throats at the earliest financially-advantageous opportunity, and to sell their flesh for profit. This foundation of deception and betrayal pervades all societies based on herding animals, which is virtually all societies in the world today. It corrodes our self-respect and gives rise to the hidden ocean of deception that permeates our human relations and all of our cultural institutions. The deception is so profound that many of us have constructed and walled ourselves into a "rather not talk about it" cocoon, so we can avoid acknowledging our participation in the culturally-mandated violence.

The ongoing deception-betrayal of innocent and vulnerable animals lives in us and at the core of our culture. Its roots lie in our deception-betrayal as children, propelling us to create economic and social systems rooted in this behavior, and that especially reward those who are skillful at deception and betrayal. These people inevitably accumulate more wealth and power, aided in this by technological multipliers, and thus we increasingly find ourselves corralled in a system permeated by the deception and betrayal we consume and that we inflict on animals by the millions daily, generating rampant corruption and inescapable tension, social fragmentation, and injustice.

The scientistic narrative of natural selection legitimizes the exploitation that pervades the system at every level. Though as individuals we naturally yearn for honest caring, transparency, and authenticity in our relationships and institutions, our culture's essential herder deception runs deep and wide, and has been saturating the fabric of our society for several millennia. It fools us into believing that deception is natural, justifiable, and necessary, polluting the field of harmony and freedom at both the individual and collective level. The darkness of falsehood is a vicious toxin, clouding our awareness, and imprisoning us in exploitable delusion. By practicing discernment, we can begin to understand the various masquerades in which deception engages, and how it works to overwhelm virtually all of our institutions, and steal away our wisdom, peace, grace, and freedom. There is an old African proverb that fittingly sums up the situation in which we find ourselves today: "The sheep spends his life in fear of the wolf, but it is the shepherd who kills him."

Science, Money, and Narrative Control

For example, science as it is now practiced today has become primarily Dark Science. Science is paraded and praised in official narratives as the objective search for truth through deductive reasoning and inductive peer-reviewed experimentation and inquiry by unbiased researchers in a community atmosphere of open and respectful questioning and debate. This is a deceptive mask that hides the reality of Dark Science, which has become pervasive. Dark Science has an agenda, which is to control and dominate nature and animals, and to increasingly concentrate power in the hands of a wealthy ruling class that controls the funding of science through predatory philanthropy as well as through capturing governmental, university, and corporate research departments and the media and educational narratives.

Money buys influence and loyalty. Massive money buys all-pervasive control of both general public narratives as well as specialized and institutional narratives, and also the ubiquitous and innocuous mental narratives, assumptions, and paradigms through which we are conditioned to perceive and interpret our entire experience. Dark Science has been working assiduously and successfully for many generations, gradually accumulating the wealth, power, trust, and influence enabling it to insinuate its technocratic and materialistic version of reality ever more deeply into the heart of every institution, and into the unsuspecting hearts and minds of the populace.

Billions of dollars flow to armies of scientists who are working to develop ever more devastating military-type technologies to bomb, destroy, manipulate, target, and surveil both foreign and domestic groups of people, and to researchers whose agenda is to poison and kill animals and insects, to destroy microorganisms, and to genetically engineer patentable life-forms, including plants, animals, and human beings, all to further concentrate profits and power in the hands of a few. Dark Science claims to be a force for our good, bringing more comfort, convenience, safety, predictability, and security to our lives. Are we happier, healthier, and more fulfilled because of the technologies that increasingly invade, track, and define our lives? Cancer, diabetes, obesity, auto-immune and neurological diseases, and depression, anxiety, substance abuse, and suicide, as well as economic inequity, pollution, starvation, crime, hunger, and conflict are surging to unprecedented levels.

It is clear that Dark Science serves an agenda that centralizes power, which is what the Trilateral Commission, the Council on Foreign Relations, the Club of Rome, the Bilderberg Group,[2] and now more recently the World Economic Forum, the World Health Organization, the United Nations with its Agenda 2030, and other plutocratic organizations have been promoting for decades, and their forebears for centuries. The primary characteristic of this globalist New World Order is centralization of power: highly-concentrated control of money, media, science, government, information, education, and human beings by a cabal of globalist robber barons working through an army of technocrats. In many ways, humanity is being factory-farmed, and individual human rights, economic freedom, and bodily autonomy are sacrificed and destroyed "for the greater good."

Inversion of Commerce, Government, Education, Medicine, and Media

Along with Dark Science, we now have a pandemic of Dark Commerce. Whereas commerce itself, like science, is a potentially beneficial and healthy practice engaged in by humans for millennia, Dark Commerce, like Dark Science, hides behind a mask of benevolence, and is actually a tool of enslavement, relentlessly concentrating wealth and power into the hands of a few. This financial elite operates through control of the Federal Reserve and other privately-owned central banks, as well as through the World Bank, the Bank for International Settlements, the International Monetary Fund, and massive asset management firms like Vanguard, BlackRock, State Street, and others. Wielding enormous financial and political power, they dominate economic institutions and determine corporate, medical, financial, and government policies as well as media narratives.

In a similar way, government is recognized as a potentially beneficent and necessary institution to help us humans cooperate and organize our interactions, given the large-scale nature of our world today, but in place of government, we primarily have what has become Dark Government, which is virtually completely unresponsive to the actual will of the people and instead serves the agenda of the wealthy ruling class, as research has clearly demonstrated.[3] Every level of government—local, state, national, and global—has been infiltrated by special interests that use bribery, bullying, blackmail, and social pressure to enforce an agenda of relentlessly eroding our human rights under the guise of increasing our safety and security. As but one example, it is well recognized that the CIA has developed a vast repertoire of subterfuge techniques to control media and cultural narratives, divide populations to increase social unrest, manipulate elections, carry out deceptive false flag operations to incite violence, fear, and confusion, and to assassinate, blackmail, or imprison prominent leaders and whistleblowers. It has thus been able to successfully overthrow elected governments worldwide, and to sabotage populist movements that challenge the power of the ruling cabal.[4] We can see its nefarious influence everywhere we look, including domestically, and it is but one of the many tools serving the unelected ruling class in maintaining its hegemony over humanity.

Instead of education, which wears the mask of teaching young people to become more aware, informed, and better able to think clearly and critically, we now have the widespread specter of Dark Education, which is a coordinated assault on young people's physical, social, mental, emotional, intellectual, and spiritual health. Dark Education, like Dark Government, is increasingly centralized, and serves to reduce capacities for creativity, curiosity, and critical thinking, so that young people are indoctrinated into disempowering narratives and trained to unhesitatingly obey all authority figures, and to be dominated by them. Dark Education prepares children to be willing fodder for Dark Science, Dark Medicine, Dark Commerce, and the other dark institutions that characterize our world today.

The practice of medicine has been similarly corrupted to a large degree by Dark Medicine. From infancy, we are all bombarded with messages that our health depends on submitting to doctors, drugs, and invasive procedures, and that we are under constant attack by dangerous pathogens that can harm us, and that other people can make us sick. We are relentlessly conditioned to ignore the possibility of enhancing our health through diet and lifestyle improvements, and through connecting with nature and striving spiritually to fulfill an inspiring purpose with creative and beneficial endeavors. Dark Medicine strives to undermine our confidence in our inherent health and natural immunity, and promulgates many types of harmful substances and protocols that further erode our health. Two of the primary deceptive narratives used by Dark Medicine to disempower people and monopolize wealth and power are the germ theory and the gene theory. We are indoctrinated from infancy into both of these reductionistic false narratives, and to see ourselves basically as victims of whatever genetic hand we have supposedly been dealt, and as innocent victims of nefarious viruses and bacteria relentlessly working to undermine our health. We are strictly discouraged from adopting a more holistic perspective, which would reduce our reliance on pharmaceuticals and procedures, and also reduce medical industry profits and power. When we believe these fear-based narratives— promulgated through the myriad avenues of the media and through the vast armies of indoctrinated personnel in the medical-pharmaceutical-governmental-educational-technology complex— that our health is dependent on doctors and medicines, then we are at their mercy, and they have little mercy. Physical and mental poisons are spewed relentlessly and if we allow them in, it is essential that we also be able to cleanse and eliminate them, or our health deteriorates, which also erodes our freedom.

Serving and empowering all of these dark institutions is the media, and mainstream media has today become the Dark Media. While journalism and media serve the vital role of providing a public forum for sharing information and discussing various sides of issues, the primarily Dark Media we have today is controlled by Dark Commerce, Dark Science, Dark Government, and Dark Medicine, especially Big Pharma. Perspectives that do not serve the New World Order agenda of centralization of power and information in the hands of a few are either ignored or actively censored. Legacy media, such as the NYT, BBC, CBC, CNN, and NPR, were among the first to be captured, followed by the internet giants comprising social media and information searches. It is difficult to overstate the damage continually wreaked on our society by relentlessly deceptive Dark Media outlets as they censor and disable honest communication and dialogue, hide information via controlled search engines and through corrupt "fact-checkers," and churn out harmful misinformation to divide, confuse, and disempower the population so that we willingly acquiesce to official narratives that are formulated to consolidate power in the hands of a few.

Dark Food: The Hidden Foundation

Underlying all of these dark institutions is the spinning fury at the core of our culture that is also the most invisible and unrecognized: Dark Food. Eating food could be—and should be—a celebration of the abundance of grains, nuts, seeds, beans, berries, fruits, mushrooms, vegetables, and other plant-sourced gifts from nature that allow all of us to be nourished on a small fraction of the land and other resources currently required to feed us animal-based foods.

However, being born into a culture that compels us to eat the extreme misery, wastefulness, and toxicity of animal-sourced foods, and to consume a vast array of factory-produced, chemically-laced junk foods, our natural empathy, intelligence, health, and respect for the sacred feminine dimension of life degenerate, and we fail to recognize that the foods we are eating are Dark Foods. The agricultural practices that employ widespread poisoning with pesticides and chemical fertilizers, anti-natural monocropping, extensive drugging and injecting of animals with hormones and poisons, genetic engineering of plants and animals, and so forth, are all manifestations of Dark Food's accomplice, Dark Agriculture, masquerading under euphemisms such as "the Green Revolution" and "bioengineering."

Thus, from the ancient foundation of Dark Food, we find that, over the centuries, we have been using Dark Science to increasingly imprison and destroy the vitality, joy, and health of animals, wildlife, ecosystems, indigenous cultures, and ourselves. Animals have thus gone from being free from human interference to being occasionally hunted, to being herded, to being imprisoned, and finally to being forced into either extinction, or into hyper-confinement, forced-medication, and genetic mutation as mere patentable property objects for human exploitation. As Dark Food, Dark Agriculture, Dark Science, and the other dark institutions have been devastating to the billions of animals routinely mutilated, raped, and killed for food and other products, the same centralized agenda is now targeting human beings.

If we acquiesce to sowing seeds of misery, disease, and slavery in billions of animals whose interests are, to them, as significant as our interests are to us, how can we expect to be worthy of lives of freedom, health, and abundance for ourselves? The boomerang effect operates with uncanny precision. Reducing animals to livestock, we are causing the same to happen to us.

Spooking the Livestock

For example, it is not difficult for a handful of relatively incompetent shepherds or cowboys to successfully herd several hundred sheep or cows into a corral with a chute so they can be trucked off to be profitably hung upside down and stabbed to death. The main technique used is spooking them. Spooking the animals causes them to stampede in the desired direction. By simply applying some spooking actions, like loud shouts and shocking sounds, or slaps, whacks, and abrupt, frightening movements, the animals predictably flee away from what is spooking them, in the direction they're being guided, right to their terrifying demise. By riding horses, and using dogs and fences, the process is even more manageable and predictable.

The herders may have, up until this particular roundup, posed as benefactors to the animals, making sure they had food and water, and most importantly, safety and security. Now however, their true intent and purpose is revealed. The good shepherd's mask comes off. The formerly friendly herders show their true faces and the animal victims seem powerless to resist or escape. They have learned to trust and obey their abusers, and this prevents them from protecting themselves and their offspring.

However, perhaps in all the confusion of the roundup, a few unusually courageous and wily cows or sheep might be able to slip away into the surrounding forest, unnoticed by the herders, and live out their days in peace, free from human exploitation. Or even more remarkably, perhaps all the cows or sheep might awaken from their complacency, and refuse to comply with being spooked and bullied by the tiny handful of humans, and decide instead to turn and easily trample them. They then would be free to live out their lives in peace and would pass this freedom to their offspring as well, and again be able to fulfill their purposes in nature as they had for thousands of generations before the advent of exploitive human herders.

Clearly, we are in an analogous position today, and the vast mass of humanity is being spooked, often quite clumsily, by a parasitic cabal that takes advantage of our conformity, complacency, spookability, and compliant gullibility. Rulers have been studying and perfecting these techniques for centuries, and since World War II, technological methods of behavior management have been explored and rapidly increased through, for example, the CIA's MK-Ultra mind control research operations[5] that revealed ways to take advantage of human malleability.[6] It is clear that the ruling class is attempting to herd us into the chute of complete technocratic oppression, and the tragic existential misery to which that leads. The captured media is the main tool used to spook the public, and the herders now ride their horses of power as authorities in governmental, corporate, and academic institutions, with a whole army of herd-dogs in the form of indoctrinated journalists, public health bureaucrats, and medical personnel, and with plenty of fencing installed to censor alternative views and to stifle debate, critical thinking, and community solidarity.

It is essential to question the bogus fear-based narratives that attempt to stampede the global populace into abject submission. Refusing to be spooked or to comply with the mandates and social pressures to conform, each of us can endeavor to exemplify the noble qualities of human dignity, critical thinking, self-reliance, compassion, justice, and freedom, and to educate others about the criminal hidden agenda being forced onto humanity by its would-be herders. Fortunately, there are many sources for further information to learn, and to share with others, and some of the primary ones are listed in the Resources section of this book.

Among human herders, it is a regular practice to "cull the herd" when it gets too big, and is always considered to be in the best interest of the herd, and of the herders as well. Culling is a euphemism for selective killing, and it seems quite obvious that this common agricultural practice is also boomeranging on humanity under the guise of safety and medical security.

When wild, free-living animals are put into an enclosure, they will immediately seek a way to escape. But animals who are born into enclosures and know nothing but the prison cell in which they live do not try to escape, because they have never known anything but incarceration. They have to be literally picked up and carried out by a rescuer in order to escape their imprisonment. We humans are much the same. Some of us may still, in some way, remember our connection with nature and with the sovereignty of our being, and attempt to escape from social enslavement as best we can. Unfortunately, however, it seems that many find comfort in obedience to authoritarian control and in relinquishing responsibility, autonomy and creativity. This is tragic, and makes the situation much more dangerous and difficult for those who yearn for freedom and who resist the growing tyranny. It also reveals the depth to which we have allowed cultural forces to poison our inherent wisdom and awareness.

Escaping from the slavery of eating animals is foundational, and we find that our example is often enough to inspire others. Many appear, instead, though, to be threatened by our freedom from the cultural food program. How do we skillfully respond to this? We cannot pick others up bodily in order to rescue them from the prison of meat-eating. We also see that many of us who have freed ourselves from eating animal-sourced foods are nevertheless still imprisoned by the fear of questioning medical, academic, and governmental authorities. With awareness, we can discern the oftentimes invisible cages that not only imprison us, but also comfort us and erode our inner clarity and strength which, if activated, would propel us out of suffering and addiction, and reconnect us with the joy of freedom and creative engagement.

It is now critical that each of us rise up, disconnect from TV, radio, mainstream journalism, and social media, promote animal liberation, and get to work co-creating communities of freedom, awareness, food sovereignty, and decentralized autonomy. If we insist on violating animals and on allowing ourselves to be spooked as we spook animals, the intelligence agency spooks will have their way and our future will be as dystopian as is the future to which we casually condemn millions of farmed cows, pigs, chickens, fishes, and other sentient beings every day. Liberating animals, we create the foundation for our own freedom. Otherwise, we are, like them, trapped in the masked deceptions of the dark institutions that spring unstoppably from the violence of herderism and the Dark Food system into which we have all been born.

There is an ongoing spiritual quickening in the heart of humanity, and as we take time daily to reconnect with the eternal essence of our true nature, we can contribute to the benevolent revolution that liberates animals, and thus ourselves. It is essential that we connect ever more authentically with our inner wisdom in order to discern the dark forces masquerading as our benefactors, and learn to take responsibility for our health and our relationships on every level. Every moment of every day is an opportunity to question, learn, and grow, and to contribute to reclaiming our health, transforming the spooking delusions of fear, alienation, and separation into the bright serenity that comes from understanding our true nature, and treating all beings as we would like to be treated: with kindness and respect.

CHAPTER EIGHT

THE VACCA-CINATION
OF HUMANITY

"Never have so many been manipulated so much by so few."
—Aldous Huxley

"Everything the government is doing right now is designed to make you
fat, weak, stupid, depressed, lazy, and reliant on crumbs they wipe off
their plates. Health replaced by pharmaceuticals. Education replaced
by programming. Hard work replaced by handouts."
—Ian Smith

"I think you have the same rights as a farm animal if you're just going to
be injected with whatever the government wants to put into you."[1]
—Del Bigtree

The War Against Germs

Our word vaccination comes from the Latin root *vacca* meaning
cow and the derivative word *vaccinia*, which refers to cowpox
disease. The vacca-cination of humanity is the agenda of turning
humans into cows: livestock to be exploited. Edward Jenner of

England coined the word vaccination in 1798 to describe his procedure of taking pus from the lesions of people sick with cowpox, and injecting it into healthy people. His theory was that this would provide a rehearsal for the body's immune defenses and thus help protect them from smallpox. This practice of vaccination has grown and spread since then, to the point that in recent decades it has come to be considered a primary weapon in mainstream medicine's ongoing and lucrative battle against the decillions of "germs" that live in us and around us all the time.[2]

Whether there is any truth to the efficacy of vaccination is still a hotly-debated topic, and with its increasingly obvious harmful effects on vast numbers of people, it's critical that we understand the source and significance of this prevailing medical practice, and the germ theory in which it is embedded. Otherwise, we will find ourselves continuing to be reduced to the status of medicated cash cows for the industry. The hidden key to the only sure-fire way to establish peace, freedom, and justice in our human world is understanding that the well-established and brazenly bigoted narrative of absolute human superiority has disconnected us from animals and from the natural world, and that this undermines all aspects of our individual and collective health.

The Pharmaceutical Juggernaut

In fact, while our routine abuse and consumption of millions of animals daily brings wealth to the large animal food-based corporations like Smithfield, Cargill, and McDonalds, it brings even more wealth to the chemical-pharmaceutical-medical complex which is also dependent on animal agriculture for its massive profits. Profit margins in the food industry are much tighter than in the pharmaceutical industry, and because people have to eat, these food corporations are increasingly diversifying into and profiting from plant-based meats, cheeses, and other foods to complement their more established animal-based ones.

In contrast, the pharmaceutical industry requires a reliable torrent of sick people dependent upon its products, and the concentration of toxins in animal flesh, dairy products, and eggs guarantees this reliable flood, as long as people can be conditioned to consume them. Big Pharma is a virulently anti-health, anti-freedom, and anti-vegan industry. Healthy, free-thinking, compassionate people are its most threatening concern. All of its products are developed through vivisection, and millions of animals are tortured and killed annually by pharmaceutical researchers in their quest for profitable drugs. The main markets for these drugs are the farmed animals who are heavily medicated (as are animals in the pet industry), and consumers who are prescribed medications for their resulting diseases.[3]

With its high profit margins, the pharmaceutical industry is not only the most lucrative industry, but also one of the most corrupt. In recent history, for example, Pfizer was required to pay the largest criminal fine in U.S. history, over two billion dollars, and GlaxoSmithKline topped that, paying the largest combined criminal and civil fine ever, over three billion dollars. Johnson and Johnson, Merck, Eli Lilly, and the other drug companies are also routinely fined huge sums for criminal deception and negligence.[4] They seem to consider it as merely a relatively minor cost of doing business. When it comes to their enormously profitable vaccine products, however, these corporations enjoy complete legal and financial immunity. This is due to their successful legislative lobbying, and the consequent passage of the 1986 National Childhood Vaccine Injury Act, as well as the PREP Act and other protective legislation over the recent decades. This government interference removes all corporate liability for vaccines, no matter how deadly and harmful they may be.

The pharmaceutical-chemical complex rakes in enormous profits in three areas besides vaccines. First, it profits handsomely from the over ten thousand drugs, hormones, antibiotics and other chemicals approved to be inflicted on the billions of animals imprisoned and exploited for meat, dairy products, eggs, and pet foods. Virtually all factory-farmed animals are force-medicated with pharmaceutical injections, antibiotics, hormones, feed additives, sprays, and baths, and many animals in small backyard operations are medicated as well. Second, there are billions of dollars more in annual sales of pharmaceuticals to those of us who eat these toxic foods and need relief from the resulting cancer, diabetes, heart disease, obesity, liver disease, kidney disease, arthritis, and many other physical afflictions directly linked with diets high in animal-based foods. Third, and largest, are profits from the sale of drugs for psychological disease and distress of various kinds. These drugs have been aptly described by psychiatrist Peter Breggin, MD, as neurotoxins that poison the nervous system.[5] The animals exploited for food are afflicted with severe depression, anxiety, chronic pain, insomnia, and traumatic stress, and the drug companies reap enormous profits from humans who purchase, cause, and literally eat all of this mental violence, despair, and misery, and are afflicted with similar conditions such as depression, anxiety, stress, and insomnia, for which they purchase pharmaceuticals.

This provides a glimpse into how the boomerang effect benefits these nefarious corporations and destroys our physical, mental, financial, and social health. Besides all this, the millions of animals kept as "pets" are routinely medicated and vaccinated through annual check-ups and "shots," which serves to condition their caregivers and society at large in the idea of regular and ongoing vaccination. We humans are now also expected to dutifully line up for annual shots as has been done in the pet industry for decades.

With these massive profits, Big Pharma buys and controls the medical narratives in the media, as well as in schools, medical and veterinary training programs, and academia, and also in governmental agencies and institutions at all levels. As but one example, in 2021 Pfizer listed nearly 500 academic, civic, scientific, and medical organizations to which it had provided generous philanthropic contributions.[6] These included the Chicago Urban League, the National Consumers League, the Immunization Partnership, the Advertising Council, and a remarkably long list of universities and medical science organizations. It would have been an obvious conflict of interest for Pfizer to promote its injections to the population directly, so its policy is to cleverly mask its involvement by paying these civic, medical, and educational organizations to push the mandates for them. As journalist Lee Fang notes, "Pharma is unique [in terms of] the raw amounts of money they spend to control the entire public sector."[7] Additionally, Pfizer funds mainstream media news narratives ("brought to you by Pfizer")[8] through its enormous annual advertising budget of about three billion dollars.[9]Another example is the fact that the vast majority of Patient Advocacy Organizations (such as American Cancer Society, American Heart Association, Alzheimer's Association, American Diabetes Association, etc.) have top management and board members who have significant financial ties with the pharmaceutical industry.[10] With these pervasive conflicts of interest with the pharmaceutical complex, it is obvious that the last thing these patient advocacy organizations would like is a robust humanity free of the diseases that are foundational to their wealth, power, and prestige.

The pharmaceutical industry's worst nightmare is a world of healthy people eating whole, organic vegan foods and taking responsibility for their health, and thus having little need for their poisonous products. Neither my wife Madeleine nor I, for example, have bought any pharmaceuticals from a drug store or doctor for any medical condition in the past fifty years. This is simply a recognition that our health is primarily in our own hands. The fact that it is unusual says more about how much our society has changed over the past hundred years than it says about us. We have used a variety of non-medical and non-pharmaceutical approaches that have been helpful over the years, and millions of people behave like us in this regard.

For example, many people opt for an approach that focuses on the mostly unrecognized efficacy of spiritual healing, a broad subject that covers many systems and practices that can be remarkably effective. Mary Baker Eddy's classic book, *Science and Health*, illuminates the essential principles of spiritual healing. The movement she founded in the late nineteenth century, Christian

Science, flourishes with a worldwide network of trained Christian Science practitioners whose livelihood is based on healing people through spiritual means, using no material methods at all, not only of emotional, financial, and relationship difficulties, but of virtually all types of physical diseases, conditions, and mishaps. Some Mahayana Buddhist approaches to spiritual healing are based on a similar cultivation of awareness, developing the understanding that the physical level is a manifestation of consciousness, and that authentic healing requires us to address this higher level. With these types of spiritual healing, physical symptoms are understood to be manifestations of underlying emotional or mental dis-ease or misperception, or the ripening of seeds from past actions. The Medicine Buddha practices in Vajrayana Buddhism also approach healing from this perspective. Faith healing is also a path that has helped countless people over the generations, especially in the Christian tradition, and in other traditions as well. The power of prayer to facilitate healing has been extensively documented by Larry Dossey, MD, and others.[11]

Many healing approaches focus more on energy, and on clearing energy blockages or stimulating and transmitting healing energy. Some examples are Healing Touch and Therapeutic Touch, as well as Reiki, acupuncture, acupressure, chi gong and other chi practices from the Taoist tradition, including Tai Chi, and pranayama, kundalini, and yoga practices from the Hindu tradition. Other healing systems—such as the ancient Ayurvedic healing tradition from India; Traditional Chinese Medicine, which includes acupuncture, moxibustion, herbs, and other approaches; shamanic healing systems from indigenous traditions worldwide; homeopathy, which facilitates the use of healing information in potentized attenuations of natural herbs and minerals; and finally, the exceedingly rich traditions of healing plants, herbs, and other natural substances—are still practiced globally. This is just a brief sampling of the systems and practices that are part of our human heritage, and there is a myriad more, for example using music, art, poetry, movement, dance, meditation, immersion in cold water and other aspects of nature, fasting, laughter, family dynamics, magnetism, various forms of purification, and countless more. The often-miraculous healing power of love has been recognized since ancient times, as well.[12] Love as a healing power has been explored and advocated by Peter Breggin, MD,[13] Bernie Siegel, MD,[14] and many others. All of these are predictably ignored and repressed by the World Health Organization and its worldwide medical-media cartel in order to promote its reductionist methods that monopolize profits and power in the hands of the plutocrats.

Each one of us can make a daily effort to take responsibility for our health and eat only healthy organic unprocessed plant-sourced foods, exercise and move regularly, connect with our creative impulses, take responsibility for the quality of our relationships, do our best to live every day with an inspiring purpose, and engage in spiritual practices that bring inner peace and deepen our understanding of our original nature. Our companion book, *The World Peace Way*, discusses these practical keys to healthy living in greater detail.

With over three registered lobbyists for every member of Congress,[15] Big Pharma spends more lavishly than any other industry in lobbying federal, state, and local governments, and in contributing to election campaigns to influence elections at every level. With its enormous wealth, it funds think tanks and legal organizations as well as advertising and public relations campaigns and predatory "philanthropic" projects in order to completely dominate media, public discourse, and governmental policy, as well as the education of scientists, doctors, veterinarians, health-care professionals, and teachers. Even the medical journals, which are an essential factor behind the medical industry's esteemed status, and dictate all its protocols, have been thoroughly corrupted by Big Pharma, as Dr. Marcia Angell writes,

> It is simply no longer possible to believe much of the clinical research that is published, or to rely on the judgment of trusted physicians or authoritative medical guidelines. I take no pleasure

in this conclusion, which I reached slowly and reluctantly over my two decades as an editor of *The New England Journal of Medicine*.[16]

Fear breeds disease, and the pharmaceutical industry markets fear in all its forms. It thrives best when people are stressed, unhappy, disconnected, misinformed, exposed to a wide variety of fear-based news stories and chemical toxins, and unable or unwilling to effectively take responsibility for their physical, mental, and spiritual health. Big Pharma carefully cultivates narratives, such as the germ theory, that guarantee that people will interpret sickness incorrectly, and see it not as a manifestation of either unresolved inner issues or of the body's intelligent cleansing and self-healing capacities, but rather as an attack by what it proclaims are innumerable invisible enemies that are constantly threatening us and trying to harm us.

The germ theory fits in perfectly with animal agriculture and with our herding culture's essential orientation. We ourselves are the invisible killers and harmers of billions of animals, and our culture's deeply-rooted shame, fear, and numbing, in causing and eating relentless violence, resonates profoundly with the victim mentality of seeing ourselves in an ongoing war against nature, animals, and the web of life. Our attitudes and quality of consciousness are in many ways determined and conditioned by our life experiences, and, on the other hand, our life experiences determine and condition our attitudes and the quality of our consciousness. Nothing is more harmful and pathetic than the vicious circle of our animal abuse, which gives rise to our victim mentality, generating the germ theory and our war against nature and microbes, which encourages even more abuse of animals, and so on, further amplified by technology and resonant cultural institutions.

The living web of microorganisms that constitutes our microbiome and pervades our body is the blessed foundation of our life and makes our life possible. Yet the pharmaceutical-medical-chemical-herder narrative turns this beneficial web into an adversary, converting sovereignty into slavery, health into disease, meaning into absurdity, and harmony into dissonant ongoing warfare against invisible antagonists. Cows, pigs, and other animals have been experiencing the resulting abuse and exploitation of this cultural narrative for centuries. Inflicting it on them, we find it increasingly attacks all of nature, and relentlessly invades our bodily, mental, and cultural landscape as well.

Circles of Poison

Herderism's self-serving narrative of reductionism and materialism promotes exploitation of the vulnerable by the powerful, and it is the key driving force that enables a tiny ruling minority to amass phenomenal wealth at the expense of humanity, animals, ecosystems, and future generations. Just as the last thing the Pentagon and CIA desire is peace, and so they constantly work to increase conflict and tension in the world to boost their perceived status and gratify their desire for copious funding, the last thing the medical-pharmaceutical complex wants is empowered and healthy people in a harmonious relationship with nature. It promotes fear-based narratives constantly through the mainstream media it dominates, as well as online media allies like Google, Apple, Facebook, Twitter, Linked-in, and Wikipedia. The pharmaceutical complex works with its partners, including Big Agra, Big Food, Big Medica, and Big Chema—as well as the governmental agencies it occupies, such as the CDC, FDA, USDA, NIH (National Institutes of Health), NIAID (National Institute of Allergies and Infectious Diseases), the WHO (World Health Organization), the United Nations, and also the most wealthy and influential "philanthropic," "professional," and "educational" institutions such as the Rockefeller Foundation, the Gates Foundation, the Wellcome Trust, CEPI (Coalition for Preparedness Innovations), GAVI (Global Alliance for Vaccines and Immunization), the AMA (American Medical Association), state medical licensing boards, public universities and most private ones, medical schools, and academia in general—to increase its power and wealth by continually investing in and controlling the medical narrative. It's essential to understand that the WHO, the preeminent global public health organization, receives substantial funding from the Gates Foundation and other private foundations that profit directly from vaccine and pharmaceutical sales.[17] It oversees the vast global pharmaceutical-medical complex and operates, in many ways, as Dr. Peter McCullough and others have stated, as a worldwide criminal syndicate, dictating policies to national governments, promoting disease and drugs, while being immune from any accountability.[18]

Big Pharma sells chemicals, and as such, it is a branch of the petrochemical industry, which is itself a subset of the petroleum industry. Animal agriculture is the foundation of the wealth and power of all three. For example, as mentioned earlier, if everyone in the world adopted a plant-sourced diet, the world population could be fed using only one billion hectares of land instead of four billion.[19] A full three billion hectares, an area the size of Africa, which is to say, larger than the United States, Mexico, Europe, and Australia combined—currently being used to grow livestock feed or to graze livestock, and doused with petroleum-based pesticides, herbicides, and chemical fertilizers—could be liberated from unnecessary agricultural abuse, providing much-needed habitat for wildlife and a massive healing for our ecosystems: rivers, forests, prairies, aquifers, oceans, soil, air quality, and so forth.

This would mean an immediate reduction in the amount of carcinogenic chemicals ending up in our water, air, food, and bodies, and thus a significant drop in the amount of disease and chemical medications we'd be swallowing and injecting into our bodies and subsequently eliminating through our sewer systems back into the waters to continue harming animals, ecosystems, and us. There would also be a correspondingly significant reduction in the need for petroleum-based pesticides and natural-gas-based chemical fertilizers, as well as petroleum to run machines, equipment, and factory-farm and slaughterhouse complexes, not to mention the associated plastics and pharmaceuticals, and the devastating effects that all these have on ecosystems, wildlife, and human health.

Going further, and taking positive and proactive responsibility for our health, and eating only organic and whole, unprocessed plant-sourced foods, preferably grown in our own gardens or purchased through local markets and co-ops, we could easily further slash our consumption of disruptive, harmful chemicals, enhance our health and freedom significantly, and drastically reduce the vast wealth and power of the pharmaceutical-petrochemical-medical complex, and its devastating capacity to dominate the conversations we are having to its own advantage. As a vegan advocate for forty years, it has become obvious that, similar to the meat, dairy, egg, and fishing industries, the petroleum industry's twin offspring—the chemical industry and the pharmaceutical-medical industry—fiercely oppose the liberation of animals.

Both industries harm the essential foundation of health for us and for all life: the community of microorganisms known as the microbiome. The soil microbiome is ravaged and destroyed by pesticides, herbicides, fungicides, larvicides, and chemical fertilizers. Residues of these toxins in food, water, and air also attack our gut microbiome, the community of microorganisms on which our life depends, which is also attacked by antibiotics and pharmaceutical drugs. Glyphosate, for example, a key factor in the disastrous promotion of genetically-engineered foods, is now the most widely used pesticide on the planet, and virtually all non-organic foods are contaminated with it.[20] Among its other harmful effects, glyphosate is a broad-spectrum antibiotic, and directly attacks the health of our intestinal flora, causing digestive issues, leaky gut, and a host of other problems. Only in recent years have we begun to understand the critical importance to our physical and mental health of these microbiome communities in the soil and throughout our body. Healthy soil microbiomes form the agricultural foundations for growing nutritious vegetables, grains, fruits, and other foods.

Similarly, a healthy gut microbiome is essential not only to proper digestion and elimination, but also, through the vagus nerve and hormone regulation, significantly contributes to our mental health, positively influencing our moods and emotional state. If beleaguered by chemical toxins and animal-sourced foods, our intestinal bacterial community tends to generate anxiety, frustration, and other emotional negativity, but when healthy, generates endorphins and an overall feeling of well-being. This empowering understanding is suppressed and ignored by the pharmaceutical/chemical industries' fear-based, fire-and-brimstone preaching of its germ theory, scaring us into believing that these microorganisms are a terrible threat to our health, so they can sell and spew more toxic chemicals throughout both the inner and outer terrain, guaranteeing further profits from disease and anxiety, and from damaged, infertile soils that now require petroleum and chemical inputs to grow food. As a business plan, it is clever and highly-successful, but of course it depends on externalizing costs onto vulnerable humans, animals, and ecosystems, as well as ruthless narrative control, censorship, and deception.

The Unyielding Dilemma

Animal agriculture brings out the worst in us, individually and collectively. It is the hidden driving force behind the arising of centralized financial and corporate power structures that parasitically control economic, political, familial, educational, scientific, and religious institutions. Corporations, which are recognized as legal persons, were created to provide wealthy individuals with financial and legal immunity from accountability. They are an inevitable outcome of herding animals over many centuries. The necessity to avoid accountability for the abuses we are routinely and unnecessarily inflicting on other living beings is the primary underlying psychological and cultural dynamic of animal agriculture. The largest transnational corporations, many with more resources than most national governments, are themselves dwarfed by the immense wealth and power of the large asset management and banking institutions, such as BlackRock, Vanguard, State Street, Goldman Sachs, Chase, and Citigroup. Financial researcher G. Edward Griffin sums it, "The world is now in the hands of the banking institutions,"[21] which are controlled by a remarkably small number of people. This unjust concentration of force into a few almighty hands flows directly from the enormous cumulative injustice to the billions of animals in our similarly almighty hands.

There are three necessary dimensions to animal agriculture. One is enslaving the animals, the second is killing the animals, and the third is the most essential foundation of animal agriculture, which is sexually abusing them: impregnating them against their will on what the industry calls "rape racks," and killing their babies (and also sexually abusing males to load the sperm guns). This is true for all animals in commercial animal agriculture, in both large-scale and small backyard operations, including organic, and it is not just cows, pigs, and other mammals, and birds such as chickens, turkeys, ducks, and geese, but also fishes in aquaculture operations and bees for honey production: all are essentially confine-rape-and-kill operations. The depths of depravity to which humanity plunged when we began herding animals required us to numb our natural feelings of empathy, to disconnect from our basic intelligence, wisdom, and decency, and to create elaborate narratives of superiority, and religious and scientific rationalizations of many kinds. All were desperate attempts to avoid accountability for our violent actions toward beings with interests as important to them as our interests are to us.

Now we are seeing everything come full circle. The ever-growing financial conglomerates that the herding culture created to escape conscience and accountability for its heartless abuse—of animals, nature, and human beings—are basically treating us humans as livestock. Who actually controls these? If we look at the largest financial asset management companies in the world, such as Vanguard, BlackRock, State Street, Berkshire-Hathaway, Fidelity, and UBS, each one with control over many trillions of investment dollars, we see that they own and control the stock of

virtually all existing corporations, including the seemingly competing ones. For example, they own Apple, Microsoft, Facebook, and
Google, as well as Exxon, BP, Shell, and Texaco; CNN, NBC, Dis-
ney, Fox, and ABC; McDonalds, Burger King, Wendy's and KFC;
Hilton, Sheraton, Holiday Inn, and Hyatt; Delta, United, American, and Southwest; Pfizer, Lilly, Merck, and Johnson & Johnson,
and so forth, throughout virtually all industries. What we are told
are competing businesses are actually all owned by the same plutocratic interests. They are not actually competing with each other,
but rather deceiving us into a false understanding. When we inquire more deeply into who actually owns and controls these
immense asset management firms, we discover that all of them are
owned by each other, with the exception of one—Vanguard—
which is privately owned, with a legal structure in place that cunningly hides the identities of the actual principals involved.[22]

Through these massive asset management companies, a relatively miniscule number of wealthy people are able to exert
enormous control over corporate, banking, and government policies, as well as the all-important narratives that maintain their
unquestioned power, which streams reliably through media, academia, and other institutions that they also control, thus
canceling any alternative voices. The scale of economic injustice
and monopolized power in the hands of a relative few is staggering. What do we mean here by a few? Basically, about eight to
ten thousand people, which is about one ten-thousandth of one
percent of the global population. This is the main inner circle of
power, and includes those who are at or near the tops of the interconnecting pyramids of influence and authority in our world.

First, it includes the bankers who control the central banks of
the world's nations, and the Bank of International Settlements as
well as the World Bank and International Monetary Fund, controlling money supply and distribution, and also those owning and
overseeing the large asset management firms and commercial
banks. Also included are the top management of the world's trans-
national corporations, as well as the presidents of the major

universities. There are the major governmental leaders of the world's nations and also those who are high up in political positions as well as in the intelligence communities and military apparatus. There are those who own and control the media companies, and also the high executives in the technology and medical industries. And finally, there are those who manage Hollywood and the entertainment, film, and music industries, as well as high-ranking royalty, and certain top religious authorities. This elite group meets together in various ways, such as through the World Economic Forum and semi-public, private and secret gatherings, and the people know one other, party together, and swarm together in the sense of working synchronously together to further their common interests, which are to continually strengthen their hold on power and narrative-control over the eight billion people whom they are relentlessly attempting to manage and dominate.[23]

They employ the wealthiest one percent of the world's population, the roughly 80 million people just below them in the power pyramid, who are well compensated to carry out their bidding in all these various domains, which are integrated at the highest level. This concentration of wealth and power at the top allows virtually complete control of the other 99 percent of the population. For example, in 2016, according to analyses by Oxfam, the wealth of the richest one percent was equal to that of the other 99 percent combined,[24] which is a devastating situation of outrageous injustice. And yet, it skewed even more sharply afterward, through imposed pandemic lockdowns and public health injection mandates. By 2022, the one percent had twice the wealth of everyone else combined.[25] It is the one ten-thousandth of one percent who control this one percent, and most likely it is the one one-hundred-thousandth of one percent, roughly 800 people, who form an even tighter inner circle of control. The economic, social, and political monopoly of power now possible through control of data-mining, surveillance, censorship, and perception management technologies makes it possible for this tiny fraction of humanity to rule over and exploit the vast majority.

It is obvious that a key goal of their agenda is the implementation of a worldwide financial system based on Central Bank Digital Currency (CBDC), which would basically eliminate cash and traditional currencies, and require all transactions to be made directly through the central banks using some type of universal digital passport that everyone would be required to use, most likely on a smart phone or implantable chip, or perhaps an iris scan, in order to buy anything or go anywhere. Those of us who resist compliance with this or engage in any behavior disapproved of by the central authorities could easily be targeted. Authorities or algorithms could simply revoke or limit, or geographically restrict, our ability to travel or to purchase food or fuel, and thus a worldwide inescapable technocratic slave society could be installed relatively easily in the near future, if we remain gullible and comply with coercive mandates issued by technocrats under the guise of public health, or safety, or one of the well-propagandized crises or emergencies.

Such a dystopian future is clearly being planned, and the heads of virtually all national central banks are openly promoting the adoption of CBDCs.[26] This enslaving agenda is propelled forward in many ways by engineered pandemics (more accurately called case-demics based on fraudulent testing protocols)[27] that centralize authority and destroy human and civil rights under the guise of public health emergencies. By spooking the population into acceptance of more centralized control over our lives, the plutocratic cabal can make use of available surveillance technologies, as well as the high-speed digital networks, recently constructed on a global scale, that are already facilitating the Internet of Things and the Internet of Bodies.

Because we have failed to question our culture's practice of enslaving and eating animals for food, and have surrendered our responsibility for health, education, and information to centralized forces, we find ourselves being increasingly treated the way many of us mistreat "pets," who are confined and tethered their entire lives. This is the unyielding dilemma we face. Ironically, it may also be our greatest blessing if it rouses us finally to awaken to the effects of animal agriculture and abandon it completely and gladly. It is encouraging to see that increasing numbers of people seem to be realizing this basic truth: whatever we sow in our treatment of animals, we reap in our human lives. I have been warning for several decades now that when we insist on relentlessly confining, tracking, force-medicating, abusing, and exploiting millions of animals, we create the conditions for the same thing to inexorably unfold in our human lives. The pharmaceutical-medical-petrochemical complex and those who run it and view humanity as mere livestock to be exploited are, in a paradoxical way, our teachers, revealing to us the potency of our similarly unnecessary mistreatment of billions of animals.

A beautiful and harmonious future of freedom, truth, and health is always available to us on this abundant Earth at every moment. It beckons, and it requires that we question official narratives, embrace our inner wisdom and empathy for others, and honor our true nature by respecting those who are at our mercy. Living in alignment with ahimsa and deep veganism is refusing to comply with the prevailing cultural oppression of animals, and this includes human animals as well. Silence is complicity. Going along to get along is complicity. Only through freeing animals from being mere property objects as livestock, pets, and laboratory, entertainment, and service chattel will we have a solid foundation for our own freedom, and the possibility to discern truth from the flood of deceptive fear propaganda that is turning us into *vaccas* – livestock. With this discernment, we can take back our authentic power and derail the unfolding *vacca-cination* of humanity that would enslave us and our children.

Each of us can say yes to this monumental challenge, and make the effort to embody and exemplify the positive transformation called for during the current unprecedented war against humanity and all life. Our predicament is a direct result of our ongoing mistreatment of animals, and we certainly have the power to liberate ourselves by liberating them, and by doing our best to exemplify and embody the peace, morality, justice, and compassion we yearn to see in our world.

CHAPTER NINE

THE METAPHYSICS OF MASKS

つつ

"Deceit is part of the structure of self. It is always trying to be other than it is and seeking to impress others by what it is not. To each person it presents a different face, consciously or unconsciously."[1]
—RADHA BURNIER

"God has given you one face, and you make yourself another."
—WILLIAM SHAKESPEARE

"Exposing the fraud of the germ theory and ending the public's fear of non-existent 'pandemics' is imperative to ending the reign of terror the pharmaceutical industry and pharma-controlled governments have inflicted on us."
—BRITT LIND

The Strategic Use of Deception

To make sense of things as the world's political, economic, medical, and cultural landscape rapidly changes, it may be helpful to get back to basics and take a fresh look at the idea of selfishness, and its opposite, altruism. Selfishness is caring about oneself and one's own welfare more than that of others, and implies a willingness to harm others or let others be harmed to benefit one's own position. In its more excessive forms, it manifests as sociopathic and psychopathic behavior, where people seem unable to empathize with others, and abuse them for their own advantage; even more extreme is sadism, the perverse deriving of pleasure by causing pain to others. We humans seem to naturally, intuitively, and rationally limit and discourage these selfish types of behavior and to view them as being immoral, unethical, and wrong. Harming others for our own benefit is psychopathic, and is the antithesis of moral and spiritual maturity. Altruistic actions, which help others without seeking gain for ourselves, are universally appreciated as comprising good and ethical behavior, and are globally espoused by religious teachings and The Golden Rule.

The obvious contradiction to this is the current situation of rampant injustice and inequality, whereby the wealthiest one ten-thousandth of one percent of humanity has accumulated so much wealth, and consequent power, that it can effectively dominate and exploit the entire human population by controlling governance, economics, and media narratives. Given our natural human cultural discouragement of exactly this kind of selfishness and unfairness, it becomes obvious that the only way this situation can be maintained, and even constantly increased, is through the strategic use of huge amounts of deception and division, and repression of the general public's innate awareness and capacities.

Two of the primary ways the ruling class is able to dominate and exploit their fellow humans is by deceptively disguising their sociopathic behavior as beneficial, and also by cloaking it in the garb of being natural and unavoidable. These same deceptions are already well-practiced in our culture's massive exploitation of animals, which we justify using similar narratives, emphasizing how much farmers care about their animals and how they treat them well before "harvesting" them, and that it is unavoidable and natural because we are inherently superior to animals and need their protein, calcium, and other nutrients to be healthy. In the same way, the ruling authorities controlling the medical-media complex propagate a narrative that, for example, we are in a terrible pandemic emergency, climate crisis, war, or other attack or predicament, and that "we're all in this together," so we all must forfeit our inherent rights to speak, travel, assemble, worship, breathe freely, and be secure in our bodies and affairs. The plutocrats are able to deceive us quite easily by exploiting and weaponizing our natural altruism, our tribalistic tendencies, and our life-long indoctrination into unquestioning obedience to medical, scientific, and government authorities. Through ramping up fear, they manipulate us into behavior that is harmful to ourselves, our children, and our entire society. Crises and emergencies can be relatively easily fabricated, and the responses controlled in order to concentrate prestige and power ever more firmly in their hands.

Targeting especially the more "progressive" among us on the left, by framing mandatory social distancing, masking, lockdowns, and injections, for example, as caring, altruistic behavior that helps keep everyone "safe," the ruling class has been able to quite easily deceive millions of people into paradoxically non-altruistic behavior that furthers their agenda of domination, and is devastating to our physical, mental, cultural, and financial health, and disempowers and divides us on every level. As but one example of this strategy, and the extreme ironies involved, we see this in the *New York Times*, even as late as 2022, when Covid was winding down and the dangers and complete ineffectiveness of face masking were well-established:[2]

> Those who refuse to take basic Covid precautions are, at best, being selfish — ignoring the welfare and comfort of their fellow citizens. At worst, they're engaged in deliberate aggression — putting others at risk to make a point. And the fact that some of the people around us are deliberately putting others at risk takes its own psychological toll. Tell me that it doesn't bother you when the person standing behind you in the checkout line ostentatiously goes maskless or keeps his or her mask pulled down.[3]

We find ourselves vulnerable to this fear-based deception because of our woundedness, being immersed from birth in medical and educational systems saturated with authoritarian materialism, which flow from and support the narratives and practices of the herding culture. The inescapable anxiety resulting from relentlessly traumatizing and eating animals drives our sense of alienation from nature, as well as our deep-seated fear of animals, insects, and microbes. This anxiety makes us susceptible to fear-based indoctrination, and it is reinforced by the underlying materialism of our culture that erodes spirituality and meaning in our lives. This materialism undergirds the convenient theory of natural selection and its corollary, Social Darwinism, that legitimizes the wealthy cabal's domination and exploitation of the less powerful. Blind to the enormous amount of cooperation and mutual aid in the natural world, reductionist science indoctrinates us into a worldview that the universe is ruled by random chance and heartless competition, with those who accumulate more wealth and power being honored for being worthy of that because of their superior prowess that rewards them through natural selection in the predatory economic-political arena. The fact that their wealth enables them to purchase narrative-control through financially capturing media and academic institutions ensures not just their prestige, but also their ability to use these institutions to terrorize the population as exemplified in the above quote, as well as to indoctrinate our youth, and to erode and manipulate religious institutions to suppress ethical teachings like the Golden Rule. They are able to deceptively (and ironically) portray as selfish those of us who refuse to comply with their tyrannical and self-seeking agendas.

We are conditioned to submit to the dictates of governmental and medical authorities, and to be blind to the fact that they are controlled by plutocrats. We are also trained to respect the wealthy rather than recognizing that their riches and power were often acquired through avarice, deception, and psychopathy on their part or on the part of progenitors in their family dynasties. This is a pressing problem in our culture today, where it has become increasingly obvious that our rulers are now typically invisible and unidentifiable, and operate behind curtains of corruption that mask rampant blackmail and bribery. In a culture based on materialism and herderism, those who are the most vicious psychopaths tend to achieve the highest positions of power, and this woundedness and trauma is passed from generation to generation, not stopping until we can recognize it, understand it, and refuse to comply with it. Of course, animals have been enduring the extreme abuse of herder humans for ten thousand years now, and we are unable to liberate them or ourselves for many of these same reasons. It is well understood that those in the upper echelons of the ruling class are typically born into families that impress on them their innate superiority to the masses of humanity, desensitizing them to the pain they are causing, as we have also been desensitized to the pain we are causing animals, who we are taught are inferior and whose suffering at our hands is therefore justifiable and inconsequential.

Thus, by disguising parasitic and self-centered exploitation and oppression of others as beneficial and natural, a tiny minority has been able gradually to create a situation where it can reliably fool and manipulate the vast majority. This practice of disguising faces and hiding actions is the key, and by managing the messaging about the hoaxes that are being perpetrated, it is now possible for a few people to dominate many people, just as it is possible for a few humans to dominate many livestock animals. Ironically, we similarly go to great lengths to mask and disguise animal-sourced foods. We fashion them into handy shapes and add salt and many types of plant-based sauces, flavorings, dressings, and trappings because the tastes and textures of raw animal flesh, eggs, and milk are naturally quite repugnant to us.[4]

Rising out of this food deception that relentlessly fosters our gullibility, we see, for example, that the U.S. government has been similarly refining its information warfare capabilities for proficient deception for many decades, especially since the Cold War, followed by Vietnam, and by the 9-11 false flag operations and the endless wars since then. More recently we know that billions of taxpayer dollars were spent during the Covid pandemic to influence us to mask our faces, social distance, lock down, and line up for "vaccines," and the money came from many agencies, including the Department of Defense, the Department of Homeland Security, the CDC, NIH, FDA, USAID, and others.[5] The government worked in concert with media outlets, marketing and public relations agencies, medical organizations, philanthropic and non-governmental organizations (NGOs), universities and academic institutes, big tech, and actors and musicians, as well as astroturf organizations and paid influencers. Their tactics include using subliminals, neuro-linguistic programming, chaos agents, divide-and-conquer organizations, disinformation campaigns, and other propaganda methods, both to censor opposing voices and to continually flood the population with a sophisticated and virtually inescapable fear-based mind-control agenda.[6] As but one example of a vast multitude, "Stanford's Virality Project recommended that Twitter classify 'true stories of vaccine side effects' as 'standard misinformation on [its] platform.'"[7] Covid is just one of many manipulative frauds that have been deployed by government forces over recent decades, not only against overseas adversaries, but also domestically, against the taxpaying public. As a number of researchers have demonstrated, the Covid pandemic event was initiated and organized as a military operation in the U.S. by the CIA, the Pentagon, the Biodefense Commission, and the Department of Homeland Security in conjunction with the World Health Organization.[8] Many of us still seem not to realize what is happening because we cannot believe that our own government and media sources would deliberately lie to us or seek to harm us, similar perhaps to sheep regarding their shepherds.

The use of charades, scams, masquerades, hoaxes, and disguises to dominate, control, and attack other people goes back thousands of years. The term "false flag," for example, dates from pirate days when pirate ships would pretend to be harmless by flying the flag of a friendly nation in order to approach and plunder a target ship. The

Trojan Horse is another poignant and illustrative case, going back about 3,200 years, when the major Greek kings and their military forces sailed to the walled city of Troy in Asia Minor to avenge the theft of Helen, the beautiful queen, wife of king Menelaus, by Paris, king of Troy. After many weeks of fighting and efforts, the Greeks could not take the city with its strong walls. The wily king Odysseus then had the idea for the Greeks to secretly build a huge wooden horse and leave it outside the main gates at night, and pretend to go back to Greece, but there were actually some Greek soldiers hidden inside the horse. The Trojans naively thought the horse was a sacred and important gift from the gods and brought it inside the city walls to honor it, and then the Greeks surreptitiously snuck out of the horse at night and opened the city gates, allowing the whole Greek army to enter and kill all the residents and burn and destroy the city. Through subterfuge, and the gullibility of their victims, they succeeded in their mission of revenge. There have been countless more ruses through the ages where deceptive gifts, intrigues and false-flag hoaxes have been used to trick opponents and subjects in order to advance self-benefitting agendas.

Four Foundational Ruses

Today, although we can discuss a slew of such ruses, four major ones are especially powerful, widespread, and insidious in their consequences. These four foundational ruses are animal abuse, chemical abuse, banking abuse, and medical abuse.

As discussed earlier, abusing and killing billions of animals daily for food is the defining core of our culture today, and it is foundational to virtually all the other abuses and subterfuges that are harming and exploiting people, animals, and nature in order to benefit a predatory and parasitic ruling cabal. The animal abuse ruse is based on the deception that we humans need to imprison, impregnate, and slaughter animals to get adequate protein and other nutrients. Though millions of healthy long-term vegans daily expose this devastating hoax, through widespread and deeply-rooted false narratives, such as human superiority, nutrition, taste, convenience, and tradition, it continues to exploit animals, nature, and other humans. Due to animal agriculture's inherent inefficiency, we are seeing the ongoing destruction of rainforests, oceans, aquifers, wildlife, and indigenous people, the unnecessary proliferation of hunger and starvation among less privileged people, and a massive global field of trauma affecting every dimension of the planetary web of life. This ocean of misery is all based on a fraud. It is completely unnecessary to eat animal flesh, dairy products, or eggs to acquire the nutrients needed to thrive and celebrate our lives on this generous Earth. Unfortunately, disease, conflict, and subjugation are profitable, and can be used to further centralize power.

The second ruse is the chemical hoax. We are from the womb now exposed to over 80,000 toxic synthetic chemicals that are sprayed on fields to kill insects, fungi, and "weeds," added to foods and household products to enhance performance and stability, applied to fabrics as flame retardants, injected and swallowed as medications, and inhaled, drunk, and otherwise consumed as by-products of fossil fuel burning, manufacturing, mining, agriculture, and countless other industrial processes. Prior to World War II, for example, farmers used no pesticides and lost about 20 to 25 percent of crops to "pests," and today, after 80 years of massive increases in the profusion of millions of pounds annually of toxic agricultural chemicals causing cancer, birth defects, neurological disorders and many other diseases—as well as sending insect, bird, fish, and other animal and plant populations plummeting—farmers are now losing about 40 percent of crops to "pests."[9] Profits to chemical and medical industries and to financial institutions have soared, though, and consequently this is all euphemized in mainstream narratives as the Green Revolution, and the media, completely subservient to these large corporations, reliably regales the population with a never-ending stream of propaganda about progress and the wonders of modern science, genetic engineering, chemistry, and technology.

Deception is rampant. Big Chema, Big Medica and Big Pharma, like Big Ag and Big Food, are indeed destroying our physical, environmental, cultural, psychological, and spiritual health, and at the same time masquerading as our benefactors. They are in turn owned and controlled by a handful of asset management firms that are near the top of an unrecognized hierarchical pyramid that exerts power and enforces agendas through compartmentalized layers in corporations, education, media, and government. The unsuspecting public below is targeted, and is taught to trust and obey these authorities, organizations, and agencies, and to police and malign noncompliant people. When there is an outbreak of a new disease, for example, two different investigative departments from the CDC can be called upon. One department looks for viruses and bacteria, and the second looks for toxic chemical contamination. The former department is far more generously funded and respected, and there are enormous financial and political pressures to blame all apparent disease outbreaks on "natural" factors like viruses and bacteria, rather than on toxic chemical pollution and corporate malfeasance.

As but one documented example, a serious outbreak of Zika syndrome with microcephaly was suddenly increasing in Brazil in 2016. Babies were born with unusually small heads and a team of local Brazilian and Argentinian scientists found it was most likely due to the recently introduced spraying of pyriproxyfen, a chemical larvicide manufactured by a Monsanto subsidiary used to kill mosquito larvae.[10] The scientists' research concluded that the birth defects were due to the increased use of this chemical, which harmed the fetuses in pregnant women who drank contaminated water. They called for the immediate cessation of the larvicide spraying, with possible lawsuits against the chemical company for damages. But public health authorities under the umbrella of the World Health Organization and CDC disputed this and instead of rightfully holding the chemical corporations accountable, they proclaimed that the birth defects were caused by the Zika virus, and blamed mosquitoes for spreading the virus and prescribed a massive increase in the spraying of toxic larvicides, as well as the marketing of a Zika vaccine, which further increased profits to the chemical-pharmaceutical complex and deceived the public into being subjected to even more harmful chemicals.[11] The pattern is well-established: mainstream media outlets, like internet search engines, censored the original story, and propagated only the WHO version, which became the approved and official narrative.

With every declared epidemic, chemical company liability is magically removed, and in fact, even more money is to be made by creating fear of mysterious invisible pathogens, and marketing ever more harmful chemical drugs and injections. It is well documented that virtually all government regulatory agencies have been captured by the industries they are supposed to be policing through funding structures and through revolving-door employment practices. With the pharmaceutical industry, regulatory capture is taken to unprecedented depths of corruption, as Robert F. Kennedy, Jr., explains:

> From the moment of my reluctant entrance into the vaccine debate in 2005, I was astonished to realize that the pervasive web of deep financial entanglements between Pharma and the government health agencies had put regulatory capture on steroids. The CDC, for example, owns 57 vaccine patents and spends $4.9 of its $12.0 billion-dollar annual budget (as of 2019) buying and distributing vaccines. NIH owns hundreds of vaccine patents and often profits from the sale of products it supposedly regulates. High level officials, including Dr. Fauci, receive yearly emoluments of up to $150,000 in royalty payments on products that they help develop and then usher through the approval process.[12]

In a similar manner, mainstream media narratives are controlled by the money and influence of these wealthy industries. In the corporate and education sectors it is the same. Non-compliant narratives are discouraged and, increasingly, they are brutally censored.

The third Trojan Horse is private central banks and fractional reserve banking. Banks, like chemical companies, are portrayed as our friends, providing us with needed products and services, in this case loans for our homes, vehicles, and businesses. Yet every time a bank makes a loan to someone, say for $100,000, the bank creates, out of nothing, an asset on its books of about $90,000 and collects both principal and interest on this money. If the person or business cannot pay it all back, the bank keeps all of the money it has received, plus it takes ownership of the house or business. In times of rapidly rising unemployment and economic distress due to lockdowns, inflation, and other factors, millions of homes and business are swallowed up by the parasitic banking class, destroying economic freedom, cultural health, and social stability, and causing extreme suffering and distress to millions, especially the more vulnerable, such as children, women, and the less wealthy.

Central banks, like the Federal Reserve in the U.S., created in 1913, control interest rates, monetary supply and monetary policy. The Fed is an independent, private entity run by bankers, and can be conveniently used to consolidate wealth in the hands of a few. The Bank of International Settlements in Basel, Switzerland, is the global central bank for all the national central banks, and besides being exempt from virtually all laws, is championing the push for a global Central Bank Digital Currency, which would virtually enslave humanity by monitoring and controlling all monetary transactions. Henry Ford summed it well when he wrote, "It is well enough that people of the nation do not understand our banking and monetary system, for if they did, I believe there would be a revolution before tomorrow morning."[13]

We should also remember that debt is a form of indentured servitude. When we borrow money from a bank for a mortgage, loan, or credit card purchase, we are obliged to pay the money back, plus interest, and if we don't, the consequences can be frightening to contemplate. For example, medical freedom advocate Dr. Robert Malone wrote, "There is no way I would have been as comfortable speaking out during the COVID crisis if Jill and I had not cleared off our debt before that storm hit."[14] In times of massive indebtedness to the ruling banking class, such as mid-2023 when people in the U.S., for the first time ever, topped one trillion dollars in credit card debt, freedom is severely eroded. With debt, we are afraid of being unable to repay, and losing assets to the banks, and consequently we are more easily controlled, and willing to sacrifice our freedoms and health. We may submit to injection mandates to keep our job so we don't potentially lose our house, and refrain from speaking up to avoid employment and economic consequences. Our freedoms are directly tied to our financial freedom. The plutocratic class understands this and continually works to increase indebtedness in the population, which assures not just increased profits, but also expanded capacity to dominate. Following Polonius' advice to Laertes that "borrowing dulls the edge of husbandry,"[15] I have never paid any interest for anything. Though this has meant doing without, and waiting until sufficient funds were accumulated before making purchases, the freedom conferred has been priceless.

Governments are similarly beholden to their central banks. Virtually every country now has a privately-controlled central bank, and these 214 central banks are coordinated by the Bank of International Settlements. Governments are deeply indebted to their central banks, and are similarly not free, but must follow orders and directives coming from their banking creditors. In this way, bankers have been able to amass remarkable hidden control of governments worldwide, and centralize their power, enabling global-level control, as we have seen with the Covid response and the Great Reset. The Rothschild banking dynasty is well understood to have pioneered this by loaning funds to the governments of Europe in the 18th and 19th centuries, bankrolling the nearly continuous wars and conflicts that propelled the rapid growth of their enormous wealth and power that continues to this day.[16]

The fourth Trojan Horse is medicine as it is currently practiced. Today's reductionistic allopathic medical model is based on the germ theory popularized by Louis Pasteur in the nineteenth century. As discussed earlier, the germ theory of disease meshes perfectly with not only the financial interests of the pharmaceutical-medical industry, which manufactures and implements the weapons used in its war against germs, but also with the foundational orientation of our culture's herderism, which injects a basic fear and distrust of nature, animals, and microbes into us, due to our relentlessly violent and exploitive attacks on them.

A more holistic and empowering alternative to the germ theory, championed by Pasteur's contemporary and rival, Antoine Bechamp, is known as terrain theory. The basic idea is that our health is based on the overall quality of our physiological terrain, and that this terrain is influenced by many factors, such as the quality of the nutrition and exercise we are getting, as well as sunshine, rest, and the mental and emotional factors that are always affecting our physiology because the mind and body are essentially a unified whole. This holistic perspective, though far more in alignment with reality than the germ theory, is profoundly threatening to the medical-pharmaceutical industry, and so is censored, ignored, and discounted not only in the education of doctors and nurses, but also in our general culture, and in the media, as well as in online search engines and resources like Google and Wikipedia.[17]

An extensive book, *What Really Makes You Ill?* by vegan researchers Dawn Lester and David Parker, clearly exposes the harmful deceptions foisted on the public, facilitated by the germ theory's portrayal of us as innocent victims of attacks by aggressive microbes. Their research shows that microorganisms have co-evolved with us for millions of years and are basically beneficial and serve many functions.[18] Zach Bush, MD, similarly points out that without the virome, the decillions of virus-like entities that permeate and surround our body, and the microbiome, the trillions of bacteria that digest our food and help clean up damaged cells, we would be unable to live.[19] According to researchers like Andrew Kaufman, MD, Thomas Cowan, MD, Mark Bailey, MD and Samantha Bailey, MD, and virologist Dr. Stefan Lanka, what we are calling viruses are actually exosomes, which are simply cellular debris and part of the natural process of cells in our body breaking down and their constituents being recycled so they can be replaced with new cells.[20] The deception lies in being told that these friends and natural processes are our enemies, and that toxic synthetics and chemicals are our friends.[21] The ability to discriminate ropes and snakes is essential. Could it be that the many millions of pounds of chemicals now pervading our food, water, and air, as well as the stress, fear, frustration, disconnection from nature, lack of spiritual purpose, and other factors such as the now-inescapable EMF fields, are the real culprits causing our dis-ease? By ignoring these factors and focusing on "germs," the medical-pharmaceutical complex imposes a reductionistic model, and as T. Colin Campbell, author of *Whole*, has pointed out, "Reductionism is highly profitable to the medical industry."[22]

The reductionistic approach to medicine that is today based on high-markup pharmaceuticals from the petrochemical industry, and which has been instigated and propelled to a large degree by the various Rockefeller corporations and organizations over the last 120 years, actually has roots that go back 2,500 years to ancient Greece. Plato, in his dialogue, *Laws*, describes two different medical systems in Athens at that time, one for slaves and one for "freemen." The doctors for slaves...

> hold no parley with their patients about their diseases or the remedies of them; they practise by the rule of thumb, and give their decrees in the most arbitrary manner. When they have doctored one patient, they run off to another, whom they treat with equal assurance, their duty being to relieve the master of the care of his sick slaves.[23]

Does this sound familiar? The doctors of freemen use a more holistic approach:

> The doctor who practises on freemen proceeds in quite a different way. He takes counsel with his patient and learns from him, and never does anything until he has persuaded him of what he is doing. He trusts to influence rather than force.[24]

The currently-dominant reductionistic medical model based on the germ theory, which treats the patient as a mere bio-chemical machine, and has no time to look more deeply and holistically at the person and the many contributing dimensions to the person's overall mind-body terrain, is modern medicine for slaves. It is designed to maximize corporate profits and create conditions whereby we are able to work in our jobs, but are not robust enough to creatively question the imposed narratives, discover the deeper truths of our situation, and rise up as a confident force to build a culture that honors all life and that supports all of us in participating to our highest potential.

These are but four of the most obvious Trojan-Horse frauds operating in our world today. The mainstream media is another, as are the many divide-and-conquer subterfuges. The endless wars that we are told we have to support are but more Trojan-Horse frauds with devastating consequences. With the pandemic motif now fixed firmly in place, the wealthy parasitic entities, which control international financial systems as well as corporate, media, governmental, and medical systems, are clearly attempting to consolidate their hegemony and roll out agendas that reduce human beings to mere consumers. Trojan Horse hoaxes have been working effectively for decades and centuries, concentrating wealth, power, and narrative-control into fewer and fewer hands. It has all been done by deception: projecting a benevolent image-mask behind which functions a selfish and malevolent intention to dominate and exploit.

Our Breath, Our Spirit

This ongoing plan to cull and enslave humanity has become obvious to increasing numbers of people over the past several decades as false flag events and assassinations by deep-state operatives have become more blatant and destructive. This awakening out of being fooled by slyly-engineered pretexts is essential to building a positive future for all of us. Regular meditation and other inner cultivation practices, access to communities supportive of questioning official narratives, and healthy distrust of authority figures are all factors that help us open our eyes. Extensive travel can also give us a broader view. My life, as an example, has been blessed by the opportunity to travel extensively as a vegan advocate, conversing with and learning from thousands of local advocates in all fifty states and in over fifty countries over the past forty years. We are on this Earth to learn from each other, and as the saying goes, from those to whom much has been given, much is expected.

The key to the whole thing is to make a sustained effort to look behind the benevolent-appearing masks of these powerful Trojan-Horse forces. Masks hide the truth. Masks cover up real identities and deceive us. A tremendous irony is that the masked forces exploiting animals, nature, and humanity succeeded in one of their greatest coups. They deceived us, the general population, into wearing their masks. As we now know from experience, mandated face masking leads straight to mandated injections, and the loss of basic human, medical, and economic rights, and of our dignity and purposes. What we have relentlessly inflicted on nonhuman animals boomerangs inescapably, and the exploitation, medical abuse, and other injustices we see in our human world arise because we allow ourselves to be deceived by false narratives cascading from behind fraudulent masks of authority.

Our word spirit derives from the old Latin word *spiritus*, meaning breath, and so it is essential to realize that being told to cover our face with a mask is a demand to block not just our breath, but also our spirit. Facial coverings repress our spiritual strength, and reduce our unique individual identity, blocking our ability to smile and to convey our expressions, and interfering with our ability to connect, speak, and communicate with each other. They are literally de-humanizing, and are a direct assault on our humanity, turning us symbolically into submissive livestock. Masks also block our basic sense of kinship and solidarity with other people. Looking at masked people is inherently stressful and creates an underlying sense of unease and anxiety, and masked people can easily be seen as dangerous, harmful, and "other." It is well known that robbers and criminals typically mask their faces so they can harm others without being responsible or identifiable.

The underlying practice of satanism is pursuing whatever goals, pleasures, and satisfactions we desire while trivializing the harm we inflict on others. It is not an accident that one of the hallmarks of satanic rituals is the wearing of masks, which hide the identity and persona, and allow someone to transform into a different, less accountable and more pernicious being. For many months as the 2020 pandemic unfolded, it seemed that the ruling cabal, reported by many journalists and researchers to be regular participants in pedophilia and satanic rituals,[25] was striving to spook the entire human species into participating in a mass-scale satanic masking ritual in order to initiate us into a "Great Reset" where we would no longer be sovereign beings but would submissively acquiesce to whatever freedom-crushing demands medical bureaucrats announced. Out of fear of germs, autocratic decrees, and tribal retribution, many complied with this evil. As discussed earlier, animal agriculture brings out the worst in us, and drives us to desperately seek ways to escape from accountability for our mistreatment of animals, nature, and each other. Deliberately staying unaware and repressing uncomfortable information is one way, and creating legal structures, like corporations, to shield us from liability, is another. Face masks also hide our identity and provide subconscious psychological relief, reinforced by the comforting feeling of membership in a cult of similarly faceless masks who agree to follow unquestioningly the dictates of the approved and venerated authorities.

The prestigious Cochrane Institute's exhaustive meta-analysis of all studies done on the effectiveness of masks, including the N95 mask, in preventing transmission of respiratory viruses like Covid through October 2022 concluded that they do not work.[26] The U.K. Health Security Agency in April of 2023 admitted the non-existence of evidence that even the N95 mask, the gold standard, could provide any protection from Covid.[27] In fact, the N95 masks are themselves now understood to be extremely toxic, and as reported by the National Institutes of Health, "the chemicals released by these masks had eight times the recommended safety limit of toxic volatile organic compounds (TVOCs),"[28] such as dimethylacetamide and dimethylformamide, which are known carcinogens and cause damage to the liver and nervous system.[29] According to researchers, masking itself, even with nontoxic organic cotton material, can cause significant harm, including hypoxia (depleted oxygen), hypercapnia (excess carbon dioxide), and brain damage.[30] Like many things that are unhealthy for us physically, mask-wearing seems to be psychologically addictive and reassuring. As with cigarettes, drugs, and alcohol, our bodies pay a big price. They are continually making an effort to cleanse themselves of waste products, and of the four main avenues for this—skin, feces, urine, and breath—breath arguably handles the most waste, including over 80 percent of metabolized fat as carbon dioxide, so our breath is critical for both detoxifying as well as weight loss.[31]

According to physiologists, "Exhaled air contains over 250 substances, including irritant or toxic gases such as nitrogen oxides (NO), hydrogen sulfide (H2S), isoprene and acetone."[32] Wearing a face mask literally poisons us, forcing us to re-inhale several hundred toxic chemicals. Researcher Kai Kisielinski summarizes,

> For nitrogen oxides and hydrogen sulfide, pathological effects relevant to disease have been described in environmental medicine even at a low but chronic exposure. Among the volatile organic compounds in exhaled air, acetone and isoprene dominate in terms of quantity, but allyl methyl sulfide, propionic acid and ethanol (some of bacterial origin) should also be mentioned.[33]

How could we fail to question mandates requiring us to consume bodily waste? Wearing masks forces us to reassimilate a wide variety of toxins that our body has wisely eliminated, and no research has been done on what harmful effects could be caused by mixing and rebreathing these toxins that accumulate in the dead air space behind masks.[34] Further, masks inhibit oxygen uptake and harmfully escalate carbon dioxide levels in our blood and tissues, leading to respiratory suppression and a variety of diseases. Besides the generalized discomfort, masking causes impaired communication, psychological social distancing, and altered self-expression.[35]

Masking is also linked with long-term brain damage, headaches, difficulty concentrating, impaired cognitive function,[36] testicular dysfunction, decreased cognitive development in children,[37] miscarriages,[38] immune system depression, mask-induced exhaustion syndrome (MIES),[39] skin irritations, microbial infections,[40] microplastic and chemical toxin accumulation, shortness of breath, dizziness, fatigue, amplification of the exhaled aerosol of infectious agents, and many ailments of gums, mouth, and skin.[41] The Brownstone Institute has collected over 150 scientific studies demonstrating that masks are ineffective in preventing the spread of viruses, and that masks cause many harms, both physically and psychologically.[42] Mask anxiety is of course one issue[43] and another is disinhibition, as alluded to earlier. When masked, people show a tendency to be less inhibited ethically and psychologically, and engage in harmful behavior they normally wouldn't. As social media has made abundantly clear, anonymity tends to bring out the worst in us, and masking our identities online or behind a physical mask can contribute to socially harmful disinhibition. Mask-wearing also contributes to what researchers refer to as transformation, where "the wearing of a mask can make individuals feel less like their usual self and more like the character represented in the mask."[44]

Face masking also seems to dumb us down as well. According to a study at Brown University, the measured IQ scores for young one- and two-year old children historically average about 100, but when measured in 2021, after a year of mandatory masking in the general population, the average IQ of one- to two-year olds dropped drastically to only 78.[45] This is, of course, from the point of view of the herding cabal, a very good thing. With less

intelligence, less emotional vibrancy, and a lower spiritual awareness, we are much more easily controlled and exploited. In a
similar way, scientists have been making efforts for many years
to breed and medicate cows, pigs, chickens, and other "food"
animals to make them less intelligent and less sensitive, and thus
better able to withstand the crushing boredom and stress of being
reduced to mere hyperconfined eating machines to be exploited
for flesh, eggs, and milk. The transhumanist agenda promoted by
the World Economic Forum and other instruments of the ruling
class is quite clear that we humans can be genetically and techno-
logically "hacked" to render us more easily controllable.

Our Persona Is Our Mask

The ancient Greek word for mask, *persona*, comes from "per,"
meaning through, and "sona," sound. Just as our persona is a façade and not who we really are, a mask is what we speak through
and it covers and hides our mouth and our identity so no one can
see who or what we actually are behind the cover, the disguising
image, that we are projecting to the world. We have been ironically
told that it's unselfish and responsible to wear masks. This was
done repeatedly by the disingenuous voices behind the false-flag
Trojan-Horse masks, the plutocrats who would enslave us as livestock. It is imperative that we realize when we are being
deliberately deceived. Excessive gullibility is an ethical violation,
precipitating unnecessary violence and harming not only ourselves,
but everyone around us.

The mask narrative was cleverly modeled—that we all comply
because we care for others and are unselfish—to appeal especially
to those on the left, who traditionally distrust corporate greed
and resist government mandates that destroy freedom. By framing masking this way, the left was tricked into virtue-signaling
and into naïve compliance with tyranny, and has basically been
destroyed. Its demise had been already advancing for decades,
with identity politics craftily replacing the left's traditional goals
of protecting workers' and citizens' rights and human freedom,

and opposing war and the surveillance state. It seems that now the so-called left promotes war, surveillance, toxic gullibility, and the cancellation of free speech and other essential freedoms even more than does the right, and so in many ways the left/right political model is meaningless.

We can see that a more realistic appraisal recognizes sovereignty for both animals and humans, and opposes the agenda promoted by the super-wealthy parasitic cabal, as orchestrated by globalist organizations such as the Trilateral Commission, the Council on Foreign Relations, the Bilderberg Group, and the World Economic Forum (WEF), which advocates microchipping the human population.[46] The unaccountable, unelected, corporate-led WEF also promotes the so-called Great Reset, and boasts of its agenda to use pandemic emergencies as levers to radically change societal power structures, eliminating individual freedom and privacy, for the common good, and "fusing our biological identity with our digital identity," as WEF founder Klaus Schwab puts it.[47]

Rosa Koire documented in *Behind the Green Mask: U.N. Agenda 21* how the unelected globalist ruling class works through nested pyramids of power that it has erected over the past decades, advancing a self-serving agenda through initiatives and policies originating from international levels, such as the United Nations, the World Health Organization, the International Monetary Fund, the World Economic Forum, and the World Bank, and operating through national governments, and working also through state, provincial, and local county, city, and town councils and school and regulatory boards worldwide. The green mask refers to the way that the malevolent globalist agenda of increasing its centralized control of where and how people live their lives, and destroying individual autonomy, is cleverly hidden behind benevolent-sounding phrases like "sustainable development goals," "promoting human health," "ecological stewardship," "green energy," "corporate social responsibility," "carbon credit policy," "diversity, equity, and inclusion," "integrated land management," "build back better," and so forth.

When the globalist ruling class initiates an operation to steal more of our economic, political, and cultural freedom, such as with the Covid roll-out, it is a worldwide phenomenon, with few places on Earth that escape the demands being mandated by un-elected bureaucrats. Spiritual and psychological growth can only happen within a context of freedom that honors the sovereignty of individual expressions of consciousness. Censoring free speech, forbidding the questioning of narratives, not allowing people to gather or travel, spreading fear and divisiveness, and exploiting millions of people: all contribute to an agenda aimed at centralizing power in the hands of malevolent actors. The ruling class most likely doesn't see itself as malevolent, and similarly, from the point of view of cows, pigs, and chickens, we humans are malevolent actors in our relentless mistreatment of them, though we certainly do not see ourselves that way. We are conditioned by our upbringing, as are the plutocrats, to trivialize and discount the suffering we cause "lesser" beings, and to rationalize our behavior due to our almighty power over them. This boomerang effect reveals the crux of our dilemma, and is our valuable and mostly unrecognized teacher, and it also drives what we see playing out every day in our human world.

Forcing people to wear masks is not only insidiously dehumanizing and debilitating, it ensnares us in a terribly destructive falsehood: that we are all inherently dangerous to each other. This is unprecedented and completely anti-scientific. It has always been known and recognized that healthy asymptomatic people never spread disease. Yet suddenly a few public health technocrats at the World Health Organization and the Centers for Disease Control (both completely subservient to the Pentagon, Big Pharma, and the plutocrats in the background) declared, without evidence, that asymptomatic people can spread disease. This blatant deception went unchallenged because mainstream media, Big Tech, and government agencies also comply with the same forces, as does the medical establishment. Doctors, nurses, and epidemiologists would lose their professional careers and be canceled and disgraced if they questioned anything coming down from on high, even when it goes completely against established scientific understanding.

To his credit, the courageous Dr. Peter McCullough, one of the most highly distinguished medical doctors and professors, plainly stated many times publicly that, because it is established fact that asymptomatic people do not spread disease, all the masking, social distancing, lockdowns, school closures, and so forth were completely futile and harmful. He was continually censored and attacked by the media and medical establishment for doing so. The unlawful mandates went on to achieve their desired effect, which was to unravel the cultural fabric, sabotage the mental and physical health of large swathes of society, especially children and the elderly, financially undermine the middle class, divide and weaken society, and thus push forward the agenda of a universal digital passport and currency. The ruling cabal understands well that in order to impose a new and much more repressive system, the existing systems must be severely damaged or destroyed. Through the CIA and military, the powerful bankers have been destabilizing countries to maintain hegemony for many decades, and fomenting revolutions, destroying economies, and terrorizing populations in countries throughout Asia, South America, Eastern Europe, and Africa, and have learned, through years of practice, how to fragment societies along pre-existing fault lines, such as race, sex, religion, class, and orientation.[48] Now the tactics are being unleashed domestically, and it is being done globally, with virtually every nation being targeted with divide-and-conquer fear-based campaigns. Only frightened and divided people are willing to relinquish their freedom and sovereignty.

Medical deception gushing from public health agencies (mostly all following in mandatory lockstep, from the World Health Organization at the global level, to national levels such as the CDC in the U.S., to the state and local levels) led to school closures, forced masking even of children, and closure of "non-essential" gyms, restaurants, small businesses, and churches. Liquor stores were conveniently deemed essential and stayed open. This led to a catastrophic decrease in exercise, fresh air, sunshine, socializing, conviviality, and intimacy, and a sharp increase in suicide, alcoholism, drug addiction, financial and emotional stress, isolation, despair, and death.[49] It also caused the single greatest transfer of wealth to the super-rich in U.S. history, as small and medium-sized businesses were destroyed.[50] According to researchers who undertook a meta-analysis of nearly 20,000 relevant studies for their 2023 book, *Did Lockdowns Work?*: "Most likely lockdowns represent the biggest policy mistake in modern times,"[51] and "the lives saved were a drop in the bucket compared to the staggering collateral costs imposed,"[52] contributing to a massive increase in "stroke, heart attack, diabetes, obesity, drug overdoses, alcohol-induced causes, homicide, and traffic accidents."[53] However, the lockdowns worked very well for the usual tiny fraction of the population, creating 500 new billionaires in the U.S., and shifting four trillion dollars from the middle-class to this new aristocracy of billionaires.[54] The current extreme of inequality in income and wealth is unprecedented, and has given this miniscule minority—one ten-thousandth of one percent of humanity—unparalleled power to control governments, media, education, technology, finance, and social narratives, all to further consolidate control.

The U.S. government, with the CARES Act, insidiously created and spent over two trillion dollars, an inflationary debacle directly harming the majority of the population, for pandemic relief and health care, with virtually all of the funds going to bolster the pharmaceutical-medical complex. Not one dollar went to supporting the actual foundations of healthy living, such as encouraging us to exercise more, get sunshine and fresh air, enjoy each other's company, and improve the quality of our nutrition. Sunshine, for example, boosts Vitamin D production, which regulates our immune system; stimulates the production of white blood cells, enhancing the immune system; triggers the release of serotonin, the "happy hormone" that relieves stress and uplifts our mood; improves sleep quality by regulating our circadian rhythms; and enhances skin and overall health.[55] Similar things can be said about exercise, fresh air, high-quality nutrition, and friendly interactions with neighbors, family, and colleagues. As a result of us being locked down and gyms and churches being closed, obesity increased dramatically, stress levels soared, and the general health of the population plummeted, which fits well with the goals of Big Pharma, and the globalist plutocrats in the background.

Happy, healthy people do not need or desire pharmaceutical products or tyrannical health mandates; only anxious, sick, and deceived people do. The modus operandi of the pharmaceutical complex is, "a patient cured is a patient lost," and the more expensive the "treatment," and the more chronic the condition, the better. Making positive lifestyle changes is a threat to the medical cabal's profits and power, and so is discouraged, ignored, or disparaged, and the only accepted narrative is what "the science" dictates, which is conveniently controlled by corrupt pharmaceutical mouthpieces such as the AMA, CDC, NIH, HHS, NIAID, medical schools and medical journals, as well as mainstream media, internet search-engines, and so called "fact-checking" organizations.

The entire theater furthers an obvious agenda. Completely ignored were, for example, a study published in the British Medical Journal concluding that people eating plant-based diets reduced their risk of "Covid" by 73%,[56] and several studies concluding that being overweight and obese leads to significantly increased Covid risk and severity.[57] While many researchers and medical experts such as Dr. Michael Yeadon question the existence of the so-called Sars-Cov-2 respiratory virus and of Covid itself,[58] eating a healthy plant-sourced diet has been long recognized to enhance the immune system, reducing colds and flu-like symptoms.[59] This book is not the place to go into the massive amount of deception and corruption undergirding the entire Covid pandemic debacle, from the easily manipulated Polymerase Chain Reaction (PCR) tests used to certify cases,[60] to the deliberate inflation of deaths attributed to the disease (with 94% of deaths due to preexisting conditions), and to the deliberate and criminal suppression of effective and inexpensive treatments. Lucrative bonuses were paid out to hospitals for Covid testing; for declaring positive cases; for prescribing the devastating drug Remdesivir; for declaring Covid deaths; and for putting people on ventilators, which were linked with 80-90% death rates.[61] For example, Denis Rancourt, Ph.D., testified under oath at the National Citizen's Inquiry in Canada that there was no pandemic that caused excess mortality, and that excess deaths were due to pandemic policy measures and vaccines.[62] Resources listed in the Resources section illuminate these important aspects of the situation.

Discovering Our Original Face

Ultimately, our leaders and governments are a mirror of us, the people. If we the people systematically engage in violent, tyrannical, abusive behavior on a massive scale, how are we not similarly worthy of being systemically tyrannized and abused? The overwhelming majority of our population is directly driving the system that traumatizes, mutilates, and kills billions of animals daily for food and other products and uses. We have no objective need to abuse these animals, and the wildlife, ecosystems, and human beings directly and indirectly killed and harmed by animal agriculture, because we can all thrive on a fraction of the land and resources now used, through a whole-food, organic vegan lifestyle.

As we dominate and oppress, we find ourselves not only being increasingly dominated and oppressed, but actually asking to be dominated, and policing each other, masking and imprisoning ourselves, unquestioningly complying with and even enforcing the mandates of the masked plutocrats and furthering their agenda. It's understandable. As Erich Fromm emphasized, we are indoctrinated into adopting a toxic mask—a universalized authoritarian persona—that not only craves to dominate, but also to be dominated. This hierarchical, authoritarian, and materialistic mentality is widespread among people raised in our culture, trained as we are from infancy to practice disconnecting from understanding the systemic oppression and killing of billions of animals in which we participate. Our minds have been captured and colonized from infancy and it is time to reclaim our awareness and wisdom, and to rescue our health from the deceptive forces lurking behind masks of respectability.

The reason we fall prey to these masked powers and fail to recognize their true nature is that we ourselves have become similarly masked, and hide from ourselves, from nature, and from each other. There is the element of shame also. We pay others to mistreat and stab the animals we consume, and prefer others not discuss it because we'd rather not know. In countless ways we are enmeshed in and contribute to a society of violence that exploits the vulnerable. It is well known that a universal human gesture when feeling ashamed is hiding our face from others. It is no wonder we yearn to cover our faces. Our fear of facing ourselves shuts down the natural wisdom and healthy self-esteem of our true nature, which would liberate us from meekly acquiescing to our own oppression. If we yearn to be free, we are called to free those we are enslaving. We are called to face uncomfortable truths, and to abandon our pretenses. The animals of this world yearn for freedom to fulfill their inherent purposes. Stealing their freedom and purposes, we lose our own. This is a universal principle.

In the Zen tradition, there is an ancient *koan* or meditation question, "What is your original face, before you were born?" This question reveals the primal existential and spiritual issue we all face: to discover our true nature, our "original face" before the false persona-mask with which we identify covered it up. We are called now, more urgently than ever, to awaken to and discover the transpersonal dimension of consciousness. Cultivating awareness that is transpersonal—literally "beyond the mask"—together with liberating animals, is the path that can liberate us from the prisons of fear, greed, and selfishness that ensnare our world population today. With deep and sustained self-enquiry, we can discover that the self with which we identify is actually a persona—a facade and a mask—an identification with a physical body and a long series of memories that all revolve around an illusory sense of "me," and that what we are is not this façade, but the eternal being that shares the same source as all other expressions of life, which makes all this possible.

When we receive a glimpse of our true face, we realize not just our own true nature, but the true nature of all living beings. We catch sight of the unity that pervades creation, the joy of being, the lovingkindness shining always in our hearts, and the eternal consciousness that functions through our physical bodies. We realize that we are not the masks with which we've been fitted and learned to identify. When this happens, we find that the bewildering array of masks and pretenses presented by the modern world becomes more transparent and also more repugnant. We can discern the false from the real and distinguish the eternal from the temporal. We can no longer be so easily deceived by the masked Trojan-Horse forces because we have removed our own mask, and instead of living in fear and being vulnerable to the manipulative lies that pervade our cultural landscape, we discern the machinations operating behind false facades, and smile inwardly, refusing to be cowed, aware of the eternal and indestructible reality of our true nature. We stand up for truth and freedom for all expressions of life, and practice respect and inclusion in our relations with both humans and animals. We become benevolently contagious, spreading joy, fearlessness, and love through every gesture and thought, and by unmasking ourselves, help others to do the same.

We understand that health can never come from fear and deception, which are far more contagious and deadly than microbes. We see that wellness can never develop from following the unjust, fear-based decrees of masked technocrats. Health and wellness arise spontaneously from uncovering and discovering our true face, each of us a radiant expression of benevolent and creative eternal consciousness.

A new story is yearning to be born in our human culture. It has ancient roots, and this current emergency (emerge-and-see), if we respond appropriately, can put us on a higher path of liberation and healing. Contagious with this living awareness, we can bless and attract others who are also on the path of rescuing and reclaiming. We can co-create a world of health, abundance, and respect for all. As we withdraw support for weaponized falsehoods and their promulgators, we can at last become worthy of the world of harmony for which we yearn. First, we are called to rescue animals from human exploitation, and second, to rescue ourselves from the cultural masks of internalized fear-based pride and delusion that herderism has injected into our minds from infancy.

CHAPTER TEN

CIRCLE OF SLAVERY

"There's a war going on. The battlefield is in the mind and
the prize is the soul. So, be careful. Be very careful."
—PRINCE

"Behold, I am sending you out as sheep in the midst of wolves,
so be wise as serpents and innocent as doves."
—MATTHEW 10:6

"Despise the glare of wealth. Those people who pay greater respect to a
wealthy villain than to an honest, upright man in poverty,
almost deserve to be enslaved."
—JOHN HANCOCK

Pretexts for War

The main pretext for animal agriculture, our war against animals, is
that we need their protein, calcium, and other nutrients to survive.
We also see false pretexts being similarly used in a war against us.
Wars are destructive and so collectively we instinctively avoid them.
Pretexts are therefore regularly fabricated to trick us into mistakenly
believing we've been attacked so we are willing to give up peace and

freedom, and fight the chosen enemy. Those pretexts are often false flag deceptions, like the sinking of the battleship Maine in Havana harbor to start the Spanish-American War, the attack on the Lusitania for entry into the First World War, the Gulf of Tonkin incident for the Vietnam War, the controlled demolition of three World Trade Center buildings for the war on terror and the Patriot Act that erodes our rights,[1] Saddam Hussein's non-existent "weapons of mass destruction" to initiate the "shock and awe" attack and war on Iraq, and there have been many more.

All of this, and more that will likely follow, may seem controversial to some because it runs counter to official narratives. The idea is to question all narratives as intelligently and cogently as possible, so that "we don't get fooled again," as Pete Townshend warned. We have been fooled far too many times, and we will hopefully begin to realize that any time a particular narrative is pushed hard by mainstream media and government, there is a strong likelihood that it is foolish to believe it.

The use of false-flag pretexts is based on the Hegelian dialectic that social change follows a three-part dynamic. First, a particular situation arises, which Hegel termed the thesis. Invariably, this is followed by a pushback or response, the antithesis. Out of this dynamic emerges the third element, the synthesis, which then becomes a new thesis, unavoidably calling for its antithesis and a new synthesis, and so forth, continuing the dynamic process of social change. Those with the wealth and power to manipulate and dominate the process have learned to introduce a fraudulent false-flag thesis as an emergency crisis, or problem, which provokes a reaction (antithesis) in the general population, for which the perpetrators have the ready solution (synthesis). This "solution" is welcomed because it is presented as the "only" solution to the artificially-created problem. However, it simultaneously promotes the cabal's hidden agenda of increasing its power, wealth, prestige, and narrative-control.

This problem-reaction-solution model, to be effective, requires a series of crises, or fabricated pretexts. Our perception and interpretation of these crises is carefully controlled by the explanatory narrative delivered by authorities through their reliably controlled media, government, and institutional outlets. The cleverness of this particular model of deception is that those who initially surreptitiously created the crisis can then present the solution, posing as savior benefactors. While actually stealing our freedom, resources, and autonomy, and imposing suffering and violence, they can portray themselves as benefitting society, and providing safety and security in the challenging time.

Wars, for example, have always benefitted rulers. As pointed out in *The World Peace Diet*, the oldest word for war, *gavyaa*, "the desire for more cows," reveals that wars were launched in order to increase the wealth of the ruling kings, because cows and livestock were, quite literally, wealth. Thousands fought and died to enrich the ruling class. It is the same today. Wars are contrived by and benefit the globalist plutocrats who not only profit from them, but use them as emergency pretexts to remove basic human rights and further their agenda of dominating and exploiting humanity. The framers of the Constitution understood this and provided safeguards to discourage this from happening by separating powers and explicitly taking war-making capacities out of the hands of the executive branch. Further Supreme Court interpretations have forbidden emergencies being used as pretexts for taking away constitutional freedoms. Nevertheless, over the decades, these protections have been continually eroded, and pretexts have multiplied. The war on germs, like the war on carbon, seems to be valued by the ruling cabal as an effective pretext for consolidating its power to undermine our health and freedom.

We can see pandemics being used as critical parts of nested pretexts serving the globalist agenda. A pandemic can easily be used as a pretext for governmental "health" decrees, coercing us into masking, locking down, distancing, tracking, and finally and most importantly, submitting to injections. The injections can surreptitiously contain poisons that cause more illness, creating additional profits through more medications, as well as being further pretexts to impose more medical "solutions" for the sickness caused by the prior injections. Injections also serve as a pretext for mandated roll-outs of digital passports to monitor the injections, which destroy freedom with totalitarian tracking and control, under the false guise of keeping us all "safe." These digital tracking systems open the door to the complete destruction of human freedom via a global central bank digital currency coupled with inescapable digital tracking and surveillance systems where all travel and economic transactions are monitored and controlled.

The World Economic Forum is not hiding this agenda that it refers to euphemistically as The Great Reset. Charles Mountbatten-Windsor, then prince of Wales and later, simply because of his bloodline, recognized as the king of England, was ironically the one to announce the Great Reset program to the world in June of 2020, publicly emphasizing that "we need to put nature at the heart of how we operate," and warning about carbon and climate change, and that "we simply can't waste more time."[2] This is coming from the man whose home is the gargantuan Buckingham Palace, with arguably the most wasteful, opulent, and least nature-respecting lifestyle on planet Earth.[3] Klaus Schwab's book, *Covid 19: The Great Reset*, presents this Great Reset vision, and it is easy to see its role in the relentless globalist agenda to crush individual sovereignty, euphemized as the Fourth Industrial Revolution. A fabricated war pretext is necessary, hoodwinking us into believing we have to fight a dangerous enemy that is an ever-menacing force, such as a viral contagion, or anthropogenic climate change, or overpopulation, or something else, such as a demonized race, subculture, or nation.

Fear is the primary motivator, and the mainstream worldview, founded on herderism, asserts that nature is a dangerous force to be both feared and controlled. Concomitantly, we see ourselves as a dangerous force as well, and as essentially flawed—an over-populating curse on the Earth—and that we should be both culled and also genetically altered. The globalists proclaim this narrative, and that they have the solution, which is the transhumanist agenda of the Great Reset, as Schwab told the Chicago Council on Global affairs in 2020, "What the Fourth Industrial Revolution will lead to is a fusion of our physical, our digital and our biological identities."[4,5] This fusion of identities is global-speak for, among other things, our enslavement by means of implantable devices, as he writes in his book: "Implanted devices will likely also help to communicate thoughts normally expressed verbally through a 'built-in' smartphone, and potentially unexpressed thoughts or moods by reading brain waves and other signals."[6] This high-tech transhumanist agenda is envisioned to allow authorities to digitally monitor and control not just our outer movements, communications, and transactions, but eventually our thoughts and feelings as well. A digital panopticon is the goal, and its electronic, physical, and mental ramparts are continually being erected and refined.

Hence the need for ever more powerful and ubiquitous cellphone towers and EMF fields blanketing the earth from satellites in space. We are told it will be for the greater good, and for our safety and security. War, which originated in the ruling class's urge to forcibly amass more power and wealth, is now waged primarily against the minds and bodies of the general population. Philosopher Marshall McLuhan, who gave us the important insight that "the medium is the message," foresaw this back in 1970, when he wrote, "World War III is a guerilla information war with no division between military and civilian participation." This is now known as fifth generation warfare,[7] "the deliberate manipulation of an observer's context in order to achieve a desired outcome,"[8] because increasingly, "wars are not fought by armies or guerrillas, but in the minds of common citizens."[9]

Looking carefully, we can see that the unelected globalist plutocrats comprising the World Economic Forum and its affiliates view the mass of human beings as livestock. Many of us have come to realize how effectively the agenda of this wealthy cabal has been implemented over the past decades, laying the groundwork for the pandemic false-flag operations by gradually capturing not only the

CDC, FDA, USDA, CIA, FBI, AMA, WHO, the United Nations, Congress, the executive branch, the judiciary, and even large portions of state, county, and local governments, but also virtually all mainstream media and big tech, as well as the financial, corporate, and scientific sectors, and academia and the educational establishment, from kindergarten through the universities and professional degrees. The entire system is based on enforcing compliance to authority figures. Many of us, even though we question some of the narratives that promote violence, injustice, and disease, are unable or unwilling to challenge the trumped up and controlled "science," and have thus been unable or unwilling to challenge and resist the criminally harmful pandemic response and other globalist frauds and deceptions.

One of the main reasons for this credulousness is our indoctrinated trust in doctors, educators, journalists, celebrities, and government officials. This is true in the vegan community also, and one segment of the vegan community is especially prized and respected, vegan doctors. Medical doctors rarely question animal-based foods, but these somewhat rare vegan medical doctors have, through their research and advocacy, significantly helped to legitimize the entire animal liberation movement by demonstrating clearly that exclusively plant-sourced diets can be just as healthy, and actually much healthier, than standard animal-sourced diets. However, it has been disappointing to see the paucity of medical doctors questioning official pandemic narratives. This is somewhat understandable, because if they do, they risk losing their licenses to practice, as well as their reputations and abilities to earn a living. In current medical practice, most doctors are mere corporate employees and are fired if they question the imposed protocols. They often have no other training, so this is a frightening prospect that works well to prevent most doctors and health professionals from speaking out against the obvious harmfulness of pandemic protocols. Few vegan medical doctors spoke out against Big Pharma's abuse of billions of people through the Covid directives, and many even expressly supported them. Many vegans, like non-vegans, unwisely trusting our captured health professionals, were thus deceived.

Why allow ourselves to be cast in the role of helpless victims of a malevolent pandemic pretext that serves an insidious agenda, and is a well-coordinated attack on humanity? Ultimately, as Dr. King reminded us, the moral arc of the universe, though long, bends toward justice. Truth, though now brutally suppressed through the most egregious censorship and military-grade information warfare in the history of western democracies, will eventually prevail. Even many usually obedient and unsuspecting people are beginning to question the disinformation continually spewing from official media and government sources. The globalists can no longer easily hide their agenda, and it is obvious for discerning minds to see. For example, we observe Klaus Schwab boasting a few years ago at a conference at Harvard University that, through the WEF's Global Leaders program, his organization had trained and placed about four thousand people in key positions of governmental, corporate, media, and financial power throughout the world, including Bill Gates, Mark Zuckerberg, and Jeff Bezos, as well as Macron in France, Merkel in Germany, Trudeau and Freeland in Canada, Ardern in New Zealand, and Newsome in California.[10] These have been among the most unwavering and tyrannical leaders in pushing the WEF's pandemic pretext and overall agenda, and Schwab further gloated that his WEF program had succeeded in "penetrating" over half of the federal cabinet positions in Canada, as but one example.[11]

The little dog Toto has pulled the curtain back for all to see, and ever-larger numbers are awakening from being indoctrinated conspiracy-deniers to understanding, often through damaging vaccine injuries inflicted on themselves or on acquaintances, that the pandemic fear-mongering is a fabricated pretext. The agenda to cull and control the human herd will doubtlessly continue as long as we are doing the same to animals for food. It is essential to universalize the deep vegan resolve to never comply with forces of violence and exploitation. Our increased awareness, resistance, and respect for all life is more important and urgent than ever.

Vaccine Consequences and Medical Corruption

Veganism is a philosophy and way of living which seeks to exclude—as far as is possible and practicable—all forms of exploitation of, and cruelty to, animals for food, clothing or any other purpose; and by extension, promotes the development and use of animal-free alternatives for the benefit of humans, animals and the environment. In dietary terms it denotes the practice of dispensing with all products derived wholly or partly from animals. – Donald Watson, 1944 [12]

Madeleine and I have done our best to take the example of veganism's nominal founder, Donald Watson, to heart. Watson coined the word vegan in 1944, and like him, we have boycotted not only the meat, dairy, egg, wool, leather, silk, and animal entertainment industries, but also the pharmaceutical industry over the past four decades of vegan living. The pharmaceutical industry is hideous in its torturing of millions of animals in experimental vivisection, and reaps its massive profits from drugs inflicted on animals in agribusiness, and on humans who are also exploited by being deceived into eating animal foods. Mahatma Gandhi was also ethically opposed to the exploitation of animals, and to medications that used animals as ingredients or in testing, and never tired of speaking out against the evils of vivisection and vaccination, which he emphasized cause untold suffering to animals and also to humans. He wrote, for example, in his 1921 book, *A Guide to Health*:

Vaccination is a barbarous practice, and it is one of the most fatal of all the delusions current in our time, not to be found even among the so-called savage races of the world. Its supporters are not content with its adoption by those who have no objection to it, but seek to impose it with the aid of penal laws and rigorous punishments on all people alike.

I cannot also help feeling that vaccination is a violation of the dictates of religion and morality. The drinking of the blood of even dead animals is looked upon with horror even by habitual meat-eaters. Yet, what is vaccination but the taking in of the poisoned blood of an innocent living animal? Better far were it for God-fearing men that they should a thousand times become the victims of small-pox and even die a terrible death than that they should be guilty of such an act of sacrilege.

Several of the most thoughtful men in England have laboriously investigated the manifold evils of vaccination, and an Anti-Vaccination Society has also been formed there. The members of this society have declared open war against vaccination, and many have even gone to jail for this cause.

In a certain town, a large proportion of the people refuse to be vaccinated, and yet statistics prove that they are singularly free from disease. The fact of the matter is that it is only the self-interest of doctors that stands in the way of the abolition of this inhuman practice, for the fear of losing the large incomes that they at present derive from this source blinds them to the countless evils which it brings. There are, however, a few doctors who recognize these evils, and who are determined opponents of vaccination.

Those who are conscientious objectors to vaccination should, of course, have the courage to face all penalties or persecutions to which they may be subjected by law, and stand alone, if need be, against the whole world, in defense of their conviction.[13]

As Gandhi correctly tells us, all vaccines contain cells that are directly cultured from animal blood and tissues, for which chickens, cows, pigs, monkeys, mice, horses, camels, and other animals are bred, mutilated, and slaughtered. These diseased animal tissues are injected directly into our bloodstream to supposedly help us fight a potential illness, and yet there are countless cases of these vaccines causing terrible harm, including inflicting the very diseases they are supposed to prevent, such as measles and polio.[14] In fact, as but one example, Gates Foundation distribution of polio vaccines in India paralyzed 491,000 children with vaccine-derived polio between 2000 and 2017.[15] Virologist Dr. Judy Mikowitz points out, "God did not intend for animal viruses to be injected directly into the human bloodstream."[16] As a senior researcher working directly with animal and human cell lines used in vaccines, she has been censored and slandered for speaking up about the known fact that "growing viruses in animal tissue and cells" does "introduce new animal viruses into the human population," and "if people really begin to focus on it, the entire vaccination program would crumble."[17]

Besides the inherent harmfulness of injecting diseased animal tissues directly into the bloodstream of neonates, infants, and children, as well as adults, all vaccines contain a variety of toxic adjuvants to irritate and thus stimulate the immune system,[18] as well as poisonous stabilizing chemicals and preservatives, again, injected straight into the bloodstream, bypassing the body's oral and digestive defenses. These include known carcinogens, neurotoxins, excitotoxins, and allergens such as mercury thimerosal, aluminum, formaldehyde, polysorbate 80, propylene glycol, glyphosate, and MSG, as well as squalene from sharks, limulus amebocyte lysate (LAL) from horseshoe crabs, egg proteins, antibiotics, gelatin from pigs, and aborted human fetal tissues.[19]

These potent toxins are linked directly with autism, Alzheimer's disease, arthritis, allergies, asthma, respiratory diseases, cancer, neurological disorders, and many other types of chronic disease. In fact, according to data from the U.S. Department of Health and Human Services, in the 1960s the rate of chronic disease in the U.S. was only about six percent, and by 1986, the rate of chronic disease was at 11.8 percent. This was the year the National Vaccine Injury Compensation Act was passed by Congress, eliminating all pharmaceutical industry liability for vaccine-caused harms. When this act was challenged in court, the Supreme Court upheld it, due in part to the fact that, as it said, "vaccines are unavoidably unsafe."[20,21] Following this elimination of liability for vaccine manufacturers, many more vaccines were added to the childhood vaccination schedule, and over the next twenty years the rate of chronic disease steadily climbed, up to 54 percent by 2006,[22] and up to 60 percent today, with 40 percent of adults having two or more chronic diseases.[23]

Chronic disease is certainly the ultimate goldmine for the pharmaceutical-medical cartel, compelling people to take expensive drugs on long-term or permanent bases. We have to ask if it is just coincidental that since granting Big Pharma vaccine legal immunity in 1986, the number of mandated childhood vaccine shots has gone from about six to seventy,[24] while industry liability has gone to zero and industry profits, new diseases, chronic disease, and drug-use have all skyrocketed. With this vast wealth, these criminally deceitful medical corporations have garnered control of media, government, education, and professional associations. For example, as the documentary film *Vaxxed*[25] clearly demonstrates, Dr. William Thompson, a senior research scientist at the CDC with a seemingly rare trait, a conscience, publicly admitted in 2014 to following orders to destroy his department's research showing that the Measles-Mumps-Rubella (MMR) vaccine was associated with a statistically significant increase in autism cases, specifically among young black males.[26] This demonstrated that the CDC had been completely captured by the pharmaceutical cartel, compelling this coverup and corruption, but it doesn't stop there. Big Pharma has also clearly taken over the U.S. Congress, because Congress still refuses to hear Dr. Thompson's testimony.[27] In 1984, the year Anthony Fauci became director of the National Institute of Allergy and Infectious Diseases (NIAID), its overarching agency, the Department of Health and Human Services (HHS), created a new regulation that is still law today. Despite its grossly anti-scientific and anti-democratic impact, this law reflects the globalist medical agenda, and mandates censorship of free speech and the suppression of scientific inquiry, which clearly leads directly to the medical and physical enslavement of humanity:

> Any possible doubts, whether or not well-founded, about the safety of the vaccine cannot be allowed to exist in view of the need to assure that the vaccines will continue to be used to the maximum extent consistent with the nation's "public health objectives." —Federal Register, Vol. 49, No. 107

"Any possible doubts, whether or not well-founded ... cannot be allowed to exist..." Here the mask comes off, revealing the naked corruption of science, medicine, government, academia, and media by powers lurking in the background. In this book, we can only give the briefest of overviews concerning the pressing and vast issue of the medical abuse of the population. However, there are a few more important points to be made. One is that this medical abuse was pioneered in animal agriculture and is still used there on a massive scale. The thousands of drugs, hormones, and antibiotics forcibly administered to animals exploited for food and other uses are a source of tremendous profits for Big Pharma, both directly and indirectly. As we buy and eat these foods, we are sowing seeds that result in our own medical oppression, as we can see happening.

Also, just as medical school education of doctors deliberately ignores the massive effect that nutrition has on health, and quickly glosses over it, the same tactic is followed with vaccines. Doctors are advised to tell people to eat "normally," while their medical education focuses overwhelmingly on their ability to traffic to the public a wide range of profitable drugs and procedures. Similarly, in one short class, doctors are told that vaccines are absolutely safe and effective, and are apprised of the vaccine schedule that they should know and enforce, and then the instructor quickly moves on to covering the most important material: the daunting amount of information in the curriculum concerning the various diagnostics, protocols, and pharmaceutical interventions they are expected to learn. Though we in the general public think that doctors must be trustworthy and knowledgeable regarding vaccines, the situation is similar to nutrition. They are deliberately not educated, and in many ways are miseducated, concerning them.

Additionally, doctors are financially incentivized to maximize vaccinations for their patients. For example, for the Covid "vaccines," there were three bonus programs through which the U.S. government paid insurance companies, which paid physicians according to the number of injections they administered. One was a direct bonus plan that paid doctors for each injection administered, and the other two programs dramatically increased the bonus as the percentage of the physician's client base that was injected increased. For example, in 2021, given the average of about 1800 unique patient visits per year,[28] a typical physician who administered injections to 20 percent of his or her patients would get a considerable annual bonus, about $60,000. However, a physician who administered Covid injections to 75 percent of his or her patients would receive an immense annual bonus of $382,000.[29] This provides an obvious explanation why so few doctors spoke up against the clearly harmful and ineffective injections, besides the significant risk of reprisals from their corporate employers, the pharma-controlled medical boards, and the media. We are called to ponder deeply the personal and collective consequences of living in a society where money so completely trumps not just integrity, but also overrides our inherent unwillingness to inflict harm on innocent and trusting patrons and dependents.

Plausible Deniability

The pharmaceutical cartel's business model is simple and effective: administer a broad array of vaccines to infants and children that weaken their health and immune systems, and as they get older, cash in on the chronic diseases the vaccines have caused, and that are also caused by the flood of toxic petrochemicals their sibling industry churns out.[30] They hide the entire time behind the mask of plausible deniability facilitated by their financial capture of media, medical, and government narratives and institutions, and by their legal privileges that grant them indemnification from any harm caused by their products. As Richard Pitcairn, DVM, points out, this is likely also true of the pet industry, where people take their animal companions for annual vaccines and then later pay for expensive medical treatments as the animals' conditions decline.[31]

Further, besides containing animal cells and tissues, vaccines are also invariably tested on animals, killing and causing hideous suffering to untold millions of monkeys, mice, rats, ferrets, pigs, dogs, and other animals. Because of the rapid increase in demand for monkeys to test the Covid "vaccines," for example, macaque and other monkeys were trapped and trafficked from the wild in unprecedented numbers, forcing species to the brink of extinction in a lucrative search for human-like animals to be tortured and killed for pharmaceutical testing.[32] Additionally, the biomedical industry has depleted horseshoe crab populations along the U.S. Atlantic coast[33] to extract their blood to test Covid injections and vaccines.

The new generations of injections, misnamed vaccines, use modified RNA to alter the genetic make-up of our cells so that they produce different proteins, for example the toxic spike protein in the Covid injections, to provoke an immune response. These are not actually vaccines, because they do not work like vaccines supposedly work, by introducing an attenuated version of the supposed disease agent to induce an immune response, which supposedly educates our immune system and gives it a rehearsal. They are completely different, but the World Health Organization, Big Pharma, and their conquered governmental agencies, in order to mislead the public and hide the obviously disturbing fact that this technology is new, untested, and completely different from vaccines, and to maintain its immunity from lawsuits, insists on deceitfully using the word vaccine to describe these injections.

Instead of an animal-derived disease agent, they contain a computer-generated RNA genetic sequence in order to hack and reprogram our DNA and force our body to create millions of pathogenic spike proteins. These injections are tested on animals who are killed in the process, and the Covid pandemic, for example, created such a demand for laboratory animals to be killed in biomedical research that the U.S. government was forced to spend millions of dollars on an emergency breeding program.[34]

These injections also use aborted human fetal cell lines in their manufacture. Whence come these aborted fetuses? The pharmaceutical industry has tried to keep this hidden, but a Pfizer quality auditor leaked the internal documents showing that these injections use the HEK293 cell line, as this journalist explains:

> The most prominent cell line, called HEK 293, comes from an abortion performed in the 1970's. It's labeled 293 because that's how many experimental attempts the researchers needed to get a working cell line. Therefore, though the abortion-to-experiment ratio is not precisely one-to-one, hundreds of abortions went into the project, even if they didn't result in the working line.
>
> HEK stands for human embryonic kidney. To harvest a viable embryonic kidney for this purpose, sufficiently healthy children old enough to have adequately-developed kidneys must be removed from the womb, alive, typically by cesarean section, and have their kidneys cut out. This must take place without anesthesia for the child, which would lessen the viability of the organs.
>
> The deliberate killing of an unwanted child (a little girl, in the case of HEK 293) took place in the torturous manner it did precisely to obtain her organs for research. The harvest of her organs was the direct cause of her death, prior to which, she was a living child, outside the womb.[35]

Having her kidneys cut out while alive and fully sensitive killed her, and she was subsequently disposed of as trash, like the lambs and calves thrown on dead piles by the animal food industry. The fiendish materialism pervading and promoted by medical scientism and the pharmaceutical industry is embedded in all vaccines and injections, sowing the seeds of disease in us, as their profits and narrative domination flourish. While organ harvesting started with pigs and other animals, now vulnerable infants, children, and adults predictably find the same thing happening to them, as illicit human organ trafficking has become a multi-billion-dollar industry.[36]

The basic tests that would determine whether vaccines are effective or not are resolutely refused for obvious reasons. Robert F. Kennedy, Jr., writes:

> Most medicinal products cannot get licensed without first undergoing randomized placebo-controlled trials that compare health outcomes— including all-cause mortalities—in medicated versus unmedicated cohorts. ... [Yet] none of the mandated childhood vaccines had been tested for safety in pre-licensing inert placebo tests....
>
> Because Gates and Dr. Fauci suffer the same allergy to funding studies that examine the effectiveness of their vaccines in improving health and reducing mortality, neither man has ever offered empirical evidence to support their pivotal claim that their vaccines have "saved millions of lives."[37]

But fortunately, one enterprising medical doctor in Oregon, Dr. Paul Thomas, had a long-term pediatric practice in which there were both vaccinated and unvaccinated children and in October of 2020 he published his findings in a peer-reviewed medical journal, "showing data, over time, that children receiving fewer vaccines were healthier than those following the CDC vaccine schedule."[38] Finally, someone had done the necessary placebo-controlled trial over time, comparing health outcomes of vaccinated versus unvaccinated children, and the result was clear. The vaccinated children had significantly higher rates of a broad spectrum of disorders and illnesses than the unvaccinated children. Because of his published results clearly revealing the harmful effects of vaccines, the Oregon Medical Board immediately issued an emergency revocation of his medical license, to the dismay of his patients, making him an example to health-care providers everywhere. Those who are courageous and caring enough to question the official vaccine narratives will pay a steep price.[39]

Looking historically, we can see that vaccines have become among the most profitable commodities in the world, and that this is due solely to direct interference by the U.S. government and other national governments. This interference has removed liability for vaccine manufacturers and created official policies to promote them and to censor scientists and journalists who question their safety and efficacy. For example, Pfizer reported a massive 92% growth in income and profits in 2021, and even more in 2022, becoming the first pharmaceutical company in history to exceed $100 billion in annual sales,[40] mainly due to its sales of the Covid injections directly to captured governments.[41] And yet, in 1985, the year before the passage of the 1986 law removing vaccine liability, less than one quarter of one percent of drug company sales were derived from vaccines.[42] It is hard to imagine now, but the general public in the 1960s and 1970s was not enthusiastic about vaccines, for good reason, and many pharmaceutical companies were losing money on them, with over half of vaccine manufacturers forced out of business. By 1980, only ten vaccine manufacturers were still making vaccines.[43] The few manufacturers left at that point faced hundreds of lawsuits for the damages their vaccines caused.[44] It's clear that without government intervention, free markets would have simply eliminated vaccines.

But in 1986, buckling to the tremendous wealth and power of the pharmaceutical industry, the government removed pharmaceutical industry liability for vaccine injuries and began adopting policies of mandatory vaccinations for children that have been continually increasing, and also instituted narrative-control campaigns in order to diminish "vaccine hesitancy" in the population. The result has been windfall profits for the pharmaceutical cartel, and skyrocketing rates of chronic disease, which afflicts at least half the U.S. population, and accounts for 91% of sales for pharmaceutical medications.[45] For Big Pharma, vaccines are the gift that keeps on giving. The main immunity vaccines provide is for the manufacturers themselves.

By enslaving animals, we have laid the foundations for the inevitable rise of materialistic and reductionistic science, which not only deepens the animals' enslavement through industrial and medical systems of domination and exploitation, but also relentlessly insinuates itself into our bodies, minds, and lives, sabotaging our health, draining our freedom, and numbing our feelings and intellects. Fortunately, this circle of slavery is becoming more obvious by the day. As each of us breaks free of the spell of herderism into which we have been indoctrinated from infancy, and as we liberate animals and reclaim our sovereignty and our health, we contribute to building the more conscious world that is always available to us, where peace, freedom, sustainability, justice, and abundance are possible and practicable.

CHAPTER ELEVEN

PANDEMICS, FAUX VEGANISM, AND EUGENICS

"Strive to preserve your health; and in this you will the better succeed
in proportion as you keep clear of the physicians."
—LEONARD DA VINCI

"You have to start with the truth. The truth is the only way that we can
get anywhere. Because any decision-making that is based upon lies
or ignorance can't lead to a good conclusion."
—JULIAN ASSANGE

"Never ever depend on governments or institutions to solve any major
problems. All social change comes from the passion of individuals."
—MARGARET MEAD

Bricks of Betrayal

It is clear that the ever-increasing profusion of noxious chemicals
from the petrochemical industry that end up in our food, water,
and air—and the toxic chemicals and diseased animal tissues injected into us as children, plus other adverse forces like water

fluoridation schemes, increasingly harmful EMF fields, atmospheric geoengineering projects that spray harmful metallic particulates and other pernicious agents into the skies,[1] as well as our constant bombardment by stress-inducing media messages of divisiveness, fear, and violence—work together to assure the high rates of chronic disease that ensure both a weakened population and abundant profitability. How do we free ourselves from this vicious circle that turns profitability into ever-increasing control of government, education, and media narratives and more chronic disease? The only reliable way is to sever our culture's hidden nemesis at the root: animal agriculture.

When we intrepidly explore our cultural institutions and food systems beyond the approved boundaries of inquiry, we discover, besides the disturbing levels of corruption and abuse, a shocking degree of betrayal. We are taught to trust medical, governmental, educational, media, agricultural, and scientific authorities and institutions, and it seems that many of us are incapable of comprehending that we are being targeted, exploited, discounted, mocked, and consciously abused by those who control these institutions, and that this is business as usual. It is also a mirror of our exploitation of animals, and most of us feel no remorse when we stand at the check-out stand to pay for our shrink-wrapped packages of chicken, turkey, fish, or cheese. As we betray, so we are betrayed.

Some of us, awakening out of this imposed cultural trance, and connecting with our indwelling empathy and intelligence, begin feeling healthy remorse for eating animal-sourced foods, but fall prey to a secondary cultural narrative, which is that free-range and small-scale animal agriculture does not abuse animals; only large-scale factory farm operations are merciless and ecologically devastating. However, whether the operation is large or small, the cows, sheep, pigs, chickens, turkeys, and other animals we use for food are vulnerable and defenseless in our hands. Their existential plight is pathetic. Born into utter dependance on us by our practice of raping their mothers and grandmothers over hundreds of generations, they can only look at us with eyes yearning for mercy, but they will always be betrayed, because the purpose of their being brought into our world, which we dictate, is to be exploited and killed.

Is it really better for the animals on smaller operations? No, there is the same forced impregnation and killing, and the betrayal is perhaps even more poignant and severe, because each individual animal is one of a relatively small number handled (or mishandled) by the owner, rather than being immersed in a vast warehouse or feedlot of thousands or tens of thousands of animals.[2] In our travels throughout North America, Europe, Asia, Africa, and Australia, we have visited scores of farmed animal sanctuaries, where a few fortunate farmed animals have somehow miraculously escaped the gulags and can live out their lives in relative peace. They are cared for by vegan sanctuary operators who hope to raise awareness about the plight of farmed animals by letting them be ambassadors to the public. The animals effortlessly demonstrate that they are each unique beings with personalities and preferences, and in many cases, this helps sanctuary visitors make connections, thereby inspiring more compassionate living. We have asked these sanctuary proprietors about the animals they receive from small backyard operations, as compared with animals that come from large factory farms, and invariably they tell us the same thing: animals rescued from backyard operations are usually more severely abused and sick than those from factory farms, typically through either extreme neglect or sadistic mistreatment.

Animals in backyard operations can suffer not only from neglect when small-scale farmers cannot afford feed and proper care, but also when they become targets for venting frustration and other forms of abuse.[3] When animals from small-scale operations are sent to slaughter, if they don't go to the large-scale slaughter operations, they end up in special small-scale slaughter operations where, as undercover journalism has demonstrated, they are often more severely and sadistically abused before being killed.[4] The large-scale slaughter operations with their high-speed lines also cause terrible suffering because animals often fail to get stunned properly at the beginning, and then go down the disassembly line still conscious and have feet and tails cut off, hide pulled off, or go into the scald tank and get boiled alive, or killed, as the workers say, "piece by piece."[5] But on small-scale operations, the workers have more time with each animal, and because this kind of work tends to bring out the worst in people, they begin to take out their frustrations on the hapless animals who are just there to be killed anyway.[6] When we sit down to eat our more expensive free-range, or organic, or cage-free, or "sustainable" piece of animal flesh, cheese, or egg, we really have no idea what kind of sadistic mistreatment this animal may have endured, which we have caused by our purchase, and which we are now eating. We are building our body temple with bricks of betrayal and unavoidable suffering and violence.

Free-range animals also eat more, and so cause more environmental destruction, and they also must be protected from predators more than animals confined in factory-farm Confined Animal Feeding Operations (CAFOs).[7] The rise in demand for free-range beef has caused a corresponding increase in the number of free-living horses being rounded up and sent off to slaughter or life imprisonment because they're seen as competing with free-range cattle. Because of the recent increase in small-scale and free-range animal agriculture operations, there is also a corresponding increase in the numbers of coyotes, bobcats, mountain lions, prairie dogs, skunks, raccoons, otters, eagles, beavers, cormorants, starlings, red-winged blackbirds, and other wild animals being shot, poisoned, trapped, and burned alive by "denning" by the USDA's Department of Wildlife Services.[8] Wildlife Services responds to requests from ranchers and farmers to kill free-living animals they view as being nuisances or pests, and with our taxpayer money, millions of animals are thus brutally killed every year in the ongoing war against nature and animals that is the unavoidable essence of animal agriculture.[9] This brief overview just scratches the surface of the abuse we inflict on animals for food products, and it makes little difference if the operations are large or small. There are no "good old days" when animals did not suffer egregiously at our hands, unless of course, we go back far enough, prior to the herding revolution ten thousand years ago, when animals were at least free of human ownership and confinement. But since then, the same dominating attitudes and practices result in misery, death, and disease, not just for the animal victims, but ultimately for us, the perpetrators, as well.

Pandemic of Consequences

Our ongoing betrayal of billions of animals has boomeranged especially viciously in the Covid mRNA injections, which are designed to work by altering the genetic material in our cells to create harmful spike proteins to supposedly stimulate our immune system. In July, 2022, researchers from Lund University in Sweden published the findings of their study, which showed that within six hours after injection, the Pfizer and Moderna mRNA injections begin infiltrating cells and transcribing their genetically-engineered RNA messages onto the existing cellular DNA, permanently altering the DNA in our cells.[10, 11] This included ovaries and other organs, which means that these alterations will also be passed on to children, grandchildren, and all future generations. This is completely unprecedented, and horrifying to contemplate, though it is something that animal agriculture scientists have been doing for years with cows and other livestock. In forty years of research into our mistreatment of animals, I have discovered that whatever we have done to animals, eventually we have done to each other. Cloning and genetically manipulating animals for the purpose of domination and exploitation should make us all concerned. The ethical aspect is also concerning. Forced injections, whether into non-consenting humans or animals, is, in essence, a form of rape, a nonconsensual penetration that is an egregious violation of another being's sacred vehicle, and can directly cause terrible injury and death.

It's well understood that the Covid injections are just the first of many DNA-altering injections that the globalists and their pharmaceutical cartel have planned. Their deliberate corruption of the human genome, a reflection of scientific, governmental, and industry corruption, is irreversible once perpetrated, and shocking in its potential ability to create non-human, quasi-human, pseudo-human, trans-human, and perhaps even anti-human beings. This completes the entire loop, because according to patent statutes, no one can patent anything in nature, but if an entity has been genetically altered and is thus no longer natural, then it can be patented and owned as a property object. Thus, there is some discussion that those of us who have chosen to receive mRNA vaccines are perhaps no longer legally human beings, but may now be reduced to mere commodities and be actually owned as property objects by the holders of the vaccine patents, and no longer entitled to any human rights.[12] We may no longer be considered human but instead be considered mere patented livestock property. This would have to be argued in the courts, but the legal precedents are in place.

Beyond polluting the human genome and literally transforming us from beings to commodities, there is much more to the Covid injections, and Mark Trozzi, MD, has summarized the situation well: "Covid shots make Thalidomide look like Flintstone Vitamins."[13] The use of the term mRNA, which stands for "messenger RNA" is incorrect, because the injections actually contain synthetically engineered, modified RNA, correctly indicated as modRNA, and this modified RNA is artificially encased in tenacious fat/lipid casings. These "lipid nanoparticles" act as Trojan Horses, and their use in humans was forbidden prior to 2020.[14] This prohibition was violated by the emergency-use authorization of the Covid RNA injections. The lipid casing deceives cells, allowing the modified RNA to slip into cells unmolested, without being detected and destroyed as non-self particles.[15] When a cell is infected by this modRNA, the modified RNA tricks it into making foreign, non-self proteins, and this eventually targets the infected cell for violent death by the immune system.[16] The epithelial cells of blood vessels are attacked and damaged first, causing clots and leaks, and all organs can be harmed, most dangerously the tissues of heart and brain, which do not replicate.[17] Dr. Sucharit Bhakdi provides a critical glimpse into the alarming consequences of modified RNA injections:

> The heart is one organ that cannot replace dead cells. Who has not heard of the mysterious sudden cardiac deaths that are occurring around the world? They are only the tip of an iceberg. Vaccine-induced heart disease has entered the daily agenda of young and old. The second organ that cannot replace its dead cells is the brain. Depending on where vaccine damage is done, any neurological and psychiatric affliction may follow.[18]

Dr. Bhakdi also emphasizes that these modified RNA injections can change chromosomes in our cells, causing even more auto-immune attacks because these cells are inevitably targeted as being non-self. More disturbing still, "Mutations in sperm and fertilized egg cells could render altered traits inheritable and lead to the creation of beings that have departed from the evolutionary track of the human race."[19]

Just in the first six months, the number of deaths and serious adverse events reported in the CDC's Adverse Events Reporting System (VAERS) had surpassed the combined total of reported adverse events of all vaccines for the prior 30 years. In the first eighteen months, deaths were up to 30,000 and serious injuries to about 250,000, with overall reported adverse events over 1,350,000.[20] According to a 2010 Harvard study on the reliability of the VAERS system, which agrees with other similar studies of VAERS, "fewer than 1% of vaccine adverse events are reported. Low reporting rates preclude or slow the identification of 'problem' drugs and vaccines that endanger public health. New surveillance methods for drug and vaccine adverse effects are needed."[21]

Many researchers have concluded that due to Covid's draconian medical censorship, the one percent number is most likely too high,[22] thus indicating that, conservatively, in the first eighteen months about three million people in the U.S. were killed by the shots, 25 million were seriously injured, and 135 million experienced adverse effects.[23] Even if we assume that an unlikely ten percent of events are reported, the figures are still staggering, with 13.5 million adverse effects and 2.5 million serious injuries, and every day, more events are being reported. Some of the primary injuries reported have been myocarditis, pericarditis, heart attacks, strokes, blood-clotting disorders, myocardial infarctions,[24] Bell's palsy, Creutzfeld-Jacob (mad cow) disease, Guillain-Barré syndrome, anaphylaxis, miscarriages, infertility, seizures, urinary tract infections, tinnitus, eye blood clots, blindness, mood disorders, psychosis,[25] cancer flare-ups and so-called turbo cancers, VAIDS (vaccine-induced immune deficiency syndrome) and SADS, sudden adult death syndrome, among many others. CDC and medical spokespeople have been "baffled" by the increasing prevalence of this new sudden adult death syndrome, just as they had been baffled by the continuing spike in SIDS (sudden infant death syndrome) and ADS (autism spectrum disorder),[26] both of which coincide with the vastly expanded vaccine schedules for infants and children.[27] According to Dr. Chris Shoemaker, MD, from Canada, "Some studies have shown that the vaccine has caused 20 percent of people to develop myocarditis. Myocarditis has an established death rate of 50 percent after five years and 75 percent after ten years."[28] Leaked Pfizer documents have also revealed that DNA, endotoxins, and bacterial proteins have been found to contaminate some of the injections as well.[29]

Distinguished obstetrician-gynecologist James Thorp, MD, has emphasized that the main target for the massive $13 billion HHS Covid injection marketing campaign was women, and secondarily pregnant women, for two reasons:

Number one: Every man and woman in medicine knows women make all the healthcare decisions for all members of the family. So that if they could capture the American College of Obstetricians and Gynecologists and 60,000 obstetricians, and then they got all the women, they captured the population.... Number two, if we can convince the world that it's safe, effective, and necessary in pregnancy, they've won the entire game for vaccinating the entire human population on the planet. And that's what they did.[30]

Through a Freedom of Information Act request, Dr. Thorp obtained direct evidence that copious funds flowed from the Department of Health and Human Services (HHS) to the gynecological, obstetric, and pediatric medical boards to ensure that all OB/GYN doctors would unfailingly recommend the Covid injections to the most medically vulnerable members of society, pregnant women. Any doctor who failed to recommend the injections would be fired, as happened to Dr. Thorp, who refused the funds offered him by his hospital to sign a nondisclosure agreement. Dr. Thorp has explained that these medical overlords must have been fully aware that the Covid injections would be devastating to fetuses and pregnant and nursing women, because Pfizer's own post-marketing research, which the medical authorities tried to cover up, clearly linked the Covid injections with an 81% risk of miscarriage, and substantial increases in inflammation, fetal death, fetal cardiac abnormalities, compromised placentas, stillbirths, premature labor, and babies born with malformations.[31]

It is well-understood that besides what has already been an astonishing and unprecedented initial onslaught of pain, disease, and death caused by the experimental Covid injections—all of it strenuously ignored, censored, and denied by medical personnel, journalists, tech platforms, and government agencies—there is the looming reality that injecting unidentified chemical and genetic contaminates into billions of people leads directly to depopulation through infertility, miscarriages, and young people dying, as well as the inevitable emergence of more chronic issues such as cancer, heart disease, reproductive disorders, and neurodegenerative disease, all highly profitable for the industry.

The Kissinger Report of 1974 on "Implications of Worldwide Population Growth for U.S. Security and Overseas Interests,"[32] led to population reduction becoming official U.S. policy in 1975.[33] Culling the human herd through mandated injections fits in well with the larger eugenics goals of the ruling class. The obvious reason that not everyone is dying all at once, and that there are so many different adverse reactions, and that different researchers are finding different things in the vials and in patients' blood and tissues, is that it seems to have been a vast experiment designed to cause and observe different outcomes. As emergency-use experimental products with blank inserts, the vials for the injections may have completely different ingredients via different batches, and also varying dosages of varying ingredients, with the experimenters able to observe the various outcomes for recipients, and to calibrate future scenarios.[34]

A key goal of the chemical and pharmaceutical cartel has always been plausible deniability.[35] This is essential in maximizing profits and maintaining the mask of benevolence. Creating a poison that doesn't immediately kill, but causes disability five, ten, or fifteen years later is much preferred, so that it is difficult to track causation. With the damage done, two goals are met. When people are chronically ill, they become profitable moneymakers for the industry and for the bankers in the background. Secondly, they are disabled enough so that they are incapable of vigorously informing themselves, organizing with others, rising up, and resisting the creeping enslavement being methodically implemented. Animal agriculture scientists similarly work on drugs and genetic alterations that make farmed animals more docile and compliant under stress, which boosts profits for both the animal food industry and the pharmaceutical-medical complex, working together. Reducing health is reducing freedom, and the ruling class can readily accomplish both of these aims through its control of pharmaceutical-medical corporations, media, and governmental health agencies, all the while giving the false impression of caring about public health.

Most criminal violence involves something that is visible, but the criminal violence of deception is different because it is a harm that is obscured and invisible, and that hurts and destroys people and communities in ways that are not understood or quantified. People don't know that they don't know. One acid test for deception is this: liars are motivated to resort to information censorship. The deceitful pandemic pretexts, for example, could never stand for more than a few moments if they were to be subjected to open discussion and debate in the scientific and medical communities, and by the general public.

However, over the decades, what is now referred to as the "censorship-industrial complex"[36] has been gradually built. It is comprised of hundreds of narrative-management institutes and fact-checking organizations, many affiliated with universities, government agencies, or media networks, and lavishly funded by Rockefeller, Gates, Ford, Knight, Soros's Open Society, Wellcome Trust, and other globalist foundations as well as by corporations such as Facebook, Google, Apple, and many others.[37] Additionally, for example, the United Nations recruited over 100,000 "digital first responders," worldwide during the Covid crisis whose purpose was, according to the U.N., to detect and neutralize "misinformation" and "fake news" on social media as quickly as possible by countering it with "accurate, reliable information."[38] This vast web of institutions dedicated to crushing dissent and managing information and narratives is completely interconnected not just with government intelligence agencies like the National Security Agency (NSA), the Pentagon's Defense Advanced Research Projects Agency (DARPA), the CIA, the executive branch and its agencies, and the United Nations, as well as all mainstream media outlets, but also with all the internet platforms and search engines that make up the public square where we discuss issues.[39] This censorship-industrial complex operates surreptitiously and many of us are completely unaware of the degree to which it insinuates itself into the way we view our world.[40] It is essential that we as individuals practice due diligence to raise our awareness about this situation so that we are not fooled and harmed by the ongoing flood of deception, and that we don't further the deception by imposing it on others.

As but one example of public mind control and censorship, Peter McCullough, MD, eminent medical doctor, epidemiologist, editor, and professor in his field of renal and cardiac health, and author of over 1,000 medical journal articles, courageously questioned the pandemic pretext. Even with his highly-respected standing in the medical community, he was harshly slandered and censored by the media and by medical associations, like many other leading doctors and scientists who as whistle-blowers were similarly oppressed and silenced by professional agencies and their lackeys.[41] We have seen the same tactics employed against researchers questioning animal-sourced foods, and questioning anthropogenic climate change as well.

Dr. McCullough has clearly and courageously explained that five recognized and accepted truths have been suppressed so that the deceptive pandemic pretext could be implemented.

1) There is no such thing as asymptomatic spread of disease. It has been well-recognized for decades that healthy people do not spread disease, and there is no new evidence to refute this.

2) Thus, there is no need to wear masks, to practice social distancing, to close or limit schools, churches, or businesses, or to test or track asymptomatic people.

3) Natural immunity is permanent and is vastly superior to the contrived immunity of vaccination.

4) Many effective treatments and remedies for Covid-like symptoms have been used successfully by millions, such as hydroxychloroquine, Ivermectin, nasal wash, etc.

5) The Covid injections are extremely harmful with unacceptably high rates of death and injury.[42]

At the European Union Parliament, in September, 2023, Dr. McCullough summarized research findings on the Covid injections, stating, "The vaccines have ravaged the population of the world.... It was the worst idea ever to install the genetic code by injection, and allow unbridled production of a potentially lethal protein in the human body for an uncontrolled duration of time."[43] Besides the other toxins in the injections, the injections contain modified RNA, forcing our cells to produce spike proteins to evoke an immune response: "We have the spike protein — the lethal protein from the vaccines — found in the human body after vaccination, circulating at least for six months, if not longer, and if people take another injection in another six months, that's another installation, and more circulating, potentially-lethal spike protein."[44] Dr. McCullough went on to recount the officially-recognized adverse Covid injection events in their four primary domains: cardiovascular, neurologic, blood clots, and immunological:

> The spike protein is proven in 3,400 peer-reviewed manuscripts to cause four major domains of disease. Number one is cardiovascular disease: heart inflammation, or myocarditis. Every regulatory agency agrees the vaccines cause myocarditis.
>
> I'm a cardiologist. When there's myocarditis, people cannot exert themselves in athletics. It will cause cardiac arrest.... The cardiovascular domain of damage in the human body from the vaccine is substantial. More than anything we've ever seen with cholesterol, high blood pressure, or diabetes.
>
> The second domain is neurologic disease. Stroke, both ischemic and hemorrhagic, Guillain-Barre syndrome, ascending paralysis, which can lead to death, and which has led to death, which is agreed to by all of our regulatory agencies. Small fiber neuropathy, numbness and tingling, ringing in the ears, headaches. These are all common.
>
> Third major domain: blood clots. Blood clots like we've never seen before. The spike protein is the most thrombogenic protein we've even seen in human medicine. It's found IN the blood clots. The spike protein causes blood clots. Blood clots bigger and more resistant to blood thinners than we've ever experienced in human medicine. I have patients with blood clots going on two years now and they are not dissolving with conventional blood thinners due to these vaccines.
>
> The fourth and last domain: immunologic abnormalities. Vaccine-induced thrombotic thrombocytopenia and multi-system

inflammatory disorder are early-acute syndromes, well-described and published. They have their own acronyms, all agreed-to by the agencies.[45]

Dr. McCullough also emphasized the deliberate dissemination of three false narratives propagated by what he called the bio-pharmaceutical complex, a "syndicate" comprised by the WHO, the U.N., GAVI, CEPI, the CDC, Wellcome Trust, the Gates and Rockefeller Foundations, and many other organizations: "The first false narrative was that the virus was unassailable. We have to stay in lockdown and be fearful. The second false narrative is, 'Take a vaccine; it's safe and effective.' The third false narrative is, 'It's not the vaccine causing these problems, it's Covid.'"[46] He concluded with the urgent appeal, "Don't fall for the false narrative. The medical literature at this point in time is compelling. The Bradford-Hill criteria for causality have been fulfilled. The vaccines are causing this enormous wave of illness."[47] How long will it continue?

From its inception, the Covid narrative was deceitful, with the CDC overestimating Covid deaths by 525 percent, relying on no-toriously corrupt Gates-funded U.K. academic Neil Ferguson's wildly exaggerated pandemic models, spooking everyone into a panic.[48] And then the PCR test was disingenuously chosen as the high-tech method that would determine if someone had Covid. Dr. Kary Mullis, who was awarded the Nobel prize in 1993 for single-handedly creating the PCR test, was always very clear that it should never be used as a diagnostic tool and stated unambig-uously, "Anyone can test positive for practically anything with a PCR test, if you run it long enough. It doesn't tell you that you're sick."[49] Mullis vocally condemned its use for AIDS diagnosis thirty years prior, and he had fought Fauci strenuously over its misuse to similarly promote the AIDS crisis, but he died, conven-iently, just before the Covid rollout. Again, the WHO authorities cunningly chose the PCR as the diagnostic gold standard, under-standing full well that it was easy to create false positives by simply increasing the PCR cycle rates above 30. Labs were instructed by CDC and other national and international authorities to run PCR tests at rates from 37 to 45 cycles, guaranteeing that millions of people falsely tested as positive.[50] This gave rise to a "case-demic," which created the false pretext for the coordinated worldwide declarations of medical emergencies.

In the U.S., the devastatingly inflationary multi-trillion-dollar Coronavirus Aid, Relief, and Economic Security (CARES) act was hastily passed in March 2020. It incentivized hospitals to further exploit and promote the false narrative, as the CARES funding that they automatically received would have to be returned if it was not used for: 1) testing incoming patients for Covid; 2) getting a positive Covid diagnosis; 3) admitting a patient into a Covid unit; 4) administering the notorious kidney-damaging drug nicknamed "Run!-death-is-near"[51] (Remdesivir - a twenty percent bonus); 5) putting a patient on a life-threatening ventilator ($39,000 bonus);[52] and 6) recording a death as Covid-related.[53] Besides these financial bonuses to hospitals, doctors, and health professionals to artificially inflate Covid data and death rates and boost the fear narrative, funds were provided to local towns, counties, and school systems to pressure local officials to amplify masking mandates and social distancing protocols, and to escalate the number of people submitting to the injections, without providing for properly informed consent.[54]

While the vast depth and breadth of pandemic deception is beyond the scope of this book to discuss, the essential point is that it was only through censorship, deception, and relentlessly inflicting fear and violence that the globalist cabal was able to cause such a high degree of compliance, confusion and mass formation. It is helpful to ask, "Cui bono?"–who benefits? The benefit has clearly been primarily to the unelected plutocrats who own and control large portions of the global financial system, transnational conglomerates, medical corporations, and mainstream media, and who, to implement their agenda of human domination, have created invitation-only organizations like the

Trilateral Commission, the Bilderberg Group, the Council on Foreign Relations, the Aspen Institute, the Atlantic Institute, the Bohemian Club, the World Economic Forum, the United Nations, The World Health Organization, and others.[55]

Controlled Opposition and Faux Veganism

The pandemic pretext has caused "the greatest transfer of wealth from the middle class to the elites in history,"[56] and a massive shift in power to the globalists as well, away from citizens in the lower and middle economic strata, and away from movements for justice, health, freedom, truth, peace, sustainability, and accountability. The vegan movement, which promotes all of these movements,[57] together with liberation for animals, would logically be one of the most committed and formidable foes fighting against the globalist cabal's agenda of medical tyranny bent on destroying our essential freedoms, promoting censorship and centralization of power, and additionally killing millions of animals for ingredients and testing for unnecessary injections. The globalists have been at this for a long time and understand that to be successful, they must control not only the narrative that is put forth in the mainstream media, but also control the primary opposing narratives as well. Known as controlled opposition, this tactic has worked well in their efforts to reduce the effectiveness, and manipulate the message, of the environmental movement, the peace movement, the women's movement, the workers' movement, and other popular movements, and we see it predictably with the animal liberation movement.

Money is easily translated into power. By making donations to animal protection and vegan advocacy organizations, for example, that specify how such funds are to be used, these organizations can be co-opted.[58] Prior to agreeing to accept these sly contributions, for instance, the organizations were working to educate the public about the inescapable abuse of hens in egg operations, and promoting vegan alternatives. However, when accepting a gift of a million dollars to promote "humanely-produced" eggs, one organization changed its entire messaging in order to take advantage of the fund-ing.[59] It changed to advocating for bigger and better cages, rather than empty cages, and the animal liberation message was effectively muzzled. This also serves the globalists' divide-and-conquer strat-egy, because it sows seeds of distrust among activists and engenders disagreements in the movement that weaken and destabilize it.

Animal advocates initially join the movement with a sense of idealism and commitment to animal liberation, but with time, es-pecially if they take employment at animal protection organizations, their loyalty may tend to shift toward the organi-zations that write their paychecks. It is the large organizations with the most funding and reach that are most vulnerable to be-ing co-opted, and they also tend to have the greatest ability to influence the perspectives of animal advocates and the public. With the infusion of strings-attached money into the movement, the culture of idealism and of creative non-cooperation with ani-mal-abusing forces has been gradually replaced by a culture of pragmatism and of partnership with those forces. In some cases, addressing the plight of the animals has become secondary to in-creasing the size, wealth, and health of the organizations. Thus, animal protection organizations can be subtly co-opted by pred-atory philanthropic entities that front for animal-abusing interests.[60] The movement has been infiltrated not only by Tro-jan-Horse controlled-opposition money, but also by controlled-opposition people as well. While there are undoubtedly cases of paid infiltrators, much of the infiltration is by well-meaning peo-ple who are vulnerable to this indoctrination by mainstream narratives, and who don't have the necessary understanding of the hidden forces at work. They typically haven't done the requi-site inner work to navigate their way through the maze of deception in which we are all immersed from birth.

The pharmaceutical-medical complex is the unrecognized nemesis of the animal liberation movement, as well as of animals themselves, directly torturing and killing millions in the produc-tion of drugs, and indirectly profiting from medicating the billions of imprisoned animals as well as the sick humans (and "pets") the animal agriculture-based food system generates. While vegan activists have worked hard over the past thirty years to raise awareness about the harmful impacts of animal agriculture, and the many benefits of transitioning to a whole-foods plant-sourced way of eating and living, the corporate complex, with its deep pockets, buys influence and narrative control, and commandeers the positive social capital the vegan movement has been building, hijacking and funneling it to its advantage.

Recognizing that the vegan movement is a rising and potentially formidable tide of awareness that would destroy it, the chemical-food-pharmaceutical-medical complex, through Bill Gates and others, works to shift the conversation away from traditional vegan values. These values emphasize the primary goal of liberating animals from human abuse, and prioritize foods that are whole, organic, healthy, cruelty-free, and cause much less environmental destruction. The push is on to submerge these traditional values under new globalist-inspired so-called "plant"-based foods that are highly-processed to satisfy taste and convenience, with little mention of animal liberation, and with environmental impacts reduced to just one, carbon. These plant-based foods (so-called not only because they are made with plants, but especially because they are fabricated and processed in industrial plants) are typically made using artificial colors and preservatives, and non-organic, genetically-engineered, pesticide-laden ingredients, often with large amounts of addictive salt, sugar, and fats. In the case of lab-grown cell-cultured meat products, only chicken has been approved by the FDA, and it is grown in a way similar to how biotechnology firms make drugs.[61] It is extremely energy-intensive, with a carbon footprint that is, remarkably, "orders of magnitude" worse than beef.[62] Healthy plant-sourced foods are being deliberately conflated with these toxic, environmentally-devastating "plant-based" factory-produced Frankenfoods.

This serves several purposes that promote the globalist agenda and harm the animal and human liberation movements. First, it ensures that people will continue to consume foods and products that, while "plant-based," contain poisonous chemicals and chemical residues, profiting the twin chemical and pharmaceutical industries and the bankers in the background. Second, it ensures we are assaulted by harmful ingredients that are added to lengthen shelf-life and increase addictive appeal, and that weaken us physically, mentally, and socially, so that we are more easily controllable. Third, it serves the agenda of centralization of power and control, because unlike traditional vegan foods like vegetables, fruits, grains, and nuts that can be grown locally and support local economies, mass-produced plant-based factory-made foods concentrate wealth in the hands of a few large centralized corporations. Fourth, by announcing plans to prohibit meat-eating and to force people to eat artificial meat and insects, usually in the name of "fighting climate change," veganism becomes falsely linked with globalist agendas. The reputation and image of veganism is sabotaged among people who should be veganism's allies. People who care about health, freedom, and environmental sustainability now mock vegan foods, and vegans as well, for their apparent gullibility and for promoting unhealthy processed foods.

What they are mocking is really faux veganism, which is a creation of the cabal working through the Gates Foundation, Open Philanthropy and other predatory philanthropic organizations, as well as the WEF, mainstream media, and other captured entities. However, this faux veganism is still promoted by naïve vegans who yearn to use these unhealthy plant-based dairy, egg, and meat substitutes to entice people into plant-based ways of eating, only to find that these new vegan recruits feel, unsurprisingly, unwell eating these Frankenfoods, and revert to eating "real" meat, and tell the world how they tried to go vegan but it didn't work. These foods are in many ways a Trojan Horse that allow hostile forces to destroy our movement from within. Nothing destroys progress for animal liberation more than these scenarios of people "going vegan" and eating toxic "plant-based" foods, and then feeling unhealthy, all amplified through media channels. The pattern is both familiar and predictable. There is far more corporate profit in the plant-based processed convenience foods, which are advertised and promoted in most vegan magazines and websites, than in lentils, potatoes, broccoli, cucumbers, and the other whole plant-sourced foods that are the actual foundation of healthful living. It is essential that those of us dedicated to animal liberation understand these dynamics, and also recognize and embrace the importance of human liberation, and cultivate discriminating awareness regarding the rollout of the globalist agenda, which deceptively preempts and exploits the vegan movement in order to undermine its power and credibility.

The globalist cabal is well-practiced in these methods. The environmental movement is a good example. Following Rachel Carson's book, *Silent Spring,* a vigorous grass-roots environmental movement developed, demanding that corporations be held accountable for their poisoning of water, air, and soil, and for destroying ecosystems and harming the health of the population. This was a direct threat to the power and profits of the ruling parasitic cabal, and so the movement had to be co-opted and weakened, and this proved relatively easy to do through increasing control of media narratives, academia, and governmental agencies. The Environmental Protection Agency (EPA) was created to mollify environmental activists, and some legislation was passed, and with time the EPA was virtually completely captured by corporate forces, academia was infiltrated with grant money, and media was brought to heel through advertising, predatory philanthropy, and consolidation. Whenever outbreaks of disease occurred, due to chemical poisoning of water, air, and food, the CDC and the WHO sent in agents to proclaim that the diseases were due to viruses, bacteria, and other natural causes.

The greatest blow to the environmental movement delivered by the cabal was its invention of a fake problem, anthropogenic global warming through "greenhouse gas emissions," which was systematically orchestrated and relentlessly promoted through captured media, academia, and governmental outlets. Suddenly the only environmental issue any concerned person could talk about was the so-called climate crisis, and everything else was marginalized. Josh Mitteldorf summarized the situation, "The environmental movement has been derailed by the carbon narrative."[63]

For several years, I must admit that I was somewhat deceived by the anthropogenic global warming narrative, and like many vegans, did my best to point out that animal agriculture should be considered the chief causal climate culprit. However, I was always disturbed by how this obvious vegan solution was ignored by the globalists and their controlled mainstream media and government agencies. It was also troubling to see how environmental activism addressing the devastating ecological harm caused by the chemical, pharmaceutical and animal agriculture industries was brushed aside in the ongoing hysteria swirling around climate change. Suspiciously, the environmental conversation was constantly being reduced to a single issue—anthropogenic global warming—but that warming never manifested. In spite of the breathless predictions by Al Gore, the U.N., and mainstream media, according to the National Oceanic and Atmospheric Administration's (NOAA) most reliable data, there has been no appreciable warming in the U.S. for the 17 years from 2005 to 2022.[64] While some of us are seeing higher temperatures and more drought in certain regions, these can be attributed to other causes (e.g., geoengineering, volcanic activity, solar output changes, deforestation, data collection inaccuracies, and so forth) which will be covered later.

This faux environmentalism, centered around climate change, is not only protecting the polluting corporations and covering up their rampant poisoning and destruction of ecosystems, but is also being used as a tool to tyrannize all of us into allowing our basic freedoms and personal and cultural health to be sacrificed. The defining characteristic of slavery is restricting and controlling movement. When we look at animal agriculture, the animals are confined, and it is this confinement that destroys their freedom, steals their purposes, and enslaves them. The same is true with us. With the faux climate crisis, the cabal is vigorously attempting to manufacture our consent for our own enslavement and impoverishment. Through its domination of media, education, and other institutions, it is manipulating and deceiving us into allowing ourselves to be similarly turned into livestock, confined into fifteen-minute cities and SMART communities, and, by other grotesque anti-movement mechanisms, imprisoning us in a matrix of control.

The environmental movement is not the first to be co-opted and then weaponized against us. Other movements that threatened the status quo, such as the workers movement, the women's movement, and the peace movement, were similarly co-opted and weaponized. The tactics are evident in the promotion of identity politics, transgenderism, and false flag attacks tricking us into thinking we should go to war against so-called enemies who have actually never harmed us. These faux movements, such as identity politics and transgenderism, reinforce animal agriculture's materialism by encouraging us to identify exclusively with the traits that separate us from others.[65] The ruling cabal thereby keeps us confused and divided, and harvests the social capital that legitimate movements have painstakingly built up. Stealing it, they use it to their own advantage. We can see the same thing unfolding in the animal liberation movement as well.

The vegan movement's prime goal is to liberate animals (and us human animals as well) and yet, by promoting plant-based Frankenfoods made with genetically-engineered ingredients, filled with toxic fats, chemical additives, and pesticide residues, and especially the specter of lab-grown, animal-cell-based factory-produced flesh and dairy products, the pharma-chemical-food industry can conflate plant-based and vegan, reducing veganism's public image to that of a movement that promotes toxic, artificial foods that promote human enslavement. Already many people compare highly-processed plant-based foods and veganism to the revolting Soylent Green, which, as depicted in the 1973 film of the same name, is manufactured from recycled human flesh.[66]

It is essential that we resist the temptation to use harmful narratives and technologies, like the faux climate crisis and plant-based Frankenfoods, to promote vegan living. It is never appropriate to use lies to promote truth. Means and ends are one, as seeds contain their eventual fruits. There are huge and valid environmental concerns beside so-called climate change, and there are countless healthy vegan foods, even some, like tempeh bacon and sunflower-based burgers, that while processed, are made from whole and organic ingredients. Transitional foods that imitate meat and dairy products must be carefully vetted or we will fall into the trap of harming ourselves, and thus our movement to liberate animals. When even long-term vegans are eating in an unhealthy way and suffering from the diseases this causes, it harms the credibility and effectiveness of the movement, and the animals and ecosystems we are working to defend. Unhealthy vegans eating plant-based junk food set an unfortunate example, deterring people and weakening the cause of animal and human freedom.

Additionally, we are seeing dark agendas emerging that are mocking humanity, such as the strong promotion through the mainstream media that we should all start eating bugs, grubs, and insects instead of animal flesh. This is obviously not vegan, because insects are clearly sentient,[67] but is being promoted as a type of "meat" that is supposedly more environmentally sustainable, reducing our so-called carbon footprint. However, it also undermines the real solution, which is to transition to obviously healthier, simpler, and more sustainable whole, organic plant-sourced foods.

We also see the looming phantasm, subtly and strongly promoted by the globalist cabal, of eating human flesh. The plutocrats use their predatory philanthropy to influence academia, science, and media to mock and insult humanity, supplying a flood of interconnected narrative lines that humanity is a cancer on the Earth, that there are too many of us, and that like animals, we can be eaten as livestock. The globalist cabal's apparent disdain for humanity propels its efforts to normalize cannibalism under a variety of guises: as a way of helping with food shortages, of boosting health, and of addressing the so-called climate crisis. Some examples: researchers at Stanford University published their findings that "harvesting blood and organs of children could help people achieve immortality;"[68] researchers at U.C., San Diego, tout cannibalism as "a new way to stop disease;"[69] a Swedish scientist has been advocating cannibalism "as a way to combat climate change;"[70] and, academics increasingly promote cannibalism to help solve the overpopulation problem.[71] *The New York Times* has not only been regularly promoting insects, but also normalizing cannibalism, advertising its July, 2022, "A Taste for Cannibalism?" article, for example, by posting, "Cannibalism has a time and a place. Some recent books, films and shows suggest that the time is now. Can you stomach it?"[72]

The Gates Foundation, like the Rockefeller Foundation, is a primary driver of the depopulation (eugenics) agenda, as well as the pharmaceutical and vaccination agenda. Like other globalist organizations, it not only invests in and profits from pharmaceutical and chemical companies, but also funds vaccination projects as well as so-called fact-checking organizations and public relations initiatives. These exert ongoing financial influence on media outlets, promoting vaccines, transhumanism, and genetic engineering. Gates is heavily invested in Bayer/Monsanto, and monetarily backs highly-processed and unhealthy foods and food additives, both animal- and plant-based. Many in the vegan movement see Bill Gates as an ally for this latter reason, despite that he is far from being vegan, and that the Gates foundations and organizations strenuously promote globalist agendas that destroy ecosystems, animals, and human health and sovereignty.

For all these reasons, it is essential that we diligently inform ourselves and do our best to make the journey to deep vegan living, and reject the faux veganism of highly-processed plant-based foods. These foods finance the harmful petrochemical-pharmaceutical complex, and often meat and dairy companies as well, which are heavily invested in processed meat alternatives. Of course, we all like to be able to offer "transitional foods" to people who are making the shift from animal-sourced products to vegan living, so perhaps a few plant-based foods have a brief part to play for these people. It would behoove us all to encourage new vegans to transition as quickly as possible away from these faux burgers, cheese, eggs, hot dogs, and so forth, to healthy, whole, organic plant-sourced foods.

Eugenics and Depopulation

Some environmentalists and vegans, because they are defending ecosystems and animals from human exploitation, tend toward misanthropic views that render them unsuspecting of the shrewd narratives spun by globalists who feign concern for the environment in order to appropriate more wealth and power for themselves, and to exploit and abuse humanity. Dr. Andrew Wakefield's documentary, *Infertility: A Diabolical Agenda*, clearly demonstrates, for example, that the Gates Foundation funded vaccination programs in Africa for many years that deceived local women into receiving shots that sterilized them,[73] as the Rockefeller Foundation had done in India a few decades earlier,[74] as well as polio vaccination programs that paralyzed nearly half a million young people in India.[75]

Investigative journalist James Corbett demonstrates, in *How and Why Big Oil Conquered the World*,[76] the methods whereby the Rockefeller empire, early in its development, diversified from petroleum into more highly-profitable petrochemicals, and from there into even more profitable petrochemical derivatives: pharmaceuticals. In order to most advantageously market these drugs, it used its vast wealth to fund and transform the American Medical Association over a hundred years ago, and gradually take over the education of doctors through funding the Flexner report in 1910, which attacked what it saw as competitive systems of healing based on herbs, homeopathy, chiropractic, and other natural methods, promoting instead the reductionist allopathic model as the only "scientific" one.[77]

With profits from patentable disease-causing petroleum- and chemical-based pharmaceutical drugs, Rockefeller purchased more influence, diversifying, for example, into academia (Rockefeller University), banking, and public health, as well as international politics through major funding for the United Nations headquarters in New York. A primary motivating worldview among Rockefeller and the other nouveau riche elites was eugenics—the idea that certain humans are superior to others—and that those with superior traits should be systematically encouraged to breed, and humans with inferior or objectionable traits should be sterilized or culled. Animal eugenics has been practiced for thousands of years in our herding tradition, and is a fundamental defining factor in our relationship with farmed animals. As our progenitors learned how to breed animals who gave more milk, or more eggs, or more wool, or had more edible flesh on their bones, or were more docile and more easily managed, this increase in exploitable output and profitability propelled the foundational orientation of domination and manipulation of nature in order to control and predict outcomes. Eventually, over the centuries, this became formalized as the scientific method. From its inception, science has been primarily a tool for domination of animals and nature, and is one of herderism's proudest accomplishments.

The eugenics movement is simply the application of herderism's mentality to fellow humans. The wealthy class promotes eugenics, in various guises, towards those it sees as the lower mass of humanity, which, through deception and indoctrination, becomes vulnerable in its hands. Cows and sheep are domesticated and born into complete vulnerability to the exploitive hands of humans, and the major drivers of global animal agriculture are the plutocrats who profit from stealing health and freedom from animals, ecosystems, and human beings. The natural capacities and powers of both animals and humans are suppressed by depriving them of their sovereignty and purposes, and by raising them in manipulative confinement. Through this, they can be conditioned toward docility. When we financially support and eat the exploitation of animals who have been reduced to livestock, we are directly feeding—and feeding on—the parasitic system that relentlessly reduces us to livestock.

The modern eugenics movement emerged in the mid- to late-nineteenth century, based on Darwin's theories of evolution and natural selection. Championed by Julian Huxley and by Darwin's half-cousin Francis Galton, who coined the term eugenics, which means "well-born," it was essentially a movement among the plutocrats to reduce and eliminate what they saw as inferior social, racial, and ethnic classes, while keeping enough acquiescent and obedient ones around to serve as their agents and servants. The British and American Eugenics Societies were both started in the early twentieth century. The U.S. eugenics movement spread rapidly through the efforts of zoologist Charles Davenport, who started the Eugenics Record Office to register the genetic background of every American.[78] He was strongly supported in his efforts by the American Breeders Association, which promoted the long-established science and practice of animal eugenics. He was also sponsored by the Rockefeller Foundation. William Welch, the founding director of the Rockefeller Institute for Medical Research, sat on the board of the Eugenics Record Office. With the support and funding of America's wealthy elites, eugenics became a fashionable social cause. Indiana passed the first law authorizing the forced sterilization of "the unfit" in 1907, and in a few years, there were a dozen states with similar legislation.[79]

As a natural extension of the practice of herderism, for centuries rulers had been claiming their right to power by proclaiming their genetic superiority. This was a direct result of animal agriculture, and its focus on and fixation with bloodlines and their purity, and even today, members of so-called royalty depend on their bloodlines for their power, wealth, and prestige. With the arising of a new elite class based solely on its financial triumphs, natural selection—also known as Social Darwinism—provided the needed narrative that rationalized the status of these *nouveau riche* aristocrats, and eugenics could be used to further legitimize and consolidate their power over those beneath them.[80] Academics and journalists declared that the wealthy and powerful rose to the top due not just to their superior drive and cleverness, but also due to their obviously superior genetics. In 1927, in the *Buck vs. Bell* case, the Supreme Court upheld the state forced sterilization laws,[81] opening the floodgates to an estimated 70,000 forced sterilizations of U.S. citizens who were deemed mentally, emotionally, or racially unfit. In fact, it was mainly the U.S. eugenics movement that inspired the German eugenics movement in the 1930s, which continued to thrive until the Nazi experience of forced sterilizations and other eugenic-inspired abuses revealed its racist and vicious core.[82] Considering the primitive surgical capacities back in the 1920s and 1930s when these tens of thousands of forced castrations and "terribly invasive"[83] salpingectomies were forced on people by public health authorities in the U.S., it is remarkable how this has been covered up and forgotten, together with the fact that *Buck vs. Bell* has deliberately never been overturned, and is still the law of the land today.[84]

The Rockefeller Foundation sponsored eugenics researchers at Kaiser Wilhelm University who went on to draft Germany's forced sterilization law.[85] Additionally, John D. Rockefeller, III, personally founded the Population Council in 1952, choosing Frederick Osborne, director of the disgraced American Eugenics Society, as its first president, after him, in 1957.[86] In 1972, population control became the new face of the same eugenics movement, which had always promoted preventing the poor and "feeble-minded" from having children. The Rockefeller Foundation provided funding to the World Health Organization to create a "Task Force on Vaccines for Fertility Regulation," which by 1995 had developed vaccines that prevent fertility in women, leading to a series of scandals where routine tetanus shots given to women in Africa and the Philippines were stealthily laced with the new anti-fertility antigen, HCG.[87] The Gates Foundation and the World Health Organization later sponsored much larger-scale stealth vaccination sterilization programs in Africa where tetanus vaccines given to over one million women were laced with infertility-inducing HCG, according to doctors in Kenya.[88] One doctor, Stephen Karanja, who was particularly outspoken and valiant in his defense of women in Kenya, warned, "When they are through with Africa, they are coming for you. Keep your children ready, they will come for them, they will come for you."[89]

With Rockefeller funding, prominent eugenicist Margaret Sanger founded Planned Parenthood, with the director of the American Eugenics Society, Alan Guttmacher, serving simultaneously as director of Planned Parenthood. Bill Gates' father, William Gates, Sr., served as director of Planned Parenthood following Guttmacher.[90] The Gates Foundation and the Rockefeller Foundation have both worked diligently to promote the global elite's eugenics agenda of sterilizing people in "unstable developing countries,"[91] who are coincidentally people of color, through vaccinations and medical procedures. In the U.S., eighty percent of Planned Parenthood abortion clinics are within easy walking distance of minority neighborhoods, and according to Planned Parenthood, "the abortion rate for black women is almost five times that for white women."[92] Knowing that the experimental Covid injections are linked with miscarriages, sterility, serious injuries, and death, and considering the globalist elite's prior record of administering vaccines to millions of people in Africa to deceptively cause infertility, and its deep ties to eugenics, it is no surprise that Melinda Gates announced that right after healthcare workers, black people and indigenous people should be the first to receive the Covid injections.[93]

Vera Sherav, journalist and Holocaust survivor, summed it well at the 75th Nuremberg Anniversary:

> The real viral disease that infected Nazi Germany was eugenics. Eugenics is the elitist ideology at the root of all genocides. Eugenics is cloaked in the mantle of pseudo-science. It was embraced by the

academic and medical establishment, as well as the judiciary, both in Germany and the United States. Eugenicists justified social and economic inequality. They legitimized discrimination, apartheid, sterilization, euthanasia, and genocide. The Nazis called it "ethnic cleansing" to protect the gene pool. Medicine was perverted from its healing mission and was weaponized. First, it was to control reproduction through forced sterilization.[94]

It is obvious that we've been told by authorities for decades that the Earth is over-populated with humans. This is clearly a message in alignment with the globalist cabal's agenda to radically reduce the population of humans, to make us easier to control. The ruling class has a variety of ways to manage the population of the human herd. Planned Parenthood, UNESCO, the National Education Association (NEA), the World Health Organization, and other organizations are promoting the sexualization of children through introducing pornography into classrooms under the guise of "comprehensive sexuality education,"[95] and encouraging transsexuality and homosexuality, as well as normalizing pedophilia, all of which lead to fewer births, fewer families, and a more easily controlled population that is confused and atomized, fixated on material distractions and shallow cravings that reduce others to sexual objects. The globalists are encouraging the sexual trafficking of children through eroding border security, and this trafficking has become a vast enterprise, more lucrative than the illicit arms and drug trades.[96]

The sexual confusion and exploitation of children is also facilitated by the widespread proliferation of endocrine disrupting chemicals like the bisphenols (BPA, BPS, and others),[97] which are linked to infertility in both men and women. Additionally, the proliferation of atrazine, one of the world's most widely-used pesticides, which literally turns male frogs into females that can mate with male frogs,[98] upsets the delicate hormonal balances in us as well, especially children. Dairy products also concentrate estrogen, because mother cows, like all lactating mammals, produce high levels of estrogen in their milk, which is molecularly identical to human estrogen (unlike the plant estrogen in soy).[99] This has the effect of increasing estrogen levels in dairy consumers. Again, unnaturally increasing estrogen in people can cause physical and psychological problems of various kinds, increasing the risk of breast cancer[100] and prostate cancer,[101] potentially feminizing boys,[102] and also forcing girls into early menarche. The age of first menstruation in the nineteenth century, and among traditional cultures not consuming dairy, was about 17 years, and now it is 12.5 years,[103] contributing to the unnatural sexualization of children, unwanted pregnancies, and enormous amounts of psychological and social stress and violence. These various factors can contribute to gender dysphoria, which is similarly promoted by globalist plutocrats,[104] not only because it is highly lucrative for the medical complex, but also because it reduces birth rates, and damages the fabric of society, dividing people, reducing the status of women, and making us more easily dominated and exploited. All of this ironically mirrors the perversion we routinely inflict on farmed animals by the millions every day, sexually abusing them and forcing them into pregnancy at an unnaturally early age through the use of drugs and hormones, when they are but children in human terms.

The eugenics approach to livestock (and human) management relies on breeding and culling, and for us, the narrative repeated interminably is that there are too many humans for the finite resources of the Earth to accommodate. This is certainly true if we humans are eating diets based on animal-sourced foods. Researchers already estimate that if everyone on Earth ate as much meat and dairy as people in the U.S., we would need two Earths because the U.S. is among the highest in per capita animal food consumption.[105] But if we humans transitioned to a healthy vegan way of living, we could feed everyone with much less land and fewer resources than we are using now.

What actually is the optimal number of humans on Earth? Do we know? Further, what is our purpose here? Like all creatures, we humans certainly do have a significant place on this Earth, rightly understood. We do not necessarily need to reduce our population either. The eugenics-inspired human depopulation narrative integrates well with herderism's fear-based relationship with the Earth. The purpose of the ruling elite's agenda to drastically reduce the human population seems to be primarily to make dominating humanity more easily manageable by reducing our numbers. Living in harmony with ourselves and nature, who is to say what the optimal number of humans on Earth actually is?

Perhaps it's around ten billion, as Peter Russell implies in his book *The Global Brain*. He discusses how, in a developing human fetus, at a certain point there is a population explosion of brain cells in the cerebral cortex, with the number of neurons increasing rapidly up to about ten billion cells.[106] He says that if you were a brain cell, you might shout, "Stop! There are too many of us; there's no more room!" And then suddenly the number of cells stabilizes, and from then on, intelligence increases by escalating the interconnectivity among all the cerebral neurons, not increasing the number of cells.

We may be in an analogous situation, which calls us urgently to awaken from the delusion of herderism and its disconnectedness. It is now obvious that if we all would eat organically-grown vegan foods, we could easily feed ten billion of us on much less land than we are now using. Imagining a world based on deep veganism is imagining a completely different world, not only in terms of dramatically reduced environmental impact, but also in terms of our fundamental orientation toward animals, nature, each other, and ourselves. We cannot possibly overstate the tremendous healing and creative forces unleashed by liberating ourselves culturally, psychologically, and spiritually from our tyranny over animals. Liberating animals would be such a monumental human transformation toward sustainability, respect, and kindness in our relations that we would be able to evolve into (or perhaps return to) a much more essential harmony with nature, animals, and each other, and discover and increase our interconnectivity, not just through technological gadgets, but more essentially through what we might call the inner-net—the intuitive connections that we have with each other and with animals and nature. Long suppressed by our herding culture's orientation toward materialism, domination, and exploitation, our inner wisdom beckons us to awaken our capacities.

The arrogant sense of superiority that herderism and materialism inculcate in human consciousness disconnects us from our sense of wonder and respect for life. This has given rise not only to the now-discredited eugenics movement of sterilizing and eliminating less "useful" people, but also to the World Economic Forum's transhumanist movement, which is actually the New Eugenics, using gene-editing technologies to engineer humans to our specifications, as we now feel perfectly justified doing to animals viewed as livestock commodities. Yuval Noah Harari, a high-level advisor to and spokesperson for the WEF, has said that humans are merely "hackable animals," and he further states, "Today, we have the technology to hack human beings on a massive scale."[107] For him and the WEF, a major problem that looms is that, with the emerging artificial intelligence and robotics technologies taking away jobs, there will be too many useless people. Harari states, "The big political question in the 21st century is, what do we need humans for? Or rather, what do we need so *many* humans for? The best plan we have is to keep them happy with drugs and computer games."[108] Julian Huxley's brother, Aldous, eerily predicted such a scenario in his 1931 book, *Brave New World*.

It should be deeply concerning that the WEF and the wealthy parasites who dominate the United Nations, the WHO, national governments, banks, corporations, and media, and aspire to dictate the future of humanity, have such an impoverished view of human beings and of our creativity, spirituality, and higher purposes. If we are not in some way fulfilling their need for workers, administrators, and consumers, then they consider us to be useless, and we might as well be culled, drugged, frivolously entertained, or reprogrammed. According to Harari, "We humans should get used to the idea that we are no longer mysterious souls. We are now hackable animals. The whole idea that humans have this 'soul' or 'spirit,' and nobody knows what's happening inside them, and they have free will. That's over."[109] Just as we reduced animals to commodities, we find ourselves now becoming similarly reduced. The world's most wealthy and powerful entities are proclaiming this directly to us, trivializing, degrading, and mocking humanity itself. This is the utterly predictable boomerang. How do we respond?

We are called to many questions. What are the real motivations behind the well-publicized campaigns to control and reduce human population? Why the frenetic push for more vaccines, and more genetic engineering of plants, animals, and even humans? What is driving the global campaign to increase technocracy, which further centralizes power, erodes freedom and health, divides humanity, and requires ever-more digital invasion, electromagnetic radiation, and harmful chemicals? Which humans are especially conditioned to regard their fellow humans the way most of us are conditioned to regard livestock? What actually goes on in the raising of children born into the tiny minority of super-rich families who wield such power that they dictate governmental policies globally and control media narratives worldwide from behind their closed-door meetings? How do these people become hard-hearted and capable of casually and remorselessly inflicting misery and death on millions of people, as well as on animals and ecosystems? How do the rest of us respond? These are essential questions, and they also tie in directly with the herderism that is at the core of our culture.

The sands of time flow continually. Every moment, every insight, and every interaction can be an illuminating opportunity to contribute to the healing of our world. The foundational necessity is to awaken from deceived delusion to a more accurate and empowered understanding of our situation. A benevolent revolution is possible and beckons. There are no external saviors. We are called, each of us as sovereign individuals and co-creators of our world situation, to liberate animals—and our minds—from herderism's pernicious influence. As we do this, the ruling parasites increasingly lose their grip on us, and over animals and nature as well, because we no longer comply with their narratives and implement their agenda of heartless exploitation of living beings.

CHAPTER TWELVE

THE BENEVOLENT REVOLUTION

"Human beings are exquisitely attuned to reading the mood of the mob. It's a survival mechanism. In order to fit in, we instinctively adopt the correct opinions and profess those opinions."
—CHARLES EISENSTEIN

"The strength of a person's spirit is measured by how much truth they can tolerate, or more precisely, to what extent they need to have it diluted, disguised, sweetened, or falsified."
—FRIEDRICH NIETZSCHE

"For if we fail in this our fight, he must surely win: and then where end we?... But to fail here is not mere life or death. It is that we become as him; that we henceforward become foul things... without heart or conscience, preying on the bodies and the souls of those we love best."
—BRAM STOKER: *DRACULA*

Template for Tragedy

Herderism is not just human exploitation of animals; more accurately it is the physical and sexual abuse of female animals and their very young offspring. The age-old practice of hunting free-living animals is clearly violent and in today's world is also typically destructive of ecosystems, but when our ancestors ten thousand years ago initiated the herding revolution—the most important revolution ever to occur in human society—they crossed serious and far-reaching ethical lines that brought their cultures into hideously harmful behavior relative to the animals they now owned and controlled as property. Herderism has become our cultural template and it is a template for tragedy.

Zoo animals often eventually wind up in canned hunting facilities that some hunters consider immoral because the animals have no chance to escape. Herderism is an extreme form of canned hunting where animals are bred directly into physical and sexual slavery, to be impregnated against their will, and to have their resulting babies either killed, or repeatedly raped and then killed. It is difficult to imagine the extreme trauma that this inflicts not just on all the animals involved, but on human children born into animal farming families who are compelled to witness and then participate in and promote this heinous sexual and physical violence. All of us, born into a society that routinely and viciously strips away sovereignty and meaning from millions of animals on a daily basis, are wounded by the resulting corrosion of our inherent empathy and intelligence.

When we see mothers caring for and nurturing their offspring, we know in our bones that the natural forces streaming through them are beautiful, inspiring, and essential, and that if anything should be respected, it is this maternal love, and the vulnerability of newborns. Yet these are the very life-giving forces and sacred relationships that we most callously exploit and destroy in the animals we use. By doing so, we desecrate the nurturing, life-giving forces and wisdom in ourselves as well, but we don't realize it because it's normalized and all-pervasive. Eating animal foods is not a choice we make, but an inheritance into which we are born. Though masked and generally unrecognized, we can best see it by its harmful effects.

Without breeding the animals, when and however we want, there could be no herderism. The living core of animal agriculture is the sexual trafficking of animals, and because the animals are forced onto rape racks when they are only children in human terms, as a society we are perpetrating animal pedophilic sexual abuse and animal child slaughter millions of times daily. We see, correspondingly, in our human world, escalating levels of child sexual trafficking, child sexual abuse, and the normalization of pedophilia. Pedophiles are being increasingly referred to as merely "minor-attracted people." Ritual sexual abuse and murder of children is also now recognized to be both devastating and increasingly prevalent.[1] Even the mainstream *Wall Street Journal* has investigated and reported on the undeniable fact that social media platforms are being used by "vast pedophile networks" to access and promote child sexual content and sexually abuse children.[2] This child sexual content includes high-priced black market videos of children being sexually abused, and even, shockingly, snuff films, where children are tortured to death, a predictable mirror of the animal snuff films where animals are filmed being tortured and killed. There are several reasons why there are more vulnerable children today, and why they are being increasingly exploited: engineered wars, conflicts, and disasters create a large and easily available supply of accessible and unprotected orphans; it is extremely lucrative for traffickers and their risk is minimized due to corruption of authorities; border security is now far more lax than it was in the past; state statutes and so-called child protective agencies have been weaponized against both parents and children and are used as trafficking fronts; and mainstream media, law enforcement, and governmental agencies turn a blind eye, censoring and disparaging journalists and whistleblowers who attempt to expose it.[3]

Not only are child trafficking and sexual abuse recognized to have become widespread problems. There is also a burgeoning market for organs as well as blood and adrenochrome harvested from children. Adrenochrome is a chemical compound arising from the oxidation of adrenalin.[4] As is well understood, when any mammal or bird is under stress, adrenalin is secreted by the adrenal glands.

Fishes also have a hypothalamus-pituitary-adrenal complex that responds to stress. When intense anxiety, caused by severe pain, is added to the stress, the adrenalin is oxidized and becomes adrenochrome. For example, when a lion is chasing a gazelle, the gazelle is secreting adrenalin, which gives the animal more speed and strength, but if the lion's teeth and claws start tearing into the gazelle's flesh, the pain combined with terror oxidizes the adrenalin into adrenochrome.[5] It's well-known that the blood of children and adolescents is rejuvenating to older people, and wealthy people pay for transfusions of children's blood for this reason, but the blood of tortured children containing adrenochrome takes this to a diabolical level: "There are substantial benefits from consuming it: greater health, increased vivacity, and a host of other, smaller effects. Combine those with an intense sense of euphoria and you have a substantial demand."[6]

As we sow, we reap. There is a high demand for, and black markets in, organs, blood, and adrenochrome harvested from children, and as a culture we also imprison and kill animal children for their organs, blood, and flesh, and tellingly, we are also unwittingly consuming animal adrenochrome on a massive scale as well. The animals we raise and kill by the millions daily for food are virtually all infants or children in human terms at the time of slaughter: male chicks in the egg industry are killed at one day, "veal "calves at one to 24 weeks, chickens at six weeks, turkeys at 10 to 17 weeks, goats at 12 to 20 weeks, pigs at 5 to 6 months, lambs at 4 to 12 months, and "beef" cattle and layer hens at only 18 months.[7] These animal children are stressed and producing adrenalin as they enter the kill line and smell death, with no possibility of escape, but when their body is slammed by a captive-bolt gun or they are hung upside down and stabbed, the terror and pain oxidizes the adrenalin into adrenochrome, so every steak, burger, pork roast, and piece of bacon, turkey, chicken, and perhaps fish most likely contains residues of adrenochrome, which could perhaps explain the somewhat addictive appeal of animal flesh. Anti-dog-meat activists in Korea have documented how men who buy live dogs in markets for meat deliberately kill them in a slow and painful way. This is because they experience more energy and vitality in the meat when they do so, and they attribute this to increasing the "yang energy" in the meat by torturing the dogs to death. It is also likely due to the elevated adrenochrome levels in their flesh. The fact that adrenochrome is available from human children who are forced to endure terrible suffering for profits should motivate all of us to do what we can to bring this lucrative practice to an end. To do so, though, we are called to get to the root, and understand it as the inevitable result of what we force millions of animal children to endure every day, covered up as a normal part of business-as-usual in animal agriculture.

Investigative journalist David Icke extensively documents, for historical perspective, the Sabbatean and Frankist cults that emerged in Europe several hundred years ago. They were based on turning morality upside down and guiltlessly performing the most heinous of acts. These cults apparently attracted the wealthiest and most powerful bankers, moguls, and royalty, and have been infiltrating the upper echelons of virtually all the institutions in the West, and even globally, ever since.[8]

The satanic ceremonies and sadistic debauchery engaged in by members of the globalist plutocrats in their secret societies[9] are simply based on doing to humans what we have been doing routinely to animals for the past ten thousand years. It is essential that we mature enough to open our eyes, and recognize and make these connections. As we sow, we reap, and what we do to animals we always end up doing to each other. People who sexually and physically abuse children at gatherings and rituals form bonds with each other, and with hidden videotaping, they are easily blackmailable, which makes them well-suited for high-level positions in government, media, and business.[10] They can be completely controlled by their superiors, and while they may get their worldly riches and glamor, it is a Faustian bargain. When we harm others, we always harm ourselves, but because we live in a society based on herderism, in which virtually all of us have made the same Faustian bargain through our daily meals, we project and co-create psychopathic tyrannical rulers because we behave similarly in relation to the animals whom we eat, and by proxy, sexually abuse and kill.

For us, the people, to merit living in societies of freedom, equality, justice, and health, with honorable leaders who serve with wisdom and integrity, we are called, as individuals, to do the inner work necessary to cultivate these qualities in ourselves, not just from the point of view of other humans, but also from the perspective of the unprotected and vulnerable, such as cows, chickens, fishes, ecosystems, and future generations. This addresses the root of our problems, and can heal the wounds imposed on us by the herding culture's conditioning.

No leader can rescue us if we don't make this basic change. If we fail to perform our due diligence and stir ourselves out of indifference, we will continue to manifest the tyrannically abusive leaders that our actions warrant. The world is, ultimately, a mirror, and learning is an essential purpose behind it all. This Earth school, with its notorious challenges, has remarkable potentials as well.

Retrieving Veganism

It is essential that we see through the materialist subterfuge of the globalist agenda and not allow our efforts for the liberation of animals and humans to be hijacked by these forces. Our moral compass is the spiritual truth of ahimsa and of The Golden Rule, and when we compromise our ethics and promote plant-based foods that are highly-processed and harmful to ecosystems and to human health, we are not only becoming a force for abusing and killing the free-living animals known as wildlife, but also sabotaging and exploiting our fellow humans. In addition, we are setting our movement up to be vilified by the very people who are potential allies. Many non-vegans are rightfully concerned about the devastating impact that genetically-engineered, pesticide-laden foods and products have on ecosystems and on our health, and are also working hard to defend our dignity and sovereignty. During the Covid so-called pandemic, the vegan movement distinguished itself by being notoriously willing to co-operate with, and serve as agents for, the criminally tyrannical and dehumanizing public health directives and narratives, instead of refusing to comply with them in order to defend our essential rights and sovereignty, which are the foundations of our movement. Without freedom of speech, assembly, religion, and of bodily autonomy, we are mere livestock who can never defend ourselves or our loved ones from abuse, much less defend cows, pigs, fishes, and other vulnerable creatures.

As vegans, especially new vegans, we may often suffer from a feeling of isolation because of our refusal to eat the foods that friends and family are eating. This puts us in a small minority that isn't fully accepted into the mainstream tribe because meals are essential to social bonding. Ironically, most members of the mainstream tribe also feel isolated. Belgian social psychologist Mattias Desmet explains in *The Psychology of Totalitarianism* that in the years leading up to 2020, most societies in the world were experiencing what he considers the four main conditions that are prerequisite to what he refers to as a "mass formation"—a society-wide collective hypnosis—that opens the door to allowing totalitarian oppression. These four conditions are: 1) a sense of isolation and lack of social bonds; 2) a sense of life as meaningless; 3) a sense of free-floating anxiety; and 4) a resultant sense of free-floating frustration and aggression.

It appears that Desmet's four conditions that predispose a society to a totalitarian takeover—isolation, meaninglessness, anxiety, and frustration—are generated by the kinds of pervasive digital technologies, social media, and cultural fragmentation that have been imposed on all of us by corporate and governmental forces over the past several decades. All of it naturally thrives within the larger context of herderism. According to Desmet, this psychologically painful situation was increasing in the years leading up to 2020, and so it was relatively easy for the globalist cabal to launch a false-flag pandemic in which about two-thirds of the population would be hypnotized through the resulting mass formation, crystallized around the fabricated arrival of a deadly new enemy, the virus.

This so-called emergency was powerfully addictive psychologically because it substantially reduced all four conditions. With the emergent pandemic, we suddenly had a common enemy, giving us a new sense of meaning and social bonding with each other, and a target for our anxiety and frustration. Mask-wearing, social distancing, and locking down, while dehumanizing and destructive of social health and cohesion, could be paradoxically bonding for those participating, and were deliberately designed to be so, as scientists proclaimed: "Ritual and solidarity are important in human societies and can combine with visible signals to shape new societal behaviors. Universal mask wearing could serve as a visible signal ... and symbol of altruism and solidarity."[11] The pandemic became an integral part of the scientistic religion, adding new sacraments and requiring the faithful to sacrifice significantly "for the greater good."

As a social psychologist, Desmet links this to prior, similar totalitarian events. He emphasizes how important it is for the one-third of the people who are not hypnotized and deceived by the fear-based psychological warfare to continually make an effort to publicly resist the behaviors required by the cultural trance, and to refuse to comply, and to doggedly point out the logical fallacies involved, as well as the loss of important freedoms. Even though people in a trance are virtually immune to logic and rationality, it is the undeniable existence of others who visibly refuse to participate, and who articulate their refusal, that is the main factor that will eventually help to break and dissolve the debilitating cultural spell.

This is also what we have been seeing regarding the cultural trance involved in eating the flesh and secretions of imprisoned animals. Even though it is anti-rational to do so, and causes disease, environmental devastation, and enormous cruelty and abuse to animals, workers, hungry people and the general population, it is the very presence of thriving and happy vegans who publicly refuse to participate in the cultural trance that is the greatest factor in helping to erode its power. With the pandemic, many vegans, due perhaps to their sense of isolation and their still unquestioned loyalty to the scientistic narrative, fell victim to the mass formation, and perhaps found a comforting new sense of bonding with the general population over the virus enemy that was being projected through the mainstream media. They often used the viral bogeyman to try to promote veganism by blaming the pandemic on wet markets, until that became completely untenable with the realization that the U.S. government had been surreptitiously conducting and funding corona virus gain-of-function research both in the U.S. as well as at the Wuhan Institute of Virology and elsewhere for many years prior.[12]

Although the vegan and animal liberation movements have been infiltrated, compromised, and weakened by the plutocratic ruling class's underhanded initiatives, and many have been deceived by the ongoing barrage of fear and lies, there are also remarkable new opportunities, such as forging alliances with the vital and rapidly growing freedom movements. The fraudulent medical and climate crises provide wake-up calls that can inspire us to purify our motivation and understanding, reconnect with our spiritual roots, and propel our efforts for animal and human liberation forward by raising the vibration of our awareness so that we are no longer susceptible to debilitating fears and deceit.

The Viral Hoax

Going further, many credible scientists and researchers, including Dr. Michael Yeadon, former vice-president of Pfizer, question whether respiratory viruses even exist,[13] and state their belief that there never was a deadly virus, just a global criminal fraud.[14] As a long-time high-level pharmaceutical scientist and executive, Dr. Yeadon was shocked by the Covid pandemic response's anti-scientific protocols, and the injections that followed, and spoke out boldly against them, saying this, for example, at a Trafalgar Square rally in May of 2023:

They lied about the entire pandemic. Now I started in 2020 be-lieving the virus transmitted respiratory disease from one person to another. I no longer believe that....

There was no pandemic. The deaths start only after the WHO declared a pandemic. The deaths occurred, I believe, due to mis-treatment in hospital, with ventilators and Remdesivir. I'm a pulmonary guy with over 40 years training. You never ventilate a person who is able to breathe for themselves through an unob-structed airway with an intact chest wall. All of you doctors, who sedated and ventilated patients, you're guilty of murder....

There was never any virus. PCR test is the only evidence that was ever given you, and it is wrong. And I told you early on and many others told you, you cannot use that test. The inventor even told us, you can't use that test for clinical diagnosis....

When I looked at the design of these alleged vaccines, I saw a deliberate intent to injure, to maim, and to kill.... I'm telling you that mRNA-based products can only produce injury, and that was the designed intent of these materials!

They are building factories around the world that will pro-duce materials that will injure, maim and kill people who take them.... It had nothing to do with protecting against a virus! They're trying to get poisonous materials into every one of you, and they won't stop! Even pregnant women, who have never, since Thalidomide, been exposed to experimental medical thera-pies. They wanted this in everybody! This is a murderous attack on humanity. It starts above the level of nation.[15]

Through the use of fraudulent PCR testing, which could reliably generate false positives, as well as massive media disinformation and complete control of the medical facilities and death reports, people were deceived so they could be stampeded into receiving gene-alter-ing injections. As distinguished jurist Reiner Fuellmich put it, "The vaccines were not created for the pandemic; the pandemic was cre-ated for the vaccines."[16] He and many others pointed out that the Covid injection manufacturers knew that the injections would not be effective, and would cause harm through antibody-dependent-enhancement, engineered RNA and DNA fragments, spike proteins, lipid nanoparticles, graphene oxide, propylene glycol, and other factors, and cause a variety of serious harms, as has been seen. They knew this through both their animal trials and their pre-clinical trials, and they attempted to have this evidence legally suppressed for 75 years, and demanded complete legal immunity for their injections from all nation-states. Non-vaccine alternative treatments were not to be allowed, and even respected and successful remedies had to be strictly banned. The grotesquely obvious deception that was perpetrated on a global scale with remarkable success highlights the unprecedented level of gullibility and fear attained by our human population. The Covid pandemic was clearly a significant step in the globalist agenda to depopulate and weaken humanity, and roll out a system of tracking every human via digital medical passports, high-tech surveillance, a central bank digital currency, and the emergent Internet of Things and the Internet of Bodies.

These are the ideas enthusiastically discussed by the World Economic Forum and other plutocrat organizations, trumpeted as the Fourth Industrial Revolution, which is the forced merging of biological selves with digital selves into easily controllable trans-humans, with society managed no longer by elected representatives but by technocrats and bureaucrats using artificial intelligence. Though globalists use comforting words and phrases like sustainable development, cooperation, justice, togetherness, green, diversity, equity, and inclusion, and so forth, it is essential that we actually read their plans, as set forth, for example, in the United Nations Agenda 2021 and Agenda 2030 reports.[17] The actions they are proposing would reduce humanity to managed commodity units imprisoned in a global digital panopticon, similar to the kind of future that we currently impose on billions of cows and other animals.

Dr. Yeadon has pointed out that, "the entire Covid-19 pandemic episode was and continues to be an unprecedented PsyOp upon the peoples of the world," and that it attempts to usher in a technological totalitarian tyranny. He has emphasized that Aldous Huxley feared that, unlike military or religious tyrannies, "technological tyrannies have no natural ending," and "if established, they would indefinitely become ever stronger, because they do not depend in any way for their maintenance upon the loyalty, belief or concerted actions of their supporters."[18] This is eerily similar to the technological tyranny we have imposed on cows, sheep, pigs, and other animals for ten thousand years. Our tyranny over these animals, through our evolving technology, has become ever more widespread, abusive, and inescapable for them, and we can now see that we are constructing such a tyrannical power through artificial intelligence and transhumanism. It is potentially as mighty and invincible compared to us humans, as we are compared to chickens and pigs. If it also reflects our dearth of empathy for those being oppressed, we should be deeply concerned for our children's future.

Breaking the Spell of Climate Change

The two main opposing forces to the globalist agenda of total control by the few over the many are deep veganism and spirituality. The spirit of deep veganism—which is kindness toward all living beings, and respect for their sovereignty—is also the fruit of authentic spirituality, and so it is essential to understand that deep veganism and spirituality, while seeming to be separate, are two mutually reinforcing aspects of our true nature. The globalist agenda of exploitation of animals, ecosystems, and humans can only be thwarted, ultimately, by humanity rising to a higher level of awareness and perception, where we more fully understand that what we are, and what animals are, are sovereign, sentient, and sacred expressions of consciousness, with purposes to fulfill and who are inherently worthy of respect. As we rise in awareness, we can connect ever more surely with our indwelling intuitive wisdom, which guides us into deeper and clearer perception, and frees us from vulnerability to deceptive fear-based narratives.

One of the first major hoaxes we question is that of enslaving and harming animals for food and other products and a seemingly never-ending myriad of uses. Recognizing them as beings, we naturally question and reject official food and use narratives and rationalizations. With further research and spiritual cultivation, we free ourselves from deception by other hoaxes also, for example, as we have discussed, the pharmaceutical/medical frauds that make and keep so many of us sick, confused, and afraid, such as the germ theory. We begin to free ourselves from the financial, economic, political, and educational scams that enslave us financially, politically, intellectually, and psychologically by deceiving us about the nature of banking and other economic and political systems, and by misleading us regarding history, nature, and reality, and what our human purposes are.

There is no end to the deceptions in which we are immersed, quite literally. Although it goes far beyond the CIA, it is helpful to remember what William Casey, then director of the CIA, said in 1981 at a staff meeting in the White House, "We'll know our disinformation program is complete when everything the American public believes is false."[19] Forty years later, it seems that their program is pretty close to complete. Virtually all narratives that are promoted by the globalist-controlled media, education, government, and internet information systems are harmful and deceptive, even those that we may embrace because they seem to support the causes we hold dear, such as the promotion of lab-grown meat and highly-processed plant-based "foods," as discussed earlier, and also of anthropogenic global warming, now morphed into the climate crisis, among many others.

It is essential that we challenge the ongoing fraud of anthropogenic climate change, which attempts to demonize carbon, the vital foundation of life on Earth, with a contrived "net zero emissions" goal that propagandizes us into the faith-based creed that human-sourced carbon dioxide and other "greenhouse gases" are causing something that should make us all very afraid: climate change. The more the mainstream media and the United Nations,

World Economic Forum, King Charles, the Gates and Rockefeller Foundations, and other plutocrat fronts vociferously proclaim a global emergency and "scientific consensus," and demand anyone questioning it be censored and deplatformed, the more obvious it is a grand and dangerous deceit. The agenda is to consolidate more power, and centralize control of the many into the hands of a few. Why don't they expound about the much more valid and empowering truth that there is simply no industry as destructive to our environment as animal agriculture? Yet we are all compelled to narrow the environmental benefits of vegan living to a one-dimensional caricature, the hypothesized bogey-man called climate change, and ignore animal agriculture's relentless and widespread attack on ecosystems through its massive and ongoing deforestation, aquifer depletion, soil erosion, ocean devastation, chemical pollution, habitat destruction, and species extinction.

Our society is harming the Earth's ecology in a myriad of ways, but the plutocrats manipulate media and governmental narratives to discount and ignore all this, and cunningly hammer away on only one small and dubious dimension: anthropogenic climate change. Why do we allow this? They are attempting to distract attention from the devastating environmental impacts of the meat-chemical-medical cartel, and deceive us into focusing all our attention on something which they can manipulate to their advantage as a fabricated pretext to further consolidate their power, as well as to lock down populations and destroy basic freedoms. The carbon credit system, for example, created to supposedly help reduce climate change, can easily be manipulated by wealthy corporations and governments to further oppress less affluent and industrialized countries, and mitigation mandates can be used to impose travel and food restrictions on the general population. Anomalies in the weather, now attributed to anthropogenic climate change from so-called greenhouse gases, are more likely the result of other factors, and we'll look at three of the primary ones.

First Factor: Deforestation

The impact of deforestation is well recognized, caused primarily by animal agriculture. The Amazon rainforest, the largest in the world, continues to be unsustainably ravaged since the 1980s by both the ranching industry and the livestock feed industry, cutting and burning forests to graze cattle and to grow genetically-engineered soybeans for feed for cows, pigs, chickens, and factory-farmed fish operations, mainly for export.[20] It is well understood that forests hold water, and deforestation causes flooding.[21] Forests also cool local and regional climates, driving moisture and cooler weather to continental interiors.[22] The trees in forests and rainforests are essential to healthy weather and hydrology because their evapotranspiration creates clouds, which produce precipitation, and destroying them causes droughts, which weaken trees and cause further deforestation in a negative feedback loop.[23]

> Every tree in the forest is a fountain, sucking water out of the ground through its roots and releasing water vapor into the atmosphere through pores in its foliage. In their billions, they create giant rivers of water in the air – rivers that form clouds and create rainfall hundreds or even thousands of miles away.[24]

Massive deforestation is caused primarily by animal agriculture, and secondarily by palm-oil plantations, urbanization, and, ironically, "green energy," such as clearing forests for large-scale wind turbine, solar panel, and biomass installations.[25] This is well understood to be negatively affecting weather patterns, contributing to excessive heat, floods, and droughts. Our war against forests is not only driving an ongoing mass extinction of species by destroying vital habitat. It also reduces the level of oxygen in the atmosphere,[26] which reduces the vitality of all animals, because our health depends on cellular aerobic processes that require abundant oxygen. The forests are the lungs of the Earth, as are the oceans, and our ocean overfishing and pollution is also reducing oxygen levels in the atmosphere.

Second Factor: Psychological Manipulation

The second factor contributing to weather anomalies is perception management. Besides the ongoing deforestation, pollution, aquifer depletion, soil erosion, and other environmentally destructive factors affecting weather, there are deliberate efforts being made to journalistically and psychologically manipulate us. Anthropogenic climate change is first and foremost a carefully-planned and contrived pretext. It is a psychological operation that is intended to continually escalate fear in our perceptions, so we can be more easily dominated and exploited by the plutocrats controlling government, science, education, and media. From the beginning, the narrative of global warming has been based on deceiving the world population into believing we have a horrible crisis, similar to the fraudulent Covid pandemic where many people were deceived into believing there was a disastrously deadly disease in order to further an agenda of control. Again, we are called to distinguish between ropes and snakes. With media domination, censorship of scientists and journalists, and theatrics, the globalist ruling cabal has learned to fabricate emergencies that can be manipulated to push the conditioned population in desired directions.

Science is easily bought and manipulated. Through their controlled organizations such as the Club of Rome, the United Nations, and the World Economic Forum, as well as academia and the media, plutocrats can effectively create a panic-producing pretext, and reliably enroll scientists, journalists, and technocrats, who are dependent on them for funding, to create and broadcast a complete deception. The initial seeds were planted by the Rockefeller-founded Club of Rome, the Rockefeller-funded United Nations, and their joint climate and environment summit in Rio de Janeiro in 1992. Then Al Gore was rewarded with the leading role of launching the great carbon scare in 2006 with his dramatic and frightening predictions of wholesale destruction caused by global warming, and scientists and journalists who questioned any of it were censored, ridiculed, and marginalized. However, three years later, in 2009, a large cache of emails from

Britain's East Anglia University Climate Research Unit was released by a whistleblower. This erupted into Climategate, "the worst scientific scandal of our generation,"[27] plainly revealing that the scientists at the very top of the U.N.'s Intergovernmental Panel on Climate Change (IPCC), the main driving force behind the climate-change narrative globally, had "for years been discussing devious tactics whereby they could avoid releasing their data to outsiders under freedom of information laws."[28]

This complete lack of transparency was similarly repeated later by the CDC, FDA, and the WHO in the Covid pretext. The media, as with Covid, immediately covered everything up, and people who questioned it were disciplined. For example, Dr. Judith Curry, chair of the School of Earth and Atmospheric Sciences at the Georgia Institute of Technology, said that, "After Climategate, I realized I had fallen into groupthink,"[29] and went from being part of the well-paid climate establishment to being a dissenter, and within two years was compelled to resign from academia as "unhireable."

In 2011, another batch of emails from the Climate Research Unit was leaked, with Climategate 2.0 revealing even more damning evidence that prominent scientists central to the climate change debate were writing each other about the importance of concealing data, viewing climate change as a political cause, and frankly admitting to each other that their science was weak and dependent on manipulation of data.[30] Again, the media and IPCC covered this up because the global warming narrative could not be allowed to be questioned. It was too important a lever for instilling fear, and along similar lines, the WHO, in its "International Guidelines for Certification and Classification of Covid-19 as Cause of Death," directed hospitals and doctors to code deaths as due to Covid, even without the virus being present.[31] The goal of the Covid pretext, like the global warming pretext, was to maximize our perception of a deadly threat to induce panic in order to facilitate the domination of the many by the few. Control of media and science narratives are crucial keys, as Melissa Fleming, Under-Secretary-General for Global Communications at the United Nations expressed in a 2022 WEF panel on *Tackling Disinformation*: "We own the science, and we think that the world should know it."[32] She detailed the U.N.'s ambitious program of partnering with Google, TikTok, the Gates Foundation, and "influencers with huge followings," to monopolize control over every aspect of humanity's perceptions of the U.N.'s two primary propaganda efforts: vaccination and climate change.

We are being psychologically and physically manipulated in nefarious ways that are both concealed and obvious. Lies are repeated so often by media and government "experts" that they become accepted truths, and it is serious heresy to question them. The media loves emergencies and crises because, as is well-known for decades, reporting on them increases readership, profits, and trust. Also, extreme weather events have always been with us, and there have been many in the past that we conveniently forget about now. As but one of many examples, the New York Herald's front-page headline screamed in November of 1921, "Death for Millions in Heat Wave," and there is a photo of beautiful Lake Murten in Switzerland, where I have swum, completely dried up by the scorching heat.[33]

Though weather anomalies are not unusual, now there is an agenda, and clever narrative control deliberately exaggerates them, and manipulates how we perceive and interpret them. Additionally, far more temperature-recording stations exist now than ever before, and whereas in the past they were mainly located in rural locations, now they are in hotter, asphalt-covered urban areas, and so the "rising temperatures" are also to some degree data-collection relics that narrative managers conveniently employ to boost fear. There is also deliberate mendacity, such as weather agencies and mainstream media substituting much hotter surface-level temperatures for the normally-used two-meter-level temperatures, to deceptively exaggerate heat levels.[34, 35] Climatologist John Christy sums it well, "There are groups in the world, the political elite, that like to have a narrative that scares people so that they can then offer a solution."[36]

Authentic climate scientists understand that climate is an exceedingly complex subject that is poorly understood, and that there are countless interconnecting factors that affect it, especially the sun, whose energy output changes in a variety of ways, and is far beyond our current capacities of understanding.[37] John Clauser, Nobel laureate in physics, points out that human greenhouse gas output is negligible compared with the power of Earth's cloud cover, covering two-thirds of the planet, which acts as a planetary thermostat, reliably regulating temperatures.[38]

> As viewed in visible light from space by the Sun, bright white clouds variably cover from one-third to two-thirds of the Earth's surface. These clouds, in turn, reflect about 90% of the sunlight incident on them back out into space. Sunlight that reaches the Earth's surface in the cloudless area, two-thirds of which is covered by oceans, is absorbed and evaporates seawater, in turn, producing cumulus clouds. It produces clouds at an increasingly abundant rate when the cloud-cover fraction is too small and the temperature is too high and vice versa when the fraction is too large. The resulting cloud-cover-fraction's feedback-controlled variability then provides a very powerful input-power thermostat that stabilizes the Earth-surface's heat input and its temperature. Changes in the radiative heat transfer rate (known as radiative forcing) associated with changes in atmospheric carbon dioxide is nearly two orders of magnitude smaller than the effective stabilization of the input-power provided by the cloud-based thermostat. *The role of carbon dioxide may thus be considered negligible by comparison.* It should be noted that reports of the Intergovernmental Panel on Climate Change and National Academy of Sciences repeatedly concede that the effects of clouds do indeed represent the greatest uncertainty in their climate predictions. But these organizations have made little progress in dealing with these deficiencies.[39] (Italics added)

Even though these and other factors are vastly more influential in determining climate here than anything we are doing, this is ignored by the narrative controllers.[40] Clauser sums up the situation well:

The popular narrative about climate change reflects a dangerous corruption of science that threatens the world's economy and the well-being of billions of people. Misguided climate science has metastasized into massive shock-journalistic pseudoscience. In turn, the pseudoscience has become a scapegoat for a wide variety of other unrelated ills. It has been promoted and extended by similarly misguided business marketing agents, politicians, journalists, government agencies, and environmentalists. In my opinion, there is no real climate crisis.[41]

For example, while feeding fear by trumpeting that "the era of global boiling has arrived,"[42] the U.N. and mainstream media simultaneously ignored what many researchers consider to be a significant anomalous contributing factor to temporary increased global temperatures. In January, 2022, the Hunga Tonga-Hunga-Ha'api volcano, with a summit 490 feet beneath the surface of the Pacific Ocean, erupted and according to NASA, "blasted an unprecedented amount of water into the stratosphere,"[43] approximately 150,000 metric tons of vaporized ocean water.[44] Water vapor is the primary "greenhouse gas" in the atmosphere, naturally regulating temperatures, and this volcano suddenly created, according to researchers a year later, an "unprecedented increase in the global stratospheric water mass by 13%."[45] Though researchers estimated this would be significantly "contributing to an increase in global warming over the next 5 years,"[46] discussion of the predictable effects of this unusually massive underwater eruption were suppressed in media and government narratives for the obvious reason that the global warming pretext is predicated upon human activity as the cause of the crisis. Only this could be used to instill panic and justify policies designed to erode freedom and fortify the globalist position. Saul Alinsky verbalized the basic principle, and Rahm Emanuel popularized it: "Never let a crisis go to waste."

Third Factor: Weather Modification Operations

The third primary factor causing weather anomalies is the ongoing deployment of weather modification operations, defined by the U.S. military as: "Any activity performed with the intention of producing artificial changes in the composition, behavior, or dynamics of the atmosphere."[47] By April 2010, there were over 150 different weather modification programs worldwide, with the number increasing annually.[48] Geoengineering operations, which are part of this weather modification carried out by the Department of Defense and the Department of Energy, have been obviously visible as the appearance of lingering and expanding white airplane trails in the sky over the past two decades. Geoengineering is well-recognized to be a program of spraying toxic particulates, including aerosolized barium, strontium, and nano-aluminum, facilitating this weather modification.[49]

Often called "chemtrails," and known officially as stratospheric aerosol injection as well as solar radiation management, geoengineering is deployed by military planes to block sunlight to supposedly fight global warming.[50] However, as investigative journalist Dane Wigington and others have been pointing out for many years, it is also used in conjunction with ionospheric heater technologies that are both land-based, such as HAARP, as well as on ships and military vessels,[51] that can super-heat specific areas of the upper atmosphere, causing deliberate and precise weather interventions.[52] This capacity to surreptitiously generate, for example, artificial high pressure areas that become large heat domes, creating unusually extreme heat waves, and other weather anomalies, is one of the main ruses propping up the climate change narrative.[53]

These technologies have been developing for decades for use in weather modification and weather warfare operations both domestically and internationally in order to change weather fronts and to produce droughts, floods, wildfires, hurricanes, hail storms, whiplash temperature swings, "snow" in above-freezing temperatures, and other unusual and extreme weather events. They can be effective in harming enemy nations, and used domestically as well, to create chaos, change crop yields, and manipulate commodities and real estate markets, and everything can be conveniently blamed on climate change. Weather modification technologies have been officially recognized for at least several decades.[54] Lyndon Johnson, then Vice-President of the U.S., summed the military's strategy to prioritize and develop weather warfare technologies in a speech back in 1962, boldly asserting that, "He who controls the weather will control the world."[55] Geoengineering operations, under the guise of solar radiation management, spraying millions of tons of chemicals and aerosolized metals into the sky, and used in conjunction with ionospheric heaters, can be used to raise temperatures to create panic, and if desired, to spread toxins to weaken and cull the population.[56]

Geoengineering tends to be unrecognized because few people ever look up and notice the sky, and it has been assiduously ignored (but is no longer denied) by scientific, media, and government authorities. In fact, Harvard, Oxford, Carnegie-Mellon, and other universities now offer doctoral degrees in geoengineering.[57] Nevertheless, it is part of an ongoing and deliberately ignored manipulation of weather, and harms ecosystems, wildlife, and human health.[58] Science is routinely used and interpreted in ways that serve the interests of funders of research, to influence both the weather and the explanatory stories. Andrew Montfort's *The Hockey Stick Illusion*, as but one example, clearly demonstrates how the climate narrative, like the pandemic narrative and the food narrative, is promoted by wealthy interests who determine which scientists' research is funded, whether it is accepted for publication, and to what degree it is publicized in the media.

Climate Consensus Canards

Though taken in by the carbon-blaming climate crisis narrative for several years following the epic sensationalizing efforts of Al Gore, the IPCC, and mainstream media outlets, I discovered, with more research, the telltale signs of massive and systematic censorship of many climate scientists who disagreed with the approved narrative. It became clear to me that this kind of censorship of research and information is only engaged in by the deceptive usual subjects with their centralization of power agenda. I had seen the same thing for decades with the food industry, and the similar corruption of science by the dairy, meat, and egg industries, and by the tobacco industry before that.

Al Gore's predictions in his 2006 *An Inconvenient Truth*—for example, that the Arctic Ocean would be ice-free by 2017, that temperatures would rise significantly due to so-called greenhouse gases, that the snows of Kilimanjaro would be melted away,[59] that the Earth would be in a "True Planetary Emergency" within a decade, with Miami and other coastal cities inundated by rising sea levels—are now well recognized to be wildly inaccurate (and in fact Gore and Obama have now even bought ocean-front mansions).[60] And yet these politicians and the plutocrats they serve continue to double down on the fear-based climate agenda of control. It is not allowed to be questioned, and so governmental, media, and even academic experts ignore reality, and keep the hysteria alive by simply modifying the narrative, and now instead of anthropogenic global warming, it's anthropogenic climate change. The ongoing weather warfare operations and media spin make the deceptive story plausible to us in the general population. We are being groomed to have our freedoms and health continually eroded. By creating fear through a fake virus emergency, the cabal seized more power and wealth, and inflicted terrible damage with coerced and harmful injections. There are a number of potentially similar engineered emergencies—viral pandemic, climate change, cyber-attack, food shortage, banking collapse, economic catastrophe: the possibilities are multitudinous—for which they will provide us all with "*the* solution" which forces us to sacrifice truth, and with it, freedom, health, and meaning.

It has become increasingly obvious that many, especially on the so-called left, tend to indiscriminately and unwisely trust media-created "settled science" narratives and government authorities, refusing to recognize that these authorities have been captured by the globalist plutocracy. The vegan movement has unfortunately been similarly deceived into promoting the globalist agenda because the climate change narrative is tempting to use, similar to the wet market narrative. We tend to repeat official narratives that support our agenda, dutifully trusting the so-called scientists who tell us what we like to hear. We like to exploit the human-caused climate change narrative to try to convince people to go vegan, because we can promote the story that eating animal foods has a larger carbon footprint than eating plant-sourced foods, and contributes to climate change. Yet it has become increasingly clear that the entire climate emergency idea is basically fraudulent, as over 1,900 respected climate scientists and professionals from Global Climate Intelligence Group have stated,[61] and is simply being used as a pretext by the plutocrats to instill fear, manipulate and exploit smaller farmers and appropriate their land, and impose lockdowns, economic sanctions, and travel restrictions. It is unethical to make use of falsehoods to promote something true, even if it is something as advantageous as animal liberation. This is especially true when the falsehoods we are spreading increase the power of the very forces bent on destroying our freedom and our ability to effectively work for animal liberation and positive social change.

The idea of a "consensus" of climate scientists has been ludicrous from the beginning, especially given the pervasive tactic of censoring and canceling dissenting scientists. The original claim in 2013, which still gets repeated, that 97 percent of scientists believe in anthropogenic climate change, has been unequivocally debunked as a "total fabrication,"[62] with the actual percentage being a tiny fraction of that. The consensus falsehoods, dutifully repeated by obedient media and politicians, reveal the corruption, and as Dr. Michael Chrichton emphasizes, "There is no such thing as consensus science. If it's consensus, it isn't science. If it's science, it isn't consensus. Historically, the claim of consensus has been the first refuge of scoundrels; it is a way to avoid debate by claiming that the matter is already settled."[63] In addition, the whole idea of turning carbon dioxide into a villain is nonsensical, because it is the precious foundation of life on Earth. Nitrogen is 78 percent of our atmosphere, oxygen 21 percent, argon is 0.7 percent, and water vapor is 95% of the remaining 0.3 percent, with carbon dioxide being only 0.04 percent, about 400 parts per million, and yet without this tiny bit of carbon in our atmosphere, there would be no trees, plants, or animals at all. Virtually all the biomass of forests and plants is built by atmospheric carbon dioxide through photosynthesis.

Greenhouse operators routinely enrich the air with carbon dioxide which significantly boosts the health and vitality of their plants. This increased vitality increases their output of oxygen, which enhances our health and the health of all animals, because oxygenating our cells increases vitality. It is well understood from ice core samples that in previous epochs, the Earth's carbon dioxide was much higher, for example about 800 ppm during the Jurassic and 1600 ppm during the Triassic, with no global warming or disastrous effects. This book is not the place to go deeply into a discussion of the greenhouse gas theory fraud, and there are sources in the Resources section for further information. The pattern that we see very clearly is the deliberate practice of turning things upside down. This is the essence of animal agriculture also. In our food narrative, we kill for vitality and we exploit for pleasure, and with this foundation, it goes on, to taking poisons for health, waging war for peace, censoring speech for truth, and fighting carbon dioxide and blocking the sun, both of which are the essential allies and underpinnings of life on this Earth.

The scientists and researchers from Global Climate Intelligence Group state, "Climate policy must respect scientific and economic realities. There is no climate emergency. Therefore, there is no cause for panic and alarm. We strongly oppose the harmful and unrealistic net-zero CO_2 policy proposed for 2050."[64]

CO_2 is not a pollutant. It is essential to all life on Earth. Photosynthesis is a blessing. More CO_2 is beneficial for nature, greening the Earth: additional CO_2 in the air has promoted growth in global plant biomass. It is also good for agriculture, increasing the yields of crops worldwide.[65]

Why do we allow our environmental conversations to be ruthlessly herded into the corral of climate change, which depends on esoteric climate science that has been completely politicized and corrupted and serves the globalist agenda of world domination? Animal food production can easily be shown to be environmentally devastating without resorting to the globalist catch-all carbon-footprint narrative. Animal agriculture's attack on ecosystems is relentless, massive, and exceeds any other human activity. The single most effective way to shrink our environmental footprint is to embrace an organic vegan way of living.

Further, according to Oxfam, the richest one percent of the global population causes more than twice the carbon emissions of the poorest fifty percent of the world's population,[66] so the globalist ruling class, which is definitely not vegan, obviously does not care about the importance of the carbon footprint that it unrelentingly demands we all reduce. Plutocrats regularly fly to climate conferences in their super-polluting private jets, hypocritically dictating to the world that we must all reduce our "carbon footprint." For example, they arrive in their private jets by the thousands at the World Economic Forum annual meeting in Davos, Switzerland, to repeatedly harangue all of us to reduce our "carbon footprint," and to prioritize the WEF goal to fight and minimize climate "disinformation."[67] Every year the World Economic Forum has advocated for ever more aggressive global censorship of scientists and journalists questioning the official climate narrative.

The mainstream media tells us, and we naively believe, that the powerful petroleum industry is against the climate movement because "green energy" will hurt its profits, not realizing that the globalist oligarchy that owns and controls the media also owns and controls not just all the oil companies, but all the so-called green energy companies as well, such as solar panel, windmill, and lithium battery industries, and are pushing for the transition to green energy as a way to not only increase profitability long-term, but to further appropriate land and freedom from the public. There is nothing green about green energy, either.[68] Lithium, copper, cobalt, and nickel mines for batteries are ecologically and culturally devastating, as are solar panel and windmill production, requiring enormous quantities of petroleum and massive mining operations. Forty thousand children slave in Congolese cobalt mines, as but one example, suffering extreme abuse, according to Amnesty International.[69] With each 300-foot windmill blade requiring several metric tons of lightweight and strong balsa wood, "balsa fever" ravages the Amazon rainforest and destroys indigenous peoples' habitat.[70] We are supposedly doing all this because we have to reduce carbon dioxide levels, and increasingly scientists are finding the courage to speak up, like Richard Linzen of MIT:

> Deeply flawed logic, obscured by shrewd and unrelenting propaganda, actually enabled a coalition of powerful special interests to convince nearly everyone in the world that CO_2 from human industry was a dangerous planet-destroying toxin. It will be remembered as the greatest mass delusion in the history of the world – that CO_2, the life of plants, was considered for a time to be a deadly poison.[71]

As a telling example of Voltaire's dictum that when we believe absurdities, we commit atrocities, Bill Gates and other plutocrats are investing in a scheme to clear-cut and bury 70 million acres of forest, mostly in the Western U.S., in order to combat climate change.[72] One can hardly imagine a more recklessly harmful action, especially in the mostly arid West, with trees being well understood to be vital to rain, habitat, and healthy ecosystems, and already under assault by animal agriculture's deforestation. Even climate change proponents recommend tree planting to absorb carbon dioxide (though this falsely portrays CO_2 as a pollutant). The specious reasoning behind Gates's tree-burying scheme is that these 70 million trees will either die and decay, or will be burned in fires, and in either case, they inevitably release their stored carbon into the atmosphere as "greenhouse gas."[73] So, Gates and other wealthy investors aim to convince the government to provide tax credits so they can cut down these millions of trees, and then dig enormous pits, and bury them in the Earth. They also ignore the fact that excavating soil also releases carbon.[74]

These demonic anti-life proposals arise from the similarly antilife foundation of herderism. We undermine the integrity of our efforts when we try to employ the "carbon dioxide and methane are harmful greenhouse gases" narrative in order to promote reducing meat consumption and to protect the environment. Climate science is enormously complex, and scientists can always be purchased to support clever plutocrat narratives that are designed to further enslave humanity and destroy ecosystems. The methane narrative is similar, with mainstream media claiming that cows are adding to global warming by belching methane, which is supposedly 70 times more potent as a greenhouse gas than carbon dioxide. But methane (CH4) cycles back into CO_2, which is absorbed by growing grass, trees, and plants.[75] It is similar to claiming that rain is new water, and if it keeps raining, we'll all drown. Additionally, it is bacteria that produce the methane as they help cows digest grass in their digestive tracts, and if the grass were uneaten, bacteria in nature would do the same and convert the grass into methane anyway, in its annual decomposition cycle.[76] In a similar way, the wildfire narrative is continually promoted, though it's no secret that many of fires in the ongoing rash of wildfires worldwide are being set by arsonists.[77, 78] Wildfires serve the globalist agenda to appropriate huge amounts of land,[79] and to blame the fires on climate change, which can then justify reducing our basic rights to travel, assemble, and be secure in our affairs.

Several Rockefeller family foundations, which are rooted in the petroleum industry and have extended tentacles reaching deep into the chemical, pharmaceutical, medical, banking, and media industries as well as academia, are major supporters of 360.org, Greenpeace, Oil Change International, Friends of the Earth, and other leading proponents of the fraudulent anthropogenic climate crisis narrative.[80] Journalist James Corbett writes:

> The Rockefellers, heir to an oil fortune that made the family name a symbol of American wealth, believe they're doing their namesake proud by getting out of oil [in 2016]. Fund director Stephen Heintz spoke reverently of oil tycoon John D. Rockefeller in a statement: 'We are quite convinced that if he were alive today, as an astute businessman looking out to the future, he would be moving out of fossil fuels and investing in clean, renewable energy.' It is no longer about oil. It never was. It is about control.[81]

When will our intuition and discriminating awareness kick in and empower us to avoid the temptation to credulously jump on deceptive globalist bandwagons as if they were our friends, in order to promote our cause? It is ironic that as vegans and environmentalists we allow ourselves to be fooled into promoting the agenda of the worst enemy of animals, ecosystems, and human health: the globalist plutocrats. Supporting the climate crisis agenda increasingly harms the vegan movement's credibility, weakening and dividing it. In sum, the essence of herderism is confining animals and controlling their movement, thus reducing them to livestock commodities. Similarly, the agenda of the anthropogenic climate change narrative is deceiving us into relinquishing our inherent rights to freely travel, congregate, grow our own food, and live our lives. The goal is to centralize control of the human population and confine us within continually surveilled 15-minute cities, likewise reducing us to Agenda-2030 livestock commodities. Though we live in an empire of lies, we can work together to expose deception, increase self-reliance, and embody respect for the spiritual sovereignty of animals, ecosystems, and all of humanity. We are called to be guardians of the integrity of the sacred web of life and truth.

Minimalism and Decentralization

Deep veganism as a path of both social justice and spiritual awakening is naturally allied with human justice movements, and also with the minimalist movement and the decentralization and localization movements. Minimalism is based on the age-old wisdom that joy and freedom arise from simplicity and nonviolence, including minimizing our ecological footprint. Traditionally, people who are devoted to a spiritual path become more sensitive to the impact of their consumption and use of resources. In many traditions, monks and nuns simplify their lives to better focus on internal awareness, and practice repairing, mending, and doing without, rather than purchasing. Having lived as a vegan for three years in a 1971 VW bus, and for 17 years with Madeleine in a 200 square-foot tiny house on wheels, it is clear to me that joy and freedom arise spontaneously with voluntary simplicity, and with refining the art of needing and using less. The essential ethic of vegan living is respect for others, and with time it becomes a delight to minimize our material desires in every way, and becomes increasingly painful to be involved with or witness anything that wastes and disrespects natural resources and other beings. Herderism at its core is a way of living rooted in reducing beings to objects and disrespecting and wasting them, profligately exhausting enormous quantities of land, water, and other inputs to feed animals and kill them, instead of conservatively and respectfully eating plants directly, and so it naturally breeds a mentality of consumerism, domination, and wasteful living.

Centralization of food, energy, information, coinage, land ownership, and power accords with herderism's mentality also, which is based on the strong dominating and exploiting the weak. Spirituality calls for the strong to protect and care for the weak. Animal liberation follows naturally from cultivating an attitude of spiritual sovereignty and self-reliance, and encourages growing our own food directly, cooperating with the abundance of nature, and gladly refraining from exploiting or harming animals for food or any other purpose, and respecting their need for healthy and intact habitats. In some spiritual traditions, such as Buddhism and Jainism, monastics and serious lay practitioners take vows not to own, keep, or harm any animals, and to let them live their lives free of human interference and exploitation as nature intended.

The more self-reliant we become as individuals, reducing our dependence on powerful centralized entities for our food, energy, finance, and information, the more we can create empowered and vibrant local communities that promote individual sovereignty for us and for animals. It is remarkable how much food can be grown on just a quarter-acre of land, for example, and as we learn to support ourselves from the land, and to trade and cooperate with our neighbors, we create liberated spaces of caring that can be models for more sustainable and spiritually-oriented ways of living. The primary aim of globalism and of the United Nations Agenda 30 is the centralization of energy, power, wealth, and information in the hands of a few. The more we can help to decentralize food, energy, power, wealth, and information, the more we are contributing to creating local communities that are resilient and self-reliant, and in alignment with deep vegan values of sovereignty and respect for all life. We can contribute to creating a parallel culture based on freedom, local responsibility, and decentralized autonomy.

For example, though it's only a quarter-acre, the food forest Madeleine and I have created from rocky, barren soil in northern California now, after ten years of effort, supports seventy-five fruit and nut trees and six raised vegetable beds, and provides an abundance of greens, vegetables, nuts, fruits, herbs, and berries for us, and some extra to give to our neighbors and occasionally to sell at our local farmers market. The garden becomes a haven for birds, insects, worms, and fungal and microbial networks that build soil and bring the earth to life, inviting recycling of waste water and compost, and creating a space of love that shines into the world in a multitude of ways, some visible and tangible, and some ephemeral but just as real, if not more so. Everything is interconnected, and when we grow veganically, with no chemical fertilizers, pesticides, bone meal, fish meal, manure, or other animal inputs, we build soil and fungal networks, honoring the sovereignty of all the beings in the web of life. This beautiful truth reflects nature's abundance: the more we do our best to refrain from harming others, the more joy, peace, health, and abundance we find manifesting in our lives.

We can co-create decentralized approaches to raising our own organic plant-sourced foods, establishing gardens and orchards locally, and supporting nearby farmers, and refusing to support chemical and animal-based agriculture. There are many inspiring examples of this not only in contemporary movements like Community Supported Agriculture, farmers' markets, and the Food Forest Abundance movement,[82] but also in the World War II Victory Gardens in the U.S. and U.K., and in the Dacha and Kin's Domain community movements in Russia inspired by the writings of Vladimir Megré.[83] We can become more self-sufficient and decentralized in terms of energy and water, and also in terms of education, information, and monetary exchange as well. In our many travels, we have been inspired to see increasingly prevalent examples of grass-roots activism in co-creating freedom schools for children, community gardens, and local currencies, as well as alternative energy, barter, and healthcare networks. Growing healthy, organic plant-sourced food is one of the most honorable livelihoods, and we can all work in our unique ways to heal our wounds by honoring ancient wisdom traditions that respect spiritual harmony with nature, animals, and with each other.

The Great Resist

The globalist agenda uses fear as its primary force to lower humanity's vibrational level to the point that we are willing to surrender our intellect, freedom, and sovereignty in order to be protected and secure. It is not surprising, for example, that as rates of low vibrational depression rise, increasing numbers of people are taking harmful pharmaceuticals to combat this depression, which often compounds the problem.[84] Authentic spirituality and deep vegan living raise our vibrational level and are based on kindness and respect, and on savoring and contributing to the creative exuberance of life, in order to embody healing and compassion, and to relish the beautiful adventure of fulfilling our unique mission here. We are called to rise above the ongoing flood of fear, disease, abuse, and intellectual dulling and deception that the reductionistic narrative of herderism disgorges through food, media, education, and all our cultural institutions. The globalist plutocrats harness the underlying delusions and tensions at the core of our herding culture, and channel these forces to wage psychological, medical, and physical war against humanity and human sovereignty. Our parasitic domination of animals is transposed and weaponized to become their parasitic domination of us.

Though the primary deception is fooling us into enslaving and killing animals for food, and though this is the fountain from which all the other deceptions spring, it is also essential to understand the other deceptions, if we are to keep ourselves and our movements healthy. Animal agriculture lowers our spiritual, ethical, and energetic vibration significantly so that we fall prey, for example, to the war deception, the banking deception, and many others, such as scientific and medical materialism, leading to the fear-inducing germ theory, and the relentlessly hammered idea of contagion, that we can catch a disease from someone else. Lester and Parker demonstrate in *What Really Makes You Ill?* that though we have all been indoctrinated by the medical cartel into the conviction that viruses and bacteria cause disease, and into believing that disease is transmissible, there is actually little evidence to support any of it.[85] The apparent epidemics and contagion outbreaks of history can be explained by the miserable and unsanitary living conditions resulting from urbanization, and poisoning through toxic chemicals, vaccines and medications, heavy metals, and electrical fields. According to researchers cited by Lester and Parker, so-called viruses are in actuality exosomes, harmless packets of genetic information used by all organisms for millions of years to helpfully communicate with each other, and bacteria work primarily benignly, cleaning up decaying and poisoned cells and do not cause harm, except in certain cases where their waste products can be excessive, but the bacteria are not the underlying cause of disease. As a child I was conditioned to believe in contagion by the adults around me, and the "cooties" games we would play, but the new method of forcing children to wear face masks takes the nefarious germ theory indoctrination to a much more sinister and visceral level. As long as we fail to question the medical propaganda, we will be easy prey for the next pandemic narrative, which is surely coming. We humans are more telepathic than we realize, and both our fear and our joy are contagious, which is why it is essential that we cultivate our awareness so that we are positively contagious, benefitting others by radiating inner peace, confidence, and lovingkindness.

Some of the other deceptions that imprison us in delusion are the absurd and purpose-crushing "life is just the result of a big bang and random occurrences" doctrine; and all the other delusional dogmas of scientism that facilitate medical-pharmaceutical exploitation and reduce animals, humans, and life itself to mechanistic meaninglessness, with the goal being to break our spirits, just as we do to animals. Further significant falsehoods relevant to our current plight include the eugenics-inspired population crisis, the pandemic and vaccination pretexts, the climate-change fraud, and the trans-sexual and trans-humanist "technology can save us" hoax. This latter includes lab-grown meat, genetic engineering, artificial intelligence, microchip implants, SMART technologies, and virtually all the "woke" narratives promoted in mainstream media.

The basic technique is to surreptitiously weaponize our good intentions against us, while posing as our benefactors. For example, our healthy yearning for justice can be weaponized to deceive us into endorsing political persecutions and war, our desire for health and security weaponized into promoting harmful lock-downs and injections, our aspiration for truth weaponized into advocating fraudulent fact-checkers and censorship, and so forth. If we unquestioningly internalize official narratives and undergo Milgram's agentic shift that overrides our inherent compassion and self-reliance, we may well become authoritarian agents who police and persecute colleagues and neighbors.

Once we are able to make the connections, see the patterns, and unlearn what we've previously learned, however, our innate intelligence awakens, freeing us from gullibility and providing helpful immunity from being tricked and coerced by these techniques. A reasonably accurate gauge is simple: any narrative being consistently promoted by NPR, the BBC, Reuters, CNN, CBC, Fox, The New York Times, The Atlantic, the United Nations, the World Economic Forum, the World Health Organization, and other mainstream outlets and institutions is almost certainly a dangerous deception. Conversely, what is ignored by media outlets is hidden on purpose and is worth researching, such as the damaging effects of 5G and other EMF radiation, of geoengineering chemtrails, of vaccines and other pharmaceuticals, of fluoride and other toxins delivered through our drinking water, of forced mask-wearing, of chemical residues in food, clothing, and household and personal care products. Correspondingly, mainstream media also downplays the many benefits of sunshine, gardening, fresh air, earthing,[86] whole and organic vegan foods, meditation and other spiritual practices, and spiritual healing.

While mainstream legacy media outlets, together with social media and Big Tech digital platforms, are still capable of deceiving many of us, we are increasingly recognizing that what is destructive and evil usually doesn't look "evil," but is presented as caring, benevolent, trustworthy, and science-based, and draws us in with promises of safety and respectability, with an underlying justification that the ends justify the means. If we are succeeding in our inner work, we will not be easily drawn in by these deceptive pretexts because our vibratory frequency will not respond to appeals based on security, and which require us to surrender our autonomy and our ethical principles. As we develop our ability to see behind the deceptive masks, we can question who is actually benefitting from these ends-justify-the-means narratives and fabricated pretexts. We will be guided by an inner moral compass instead of by authoritarian fear-based narratives.

It is time for all of us who are making efforts to support animal liberation, health freedom, and environmental sustainability, peace, and justice to deepen our inner work so that we are no longer led astray by the siren appeals of the globalist deceivers. Instead, we can connect more authentically with our intuitive wisdom, find our common ground, and work together to co-create parallel social structures that embody the positive future that is both possible and beckoning. Liberating animals, we can authentically and confidently reclaim our freedom. Doing our best to fulfill the Golden Rule in all our relations, we become exponents of the benevolent revolution that is based not on developing more sophisticated and complex outer gadgetry, but on aligning our consciousness with the spiritual truth that one life lives through us all. Buckminster Fuller presciently emphasized that the most effective way forward lies not in fighting institutions that are corrupt and abusive, but instead, in creating healthy and empowering alternatives that parallel the existing ones, eventually rendering them obsolete and replacing them.

Hells, created through self-centered delusion and amplified by materialist science, can transform into paradises of abundance and lovingkindness. Instead of large and small vortices of imprisoned, diseased, exploited animals, leading inevitably to centralized tyranny and the same fate for us, we can create gardens, orchards, and food forests of health, abundance, and decentralized autonomy. Each one of us, individually, is capable of significantly contributing to the awakening of human consciousness. Reclaiming our sovereignty, integrity, and creativity, we can help rescue animals, nature, and our culture. We give thanks that we still have the freedom and healthy sense of urgency that enable us to contribute to the rising tide of human effort dedicated to building a positive future for our children, and for the future generations of all beings.

Keys to Healthy Living

We live in a culture that has, in many ways, forgotten its purpose and the purpose of human life. We consume relentlessly while the Earth, animals, and those less affluent bear the brunt of our voracious appetites. The pressure builds relentlessly, and we all feel it.

What are the keys to successfully living an authentic and healthy life? With understanding and practice, we can rejuvenate the five interconnected dimensions of health: environmental, cultural, corporeal, psychological, and spiritual. I have found that there are six essential keys to opening doorways into harmony, joy, and abundant health. They are nutrition, meditation, relationships, movement, nature, and creative expression.

The keys to all requisite wisdom lie within us. The companion volume to this book, *The World Peace Way: Six Keys to Health and Harmony for All,* offers an overview of some of these beckoning and practical keys to reclaiming our health and rescuing our world.

CONCLUSION

◦◦

"Though the problems of the world are increasingly complex,
the solutions remain embarrassingly simple."
—BILL MOLLISON, THE "FATHER OF PERMACULTURE"

Institutionalization and Invisibilization

Thank you, dear reader, for taking this journey through which
we have attempted to illuminate the essential dilemmas we collectively face. We have explored the underlying social,
psychological, and economic dynamics driving the disastrous
consequences of animal agriculture to our health, spirituality,
and freedom, and provided some practical keys to help address
the situation. It is not possible to overstate the hidden detrimental
impacts of our culture's food orientation. Our abusive enslavement of animals guarantees the same, eventually, for us.

In 2018, I gave a lecture at California Polytechnic Institute in
San Luis Obispo, sponsored by the Ethical Eating Club. After the
lecture was over, it was early afternoon, and our host, an organizer
with the Central Coast Vegan Network, offered to give us a short
tour of the campus.

Being from the Boston area, I had been under the false impression that Cal Poly is a west-coast equivalent of MIT, focused on mathematics and engineering, but soon realized that it also has a large animal agriculture department with over 6,000 acres of ranching operations. Like most of the public state-sponsored land-grant universities that have been set up in virtually every state, there is a strong emphasis on teaching the "science" of animal agriculture to young students.

We drove by the "poultry center," where chickens were crammed into a windowless shed and students were being instructed in the science of exploiting birds. There was a similarly bleak "swine center." We visited the "dairy science" center and besides seeing cows in pens, we got out and visited the roughly fifty calves who were each confined to a small, dark fiberglass doghouse-type structure. The stench of urine- and feces-soaked hay permeated the area, and the calves, some so young they could barely stand, looked at us with the most beautiful, trusting, and inquisitive eyes imaginable. Their painful separation from their mothers, their distressing isolation, and the complete frustration of their natural yearnings made the absurdity and violence of their plight palpable and haunting. I tried to go to all of them and apologize for the hideous abuse they would be enduring at human hands.

Finally, we went by the "meat processing center." We entered and were asked by a young woman in a white hardhat and a hairnet if she could help us. She informed us that because it was Tuesday, they would be teaching other students the science of pig slaughter. She said that we could watch the "harvest" of the pig through the window of the room at the end of the hall where many students were congregating. If the unfortunate pig had to endure this, I felt I could at least witness it.

The students, about twenty or so, were mainly young women undergraduates in the veterinarian or animal science program, and were all waiting for the pig to enter the room. Soon I heard a loud squealing sound and saw a door open and the back of a large pig move into a huge metal box and then a man reached over and down with an electrical shocking device and held it for a good ten seconds on the back of the pig. Then a mechanical hoist was attached to the leg of the pig and the pig's huge stunned body was lifted over to the middle of the front of the room. I couldn't see what happened next because it was behind the students who were all watching, but I could see the pig suddenly shake and twist her free leg, and simultaneously many of the students squirmed, fidgeted, and looked away or at the floor, so I knew the arteries in the neck were being cut and the pig was bleeding out. In less than a minute, in front of our eyes, she was scientifically reduced from a living being to a dead object. Next the corpse was mechanically lifted to the right into a large, shiny steel bin with a lid, and after the lid was closed, there was an enormous frothing, with white foam spilling out onto the floor, and with occasional mechanical whirring and grinding sounds. Then the lid opened and the now white body of the pig was roughly spun and lifted by mechanical levers and brought back by the hoist to the center of the room.

I knew that at this point the teachers were going to dissect the pig and teach the students about the pig's anatomy, and so I left the building, feeling that I had just witnessed a bizarre scientific satanic ritual of indoctrination. The pig had been sacrificed on the glimmering steel altar of the scientific establishment of human domination and entitlement, and the leaders of tomorrow were being ever more potently desensitized in order to be future enablers and legitimizers of our culture's defining and ongoing atrocities of animal oppression.

The young women were perhaps drawn to that "education" by idealistic yearnings to build careers helping animals as veterinarians, or feeding a hungry world as agricultural scientists. These ideals were being hijacked and corrupted by animal agriculture and its science, which require obedience to the established narrative for those who will reap their rewards. Could the young women understand that the system of animal agriculture they were being compelled to embrace is not only completely obsolete and unnecessary, but is also destroying our health on every level? Probably not, because their career success demanded that their rationality, empathy, and intuition be suppressed to maintain social and academic approval, and to assimilate the protocols and worldview of animal agriculture. It is the institutionalization and invisibilization (to coin a word) of this repression that we now are called to see clearly and to address.

Science, now become scientism, the pseudo-religion of our modern culture, is used to legitimize this destructive behavior by inculcating the pervasive materialism that reduces beings to mere physical objects and rationalizes their abuse. The sacred feminine dimension of consciousness that recognizes beings as beings, and that naturally yearns to respect, celebrate, and protect life, is systematically and harshly repressed. Our youth are ironically trained to steal and destroy the bright light of life shining in the eyes of animals and their offspring.

We are vehicles of this light, and our lives are meant to be its expression through our unique capacities for creativity and loving-kindness. Animals are also vehicles of this light, and we are called to respect them also, and to be savvy about the technology that dominates our culture's approach to living. It affects us all profoundly, surrounds us, and lures us with what it promises will be more convenience, comfort, and "safety," but we pay an enormous and often unrecognized price for these, in terms of our health, awareness, and respect for nature, animals, and each other. If we look carefully, we can see that it reduces us from creators to mere consumers, and that this undermines our essential sense of meaning and significance, and softens us up for being culled and enslaved. While I emphasize in this book how our violence toward animals harms us, the idea is not to stop our mistreatment of them so that our lives will be improved, but so that *their* lives will be improved. Empathy for others, without self-benefitting motivation, is the most lasting foundation for rescuing our world from the devastating impacts of animal agriculture.

"As above, so below:" when we consent to exploiting the animals who are below us in power, we create the conditions for us to be similarly exploited by those more powerful. We can see it in the reverse as well: "As below, so above." Liberating animals, and understanding the spiritual dynamics involved, creates a reliable foundation on which to build a culture of freedom and abundance. When we are compassionate, aware, and acting in integrity, our leaders will reflect this. Instead of allowing ourselves to be deceived by the false promises of Faustian scientism, we can explore the magnificent vistas of our minds and hearts, and work to co-create decentralized communities in harmony with the abundance of the natural world around us. As we focus our attention on raising our vibratory resonance to align with compassion, gratitude, joy, and inner peace, we open inner doorways to new insights into harmonious living, of which our present mental conditioning is completely unaware.

Rescuing Our World from Weaponized Technology

It's long past time to awaken from the toxic narrative imposed on us by the herding culture into which we're all born, and to transform our education, and all our institutions, away from the abusive hoaxes that possess them. An authentic science would realize that there is no reason to imprison animals for food and other products. Authentic spiritual, religious, and ethical teachings agree, and urge us to treat other beings with respect and kindness. These seeds of The Golden Rule and of satyagraha (Gandhi's "truth power") are being destroyed by the captured agriculture programs of universities. Virtually all our institutions are similarly captured.

Technology has clearly been weaponized to propel us toward the fulfillment of the globalist agenda of centralized control that turns the entire Earth into a digital panopticon where a few with massive wealth and power can reduce humanity to exploited livestock. We see it manifesting all around us in the form of worldwide systems of surveillance, data-mining, and information control, supported by tens of thousands of orbiting satellites and robotic drones, with genetic engineering of plants, animals, and humans, as well as trans-humanist desecration of our bodies by merging them with machines. This globalist transhumanist agenda aims to subdue our spiritual sovereignty and destroy our sense of purpose, just as humanity has similarly done with the untold trillions of animals we have enslaved in toxic and purposeless misery over the past ten thousand years.

While some of us may have been able to find meaning in concentration camps and prisons to the degree there is opportunity to have relationships and to think and question, what we have done to animals goes far beyond these kinds of scenarios. Animals have been completely stripped of their sovereign purposes in nature for many hundreds of generations. We force them to be born into existential absurdity and violence, to suffer confinement, mutilation, and sexual exploitation, knowing nothing else, and to be brutally killed as infants or children in human terms. The globalist transhumanist agenda, coupled with rapidly-developing artificial intelligence, surveillance, and mind-control technologies, has the capacity to inflict a similar level of complete physical and mental tyranny on humanity. This is a form of extreme totalitarian slavery which we can hardly fathom, and is sobering in its implications. It is difficult to imagine it, except as we see it reflected in the human-created hells into which we unrelentingly force millions of animals. The dystopian globalist agenda will continue unfolding as long as we continue complying with official technocratic narratives, and as long as we continue buying and eating the flesh and secretions of enslaved animals.

The 2020 Covid rollout was a preliminary exercise, and plainly exposed the malevolent agenda for all with eyes to see. Similar false flag mandates and contrived emergency protocols will certainly be imposed again in new guises. Without our committed and creative resistance, what is there to prevent the planned and already initiated culling of humanity, as well as the full-scale enslavement of those remaining, at an intensity similar to what we now routinely inflict on livestock animals, with future humans born into total bondage, and unable to even imagine anything else? For sheep, goats, cows, and other farmed animals, it is still going on after ten thousand years. How can we ensure that a similar fate does not befall us and our children, descendants and future incarnations over the next ten thousand years?

The way to a positive future beckons, but only as we question, and refuse to participate in, the rituals and narratives that poison us and destroy our intelligence and empathy. With a human birth, we are given the privilege and opportunity of awakening our consciousness so that we can be a force for compassion in our world. Through right understanding, we can reclaim our awareness from the delusions of conditioning that propel us to cause unnecessary suffering to others and to ourselves. The dark violence, disease, and exploitation that we see in the outer world arise from the darkness in our minds. We are multi-dimensional beings, and the living tapestry of our lives arises not only from the conditioning of our culture, and the wounds we have experienced in this lifetime, but also from experiences in other realities of which we are now typically unaware. Aldous Huxley was referring to this when he wrote that, "It's important not to prematurely close our accounts with reality."

We Convince by Our Presence

Through understanding and opening to the regenerative potential of the six keys to healthy living discussed in *The World Peace Way*—diet, meditation, relationships, movement, natural living, and creative expression—we contribute to co-creating more radiant health, beauty, and harmony for others and ourselves. This six-fold path is a spiral leading ever higher, in this life and beyond. All of these six dimensions require commitment and effort, and call us to resist the inner and outer programming of our culture, and instead to follow our intuitive guidance. Going along with cultural dictates is easy. However, the ancient wisdom reminds us that if we want to do only what is easy, our life will be hard and painful; if we are willing to do what is hard, our life will be easy and joyful.

We invariably affect others by our life choices, and our own future is also determined by our present attitudes and actions. Present and future generations of all beings gaze upon us with expectant eyes. How we choose to live sows seeds that bear fruit in all directions and dimensions. Our level of compliance with tyranny and the quality of our food choices are two especially potent determinants of our world, dictating whether we are contributing to slavery or freedom. Liberating ourselves from cultural indoctrination, we rescue animals from being reduced to mere food objects. Our almighty hands, in the act of rescuing and releasing them from ten thousand years of bondage and inescapable destruction, can at last be free to create beauty, and to joyfully serve love, truth, and freedom.

The window of opportunity is now. Each one of us has a unique and essential part to play in the imperative awakening of humanity. When we see things clearly, we know how we should live, and what we should avoid. As we free ourselves from the cultural spell of scientism, technology, and animal slaughter, which are all cut from the same cloth, our lives improve dramatically, and our example makes it easier for others to free themselves as well. Congruence is essential. With clear understanding, we embody the changes we would like to see in the outer world. Walt Whitman summed it well in these lines from his poem, "Song of the Open Road:"

I and mine, we do not convince by arguments;
We convince by our presence.

Granting respect and freedom to animals and to everyone in our world, we develop the capacity to exemplify the spirit of respect and sovereignty in all our relations. Understanding the essential harmony between the human freedom movement and the animal liberation movement, we realize how we are called to live, and how best to share these understandings with others. As awareness spreads, the globalist agenda of centralized control will be increasingly exposed and neutralized.

Healing the wounds within us, we no longer project them into the world around us. We are here on this Earth at this critical time to embody this truth in our daily lives. Cultivating our inner light, spiritual progress is assured. The historical Buddha is reported to have said, "Do not complain and cry and pray, but open your eyes and see, for the light is all about you, and it is so wonderful, so beautiful, so far beyond anything of which men have ever dreamed, for which they have ever prayed, and it is forever and forever."[1]

The main understanding to be cultivated is sensitivity to essence. From infancy, our indoctrination into herderism reduces our sensitivity to the hidden essence that is revealed by the living forms that are all around us. We are forced to stay shallow and numb as we eat and as we commodify animals, nature, each other, and ourselves. Healing from these wounds, and awakening out of materialism, we can begin to sense the spiritual essence that manifests as the tree, the flower, the bird, the cat, the little child, and as our capacity to see and appreciate the grace and revelatory power of the natural world. As our hearts open, and our empathy and intelligence are rekindled, we develop a feeling for the sublime presence which is ever peeking out and winking through the myriad forms arising and dancing in the world around us. A yearning arises in us to savor every moment and situation, to understand and protect the innocent and vulnerable, and to honor the enchanting beauty of life by respectfully minimizing the harm, waste, and inconvenience we cause. With every thought, word, and action, we radiate our intentions, and we impact the web of relations that connects us all. As we more deeply respect and understand the creative essence hidden within the myriad outer forms, the ripples we send forth naturally emanate benevolence and good will for all.

We are here on this Earth during this challenging time to help, each in our unique way, to liberate human consciousness from the deceptions and delusions that cause us to destroy ecosystems, exploit animals, and abuse each other. The dark forces of oppression are suppressing and perverting authentic religious teachings, and are attempting to make science and technology the new religion, and to centralize power into the hands of a few. It is time to re-connect with the spiritual clarity that shines in our hearts, and in the teachings of the world's wisdom traditions, and be part of the awakening of human consciousness, for the benefit of all. With understanding and patience, we can diligently cleanse the decep-tive cultural poisons from our minds and actions. This protects and blesses not just ourselves but also our children and the future generations of all living beings.

The ancient wisdom of the Golden Rule lights the path to a positive future for all of us. We each have our piece of the puzzle to contribute as we co-create communities of freedom, health, and more conscious living on this abundant Earth. It starts on our plates and extends to all our relationships. The eyes of im-prisoned animals and of our children are on us. No effort we make is ever lost. One life lives through us all, and with discern-ing awareness and caring hearts, we can rescue animals, our Earth, and ourselves from the impending globalist reflection of our ongoing mistreatment of animals. The time is now.

Remembering the Vision

I saw a great gathering, people arriving from every direction,
From every culture, race and nation,
Young and old, a great circle forming,
Till the human family, finally, gathered as one.
And then they came: walking, crawling, flying, swimming,
All species, our fellow mortals, joining us in the great circle.
And then the ancestors joined us, and beings from generations yet
    unborn,
And we were joined at last by hosts of nature spirits, and devas and
    angels,
Long neglected and forgotten, they came forth and rounded out our
    circle,
So vast, yet so dear, every being somehow close as the two hands in
    mine.
A hush: all eyes now on us, we humans, calling and sobering us,
Silent expectancy filling the air, the eyes upon us, quietly
    waiting...waiting...
Slowly we gathered our courage, our hearts beginning to open,
Till one of us raised our eyes to them and met them, and remembered,
And suddenly a beam of light flashed from one heart to another,
And then from another to another and another,
With accelerating tempo, light streams flashed across our circle,
Joining hearts with hearts, humans with non-humans, and with each
    other,
Building momentum and brightness, forging a web of living light:
Every being joined by sparkling strands, every heart a luminescent gem,
Till from the center of this vast web of jewels,
There burst forth a towering pillar of light:
Brilliant, infinite, living, radiating, pulsing love and knowing,
And suddenly as one, we all understood.
(We are this light, this light is all, Ahh...Ahh-haa!)

And then such a celebration as has never before been seen on this Earth
　　broke forth,
Such joy released! Such immense relief! Such laughter, so many tears of
　　recognition!
The hospitals emptied, and the prisons and asylums emptied,
As the great wave of understanding swept through every heart,
And the slaughterhouse doors were opened, and the doors of the factory
　　farms,
And never again would beings be imprisoned and used by others,
For compassion and understanding had been born on our Earth.

ACKNOWLEDGMENTS

Deep thanks to the spiritual teachings of the world's wisdom traditions and to the communities and practitioners whose efforts to embody and propagate them benefit us all, and to my spiritual teachers for their example, insight, and compassion.

Heartfelt gratitude to the many heroic people who translated *The World Peace Diet* into their native languages, opening doorways of further collaboration and understanding. Since *The World Peace Diet* was published in 2005, I've been able to work together with an extensive web of colleagues and researchers to whom I am grateful for insights and inspiration, and for the opportunity to cooperate, learn and participate, both nationally and globally.

I am particularly appreciative to colleagues who provided support, and who read the manuscript before publication, sharing ideas and making suggestions: Philip Nicozisis, Anil Narang, Danielle Light, Clare Mann, Judy Carman, Britt Lind, Nicky Hind, and Veda Stram. Special thanks go to Casey Taft for the original encouragement to write this book, and to Christine and John McClarnon for offering their ideas and helpful suggestions multiple times during the writing and editing process. Finally, profound gratitude to my wife and life-partner Madeleine, whose art enhances the cover, and with whom I am blessed to share this precious life. Radiating love and understanding, she has blessed me abundantly during the writing of this book.

May all be free and at peace.

INTUITIVE COOKING
Happy Dining for Body, Earth, and Spirit

BY MADELEINE TUTTLE

Here are some basic recipes, which can be repeated or mixed and matched in different ways, with a shopping list at the end. We kept the dishes pretty simple, but there is a lot of variety. Please use only whole organic ingredients if possible!

Some meals call for tahini sauce, which is easy to make; just add some water to tahini & stir until smooth. Some call for hemp hearts sauce, blending hemp hearts and water in a blender.

It can be convenient to cook pasta, potatoes, rice, and other grains in a large quantity and store them in the fridge to use later in stir fries, salads, and other meals. Some recipes call for leftover grains.

We purposefully don't mention measurements, just the different ingredients. So let your intuition create wildly and have fun!

I love to "paint" the meals: add paprika if it lacks red, or herbs, baby leaves, or sprouts if it lacks green. Turmeric, curry, or peppers for yellow, and so forth.

- **Favorite breakfast**—a Green Smoothie! Feel great 'til lunch! Blend fruits in season, bananas, citrus, kale or spinach, ginger, flaxseeds (can be ground first in coffee grinder), cinnamon, clove, nuts, & water.
- **Other favorite breakfast**—Non-sweet Cleansing Smoothie! Overnight, soak flaxseeds, chia seeds, black cumin seeds, and several almonds. In

the morning, add hemp hearts, ginger, apple, cucumber, celery, whole lemon with rind, and add fresh herbs to taste.

- **Favorite lunch**—Oatley! Soak oat flakes overnight if possible, or at least a couple of hours, add vegan yogurt with fresh fruits in season. Many creative possibilities—see Madeleine's Intuitive Kitchen YouTube channel for enticing options.

- **Other favorite lunch**—Tortillas! Spread tahini sauce or hemp hearts sauce (see above) on a tortilla and fill with lettuce, sprouts, tomatoes, cucumber, walnuts, olives, herbs, spices. Variations: add avocado, tofu, seitan, tempeh, etc.

- **Favorite dinners**—Mashed potatoes topped with veggie ragout. Boil cut-up potatoes in water. When soft, pour most of the water into a bowl and save. Add plant milk, nutmeg, a little tamari, and mash with potato masher. Add some of the water back if necessary. Steam seasonal veggies, and when *al dente* add tahini sauce, tamari, herbs, minced garlic, and mix. Add some herbs and spices to the leftover potato water for a delicious soup. Save leftover mashed potatoes for Shepherd's Pie (below)! Sweet potatoes can be used instead.

- **Spaghetti**—Cook spaghetti with chunks of winter squash in water, and when nearly soft, put broccoli flowers on top. Cover and cook until *al dente*. Pour water off (as a soup) and serve with tomato sauce, or with a grated ginger-tahini sauce (see above).

- **Salad**—Chop and mix greens, peppers, tomatoes, cucumbers, celery, onions, etc.; add tahini sauce, lemon, tamari, herbs, and spices, and mix. Variations: add tofu or tempeh cubes, leftover rice, noodles, kasha, bulgur, or cut-up boiled potatoes, or eat with bread, toast, or crackers.

- **Couscous**—Boil water and pour over couscous in a bowl with added cumin seeds. Sauté onions, squash, cabbage, and a few potato chunks and curry. When soft, add tahini sauce, tamari, ground pepper, mint, and mix. Place in the middle of bed of couscous.

- **Bulgur**—Boil finely cut veggies, turmeric, cumin in water, then add bulgur. Cook about five minutes till soft, and turn off heat. Mix raw spinach leaves under.

- **Polenta**—Boil water with rosemary; with whisker, stir in cornmeal. Steam seasonal veggies, add tofu, and when soft, add tahini sauce, tamari, Italian herb mix, and cayenne. Mix and top over cornmeal.

- **Quinoa**—Boil quinoa in water (approximately 3:1) for 45 minutes. Add kale when 2/3 done. Sauté slices of tempeh, then sauté mushrooms with onions. Top quinoa with sauté and fresh basil.
- **Carrot salad**—Finely grate carrots. Mix tahini sauce with lemon and tamari, add peppermint herb, and pour over grated carrots. Add pine nuts or walnuts.
- **Shepherd's Pie**—Sauté onions and zucchini in a wide shallow pan with lid. Spread peas and crumbled tofu or tempeh, top it with leftover mashed potatoes and cook until warm.
- **Rice**—Cook Lotus brand rice. Mix raw sauce containing finely-cut peppers, celery, tomatoes, parsley, walnuts, olives, lemon, herbs, and spices. Pour over cooked rice, sprinkle with lemon juice.
- **Millet with roasted leek**—Cook millet (4:1) for 30 minutes. Sauté leeks. When soft, add minced garlic and tamari. Serve over millet with a few drops of lemon and toasted sesame oil. Adorn with baby spinach.
- **Pumpkin soup**—Boil Kabocha squash (or other winter squash) in water. When soft, pour into blender. Add a spoonful of tahini and blend until smooth, the briefly blend in fresh cilantro. When served, add a little tamari.
- **Bean tortillas**—Spread fresh cooked or refried beans on tortillas. Cut up cilantro and/or other greens, tomatoes, cucumbers. Add salsa or hemp cream, cayenne, pepper, and roll up.
- **Angel-hair noodles on kale bed**—Cook angel-hair noodles. Steam kale, add roasted sesame seeds, tamari, toasted sesame oil. Serve angel hair on bed of kale, and sprinkle with paprika, toasted sesame oil, tamari, and finally, toasted sesame seeds.
- **Sablé cookies**—Mix spelt flour, Sucanat, vanilla, and a pinch of salt with liquefied coconut oil and water. Shape into long bars 1 1/2 inches in diameter. Put into refrigerator for half hour. When firm, cut into 1/3-inch cookie slices. Put onto baking pan and bake at 350 until light brown (ca. 20-30 minutes). Variation: add hazelnuts or shredded almonds or raisins.
- **Chocolate cookies**—Mix spelt flour, chocolate powder, shredded coconut, crushed walnuts, and a pinch of salt. Add maple syrup or Sucanat and coconut oil. Spread onto baking sheet and bake about 20-30 minutes. When still warm, cut into squares or bars.

SHOPPING LIST:

Allow yourself a good hour to explore and buy the following items, always *organic*, fair trade, and non-GMO. The more love you feel, the better the outcome.

The best place to "shop" is in your own organic (and veganic) garden. The second-best is at the local farmers' market or through a local CSA or food-co-op. The third best is in the organic section of your local grocery store, or through carefully-vetted online suppliers (see Nutrition and Healthy Living Resources section for suggestions also).

Grains: Lotus brand rice, millet, spaghetti, angel-hair, couscous, quinoa, buckwheat, bulgur, wild rice, cornmeal, oats, beans. (Note: we recommend acquiring a small kitchen grain mill to make fresh flour and cornmeal. Also, a hand-powered flaker to roll/flake the oat grains.)

Veggies: In season, pumpkin/squash, leek, onions, garlic, kale, cabbage, ginger, lemons, broccoli, peppers, mushrooms, carrots, lettuce/greens, sprouts, spinach, tomatoes, cucumbers, celery, avocado, cilantro, peas (fresh or frozen), potatoes, sweet potatoes.

Proteins: Tofu, tempeh, seitan, lentils, split peas, beans, and other legumes.

Herbs & spices—fresh if possible, or dried: peppermint, parsley, basil, dill, cilantro, oregano, sage, rosemary, thyme, turmeric, paprika, cayenne, curry, pepper, nutmeg powder, cumin seeds, cardamon, cinnamon, clove, etc.

Fruits: citrus, apples, bananas, grapes, blueberries, and other fruits & berries in season.

Other: flaxseeds, almonds, walnuts, hazelnuts, pine nuts, raisins, sesame seeds, tahini (sesame butter), tomato sauce, tamari or shoyu, refried beans, Real Salt (from Utah) or sea salt, vanilla, coconut oil, chocolate powder, shredded coconut, maple syrup.

Though there are commercial plant-based cheeses, milks, ice creams, burgers, etc., when ready to go deeper into healthy vegan living, it's best to refrain from processed and non-organic foods.

When you sit down to eat, look at what you created. Enjoy the colors, smells, tastes, and the love that blesses the food. The Oneness of all beings!

Bon Appetit!
Stay in touch—feel free to copy!

For more details and ideas,
see Madeleine's Intuitive Kitchen online videos.

RESOURCES

by Dr. Will & Madeleine Tuttle

Available through foodforfreedom.net, worldpeacediet.com and willtuttle.com and relevant online platforms.

AnimalSongs. Music CD by Will Tuttle. Original piano blended with voices of animals; special focus on animals used for food production. 61 mins.

Buddhism and Veganism: Essays Connecting Spiritual Awakening and Animal Liberation. Edited by Dr. Will Tuttle. Essays by internationally recognized Buddhist authors on vegan living and spiritual practice. Vegan Publishers, 2018. 250 pages.

Bursting Light: Favorite Original Piano Solos by Will Tuttle with Visionary Paintings by Madeleine Tuttle. Sheet music for 15 pieces of piano music composed by Will, plus 25 full-color images of paintings by Madeleine. Karuna Music and Arts, 2018. 132 pages.

Circles of Compassion: Essays Connecting Issues of Justice. Edited by Will Tuttle. Essays by internationally recognized authors on the intersectionality of justice issues. Vegan Publishers, 2014. 320 pages.

Conscious Eating: The Power of our Food Choices. DVD by Will Tuttle. Fully illustrated interview, plus three other programs, including a World Peace Diet keynote lecture. 110 mins.

Daily VegInspiration: Jewels from The World Peace Diet. By Dr. Will Tuttle with original art by Madeleine Tuttle. Inspiring excerpts from *The World*

Peace Diet, one for every day of the year, embellished with Japanese brush art paintings by Madeleine. Karuna Music and Arts, 2018. 160 pages.

Four Viharas Guided Meditation. CD by Will Tuttle. Meditation on loving-kindness, compassion, joy, and peace, for cultivating inner and outer harmony, with original piano music. Two versions, one for beginning practitioners, and one for more seasoned. 45 mins.

Living in Harmony with All Life. CD by Will Tuttle. In-depth monologue covering the main ideas presented in *The World Peace Diet*. 75 mins.

Madeleine's Intuitive Kitchen. YouTube channel of videos of healthy organic vegan food preparation by Madeleine Tuttle, including gardening, crafts, exercise, and music. See YouTube listing following.

The World Peace Diet: Eating for Spiritual Health and Social Harmony. By Will Tuttle. International best-selling book translated into 17 languages. This book helped launch the vegan spirituality movement and provides a broad and in-depth overview of the consequences of animal agriculture. Lantern Books, 2005, 2016. 360 pages.

The World Peace Diet audio book. CD by Will Tuttle. Contains the entire *World Peace Diet* text in an unabridged reading by the author. 31 tracks. It is 13.5 hours long, in an MP3 format.

World Peace Diet Circle: Monthly online discussion group—90 minutes typically on the third Thursday of each month: worldpeacemastery.com.

World Peace Diet Mastery and Facilitator Training Programs. Self-paced online training by Will Tuttle. Four-module and eight-module online training by Dr. Will Tuttle, includes audio and video teachings as well as additional resources and monthly online discussion group: worldpeacemastery.com.

World Peace Meditations—Eightfold Path for Awakening Hearts. CD by Will Tuttle. Eight guided meditations with original piano by Will and flute music by Madeleine, plus *World Peace Diet* passages for meditation. 79 mins.

The World Peace Way: Six Keys to Heath and Harmony for All. By Dr. Will Tuttle. Overview of practical ways to cultivate radiant health. Karuna, 2024. 180 pages.

Worldwide Vegan Summit for Truth and Freedom. Directed and produced by Will Tuttle. Eighteen video presentations on health freedom by noted vegan doctors, authors, advocates, and organizers with audio and written transcripts. worldpeacediet.com/worldwide-vegan-summit

Worldwide Prayer Circle for Animals: every day at noon we join together in an affirmative prayer: "Compassion Encircles the Earth for all beings everywhere." See circleofcompassion.org for more information.

Your Inner Islands: The Keys to Intuitive Living by Dr. Will Tuttle. A narrative adventure with teachings and practices to help readers activate the inner guidance system of spiritual intuition. Karuna Music and Arts, 2017. 150 pages.

YouTube video channel with Dr. Tuttle's lectures, presentations, interviews, and concerts, as well as "Madeleine's Intuitive Kitchen" with food, gardening, yoga, and crafts videos by Madeleine Tuttle. See youtube.com/channel/willtuttle

See willtuttle.com, foodforfreedom.net, and/or worldpeacediet.com for more information on upcoming events, plus essays, writings, meditations, music CDs, art prints, fiber art, individualized music and art portraits, ordering, contacting, and downloading. Books and audio recordings are also available through online commercial sources.

MEDICAL FREEDOM RESOURCES

⁓⁓

Bibliography

Atlas, Scott. *A Plague Upon Our House: My Fight at the Trump White House to Stop Covid from Destroying America.* New York: Post Hill Press, 2021.

Berenson, Alex. *Pandemia: How Coronavirus Hysteria Took Over Our Government, Rights, and Lives.* Washington, DC: Regenery, 2021.

Breggin, Peter and Breggin, Ginger. *COVID-19 and the Global Predators: We Are the Prey.* Ithaca: Lake Edge Press, 2021.

Coleman, Vernon. *Anyone Who Tells You Vaccines Are Safe and Effective Is Lying.* Independently published, 2019.

Cowan, Thomas and Fallon Morell, Sally. *The Truth About Contagion.* New York: Skyhorse, 2021.

Desmet, Mattias. *The Psychology of Totalitarianism.* White River Junction: Chelsea Green, 2022.

Dowd, Edward. *"Cause Unknown"—The Epidemic of Sudden Deaths in 2021 and 2022.* New York: Skyhorse, 2023.

Englebrecht, Thorsten, et al. *Virus Mania: How the Medical Industry Continually Invents Epidemics, Making Billion Dollar Profits at our Expense.* Independently published, 2020.

Handley, J. B., *How to End the Autism Epidemic.* White River Junction: Chelsea Green, 2018.

Heckenlively, Kent and Mikovitz, Judy. *Plague: One Scientist's Intrepid Search for the Truth about Human Retroviruses and Chronic Fatigue Syndrome, Autism, and Other Diseases.* New York: Skyhorse Publishing, 2014.

Hume, Ethel. *Béchamp or Pasteur? A Lost Chapter in the History of Biology* (1923) prefaced by Pearson, R. B. *Pasteur: Plagiarist, Imposter: The Germ Theory Exploded (1942).* Distant Mirror, 2020.

Humphries, Suzanne and Bystrianyk, Roman. *Dissolving Illusions: Disease, Vaccines, and the Forgotten History.* Independently published, 2013.

Icke, David. *The Trap: What It Is, How It Works, and How We Escape Its Illusions.* Derby: Ickonic Publishing, 2022.

Kennedy, Jr., Robert F., *The Real Anthony Fauci: Bill Gates, Big Pharma, and the Global War on Democracy and Public Health.* New York: Skyhorse, 2021.

Kennedy Jr., Robert F.; Hooker, Brian. *Vax-Unvax: Let the Science Speak.* New York: Skyhorse, 2023.

Ladapo, Joseph. *Transcend Fear: A Blueprint for Mindful Leadership in Public Health.* New York: Skyhorse, 2022.

Lester, Dawn and Parker, David. *What Really Makes You Ill? Why Everything You Thought You Knew about Disease Is Wrong.* Independently published, 2019.

Malone, Robert. *Lies My Government Told Me and the Better Future Coming.* New York: Skyhorse, 2022.

McCullough, Peter and Leake, John. *The Courage to Face Covid-19: Preventing Hospitalization and Death While Battling the Bio-Pharmaceutical Complex.* Dallas: Counterplay, 2022.

Mercola, Joseph, and Cummins, Ronnie. *The Truth About COVID-19.* White River Junction: Chelsea Green, 2021.

Mann, Clare. *Myths of Choice: Why People Won't Change and What You Can Do about It.* Sydney: Communicate 3, 2019.

Mayer, Thomas. *Covid Vaccines from a Spiritual Perspective.* Independently published, 2022.

Merloo, Joost. *The Rape of the Mind: The Psychology of Thought Control, Menticide, and Brainwashing.* Independently Published, 1956.

Mikovits, Judy, and Heckenlively, Kent. *Plague of Corruption: Restoring Faith in the Promise of Science.* New York: Skyhorse, 2020.

_____. *The Case Against Masks.* New York: Skyhorse, 2020.

Miller, Ian. *Unmasked: The Global Failure of Covid Mask Mandates.* New York: Post Hill Press, 2022.

Mullis, Kary. *Dancing Naked in the Mind Field.* New York: Random House, 1998.

O'Toole, Zoey and Holland, Mary, ed. *Turtles All the Way Down: Vaccine Science and Myth.* Independently published, 2022.

Palmer, Michael, et al, *Doctors for Covid Ethics: mRNA Toxicity.* Independently published, 2023.

Popper, Pamela and Prier, Shane. *Covid Operation: What Happened, Why it Happened, and What's Next.* Independently published, 2020.

Reiss, Karina and Bhakdi, Sucharit. *Corona: False Alarm.* Berlin: Goldegg Verlag, 2020. White River Junction: Chelsea Green, 2021.

Rudolph, Dustin. *The Empty Medicine Cabinet: The Pharmacist's Guide to the Hidden Danger of Drugs and the Healing Powers of Food.* Tarpon Springs, FL: Pursue A Healthy You, 2014.

Sayer Ji. *Regenerate: Unlocking Your Body's Radical Resilience through the New Biology.* New York: Hay House, 2020.

Schwab, Klaus, and Malleret, Thierry. *Covid-19: The Great Reset.* Geneva: Forum Publishing, 2020.

Seneff, Stephanie. *Toxic Legacy: How the Weedkiller Glyphosate Is Destroying Our Health and the Environment.* White River Junction: Chelsea Green, 2021.

Stevo, Allan. *Face Masks in One Lesson.* Chicago: Crafting 52, 2020.

Willis, Mikki. *Plandemic: Fear is the Virus. Truth is the Cure.* New York: Skyhorse Publishing, 2021.

Online Resources

Alliance for Human Research Protection: ahrp.org
Canada Health Alliance: canadahealthalliance.org
Children's Health Defense: childrenshealthdefense.org
Coffee and Covid: coffeeandcovid.com
The Corbett Report: corbettreport.com
Doctors for Covid Ethics: doctors4covidethics.org
The Exposé: expose-news.com
Global Research: globalresearch.ca
Green Med Info: greenmedinfo.com
The Healthy American: thehealthyamerican.org
The Highwire: thehighwire.com
Make Americans Free Again: makeamericansfreeagain.com
Millions Against Medical Mandates: millionsagainstmandates.org
Plandemic Series: plandemicseries.com
Protection of the Educational Rights of Kids (PERK): perk-group.com
Stand for Health Freedom: standforhealthfreedom.com
The Time is Now: thetimeisnow.movie
Vaccine Choice Canada: vaccinechoicecanada.com
Wellness Forum Health: wellnessforumhealth.com

What Really Makes You Ill? whatreallymakesyouill.com
World Council for Health: worldcouncilforhealth.org
Alexander, Dr. Paul Elias: palexander.substack.com
Bailey, Dr. Samantha: drsambailey.com
Bridle, Dr. Byram W.: viralimmunologist.substack.com
Childers, Jeff: coffeeandcovid.com
Christian, Dr. Francis: francischristian.substack.com
Hall, Peggy: thehealthyamerican.org
Kirsch, Steve: kirschsubstack.com
Latypova, Sasha: ashalatypova.substack.com
Makis, Dr. William: makismd.substack.com
Miller, Mark Crispin: markcrispinmiller.substack.com
Malone, Dr. Robert: rwmalonemd.com
McCullough, Dr. Peter: petermcculloughmd.com
Northrup, Dr. Christiane: drnorthrup.com
Rose, Dr. Jessica: jessicar.substack.com
Stevo, Allan: realstevo.substack.com
Tenpenny, Dr. Sherri: drtenpenny.substack.com
Thomas, Dr. Paul: kidfirst4ever.substack.com
Trozzi, Dr. Mark: drtrozzi.org

TRUTH MOVEMENT RESOURCES

Bibliography

Ball, Tim. *Human Caused Global Warming: The Biggest Deception in History*. Independently published, 2016.

Berry, Edwin. *Climate Miracle: There Is No Climate Crisis; Nature Controls the Climate*. Independently published, 2020.

Carman, Judy. *Homo Ahimsa: Who We Really Are and How We're going to Save the World*. Circle of Compassion, 2020.

Cohen, Zina. *Greta's Homework: 101 Truths about Climate Change that Everyone Should Know*. London: BM Marvel Publishing, 2020.

Cousens, Rebbe Gabriel, MD. *Creating Peace by Being Peace*. North Atlantic Books, 2008.

Debaun, Daniel, and Debaun, Ryan. *Radiation Nation: The Fallout of Modern Technology*. Icaro, 2017.

Druker, Steven. *Altered Genes, Twisted Truth: How the Venture to Genetically Engineer Our Food Has Subverted Science, Corrupted Government, and Systematically Deceived the Public*. Salt Lake City: Clear River Press, 2015.

Fensin, Alan. *The Global Warming, Carbon Dioxide Hoax: Easy to Read Proof That Climate Change Is Normal and Not Man-Made*. Burlington Books, 2015.

Firstenberg, Arthur, *The Invisible Rainbow*. White River Junction: Chelsea Green, 2020.

Freeland, Elana. *Chemtrails, HAARP, and the Full Spectrum Dominance of Planet Earth*. Port Townsend, WA: Feral House, 2014.

_____. *Geoengineered Transhumanism: How the Environment Has Been Weaponized by Chemicals, Electromagnetics, & Nanotechnology for Synthetic Biology*. Independently published, 2021.

Gatto, John Taylor. *Weapons of Mass Instruction*. Gabriola Island, BC: New Society Publishers, 2010.

_____. *Dumbing Us Down: The Hidden Curriculum of Compulsory Schooling*. Gabriola Island, BC: New Society Publishers, 2017.

_____. *The Underground History of American Education, Volume 1: An Intimate Investigation into the Prison of Modern Schooling*. Oxford Scholars Press, 2017.

Goodman, Peter. *Davos Man: How the Billionaires Devoured the World*. New York: Harper Collins, 2022.

Griffin, David Ray and Scott, Peter Dale. *9/11 and American Empire: Intellectuals Speak Out*. Northampton: Interlink Press, 2007.

Griffin, David Ray and Woodworth, Elizabeth. *9/11 Unmasked: An International Review Panel Investigation*. Northampton: Interlink Press, 2018.

Herndon, Marvin and Whiteside, Mark. *Chemtrails Are Not Contrails: The Face of Evil*. Independently published, 2023.

Icke, David. *The Trigger: The Lie that Changed the World—Who Really Did It and Why*. Derby: Ickonic Publishing, 2019.

_____. *Alice in Wonderland and the World Trade Center Disaster: Why the Official Story of 9/11 Is a Monumental Lie*. Isle of Wight: David Icke Books, 2002.

Joyce, Helen. *Trans: The New Gender Identity and the Battle for Women's Rights*. London: One World, 2022.

Keenan, Mark. *Transcending the Climate Change Deception Toward Real Sustainability*. Independently published, 2022.

Klein, Richard. *Shivering: Heating Up the Global Warming Debate*. Independently published, 2020.

Koire, Rosa. *Behind the Green Mask: U.N. Agenda 21*. Santa Rosa: Post-Sustainability Institute Press, 2011.

Korsgaard, Soren. *Deadly Deception Exposed*. Korsgaard Publishing, 2020.

Lich, Tamara. *Hold the Line: My Story from the Heart of the Freedom Convoy*. Rebel News Network, 2023.

Mann, Clare. *Vystopia: The Anguish of Being Vegan in a Non-Vegan World*. Sydney: Communicate31, 2018.

Marazzo, Tom. *The People's Emergency Act: Freedom Convoy*. Independently published, 2023.

McGooey, Linsey, *No Such Thing as a Free Gift: The Gates Foundation and the Price of Philanthropy*. London: Verso, 2015.

Mitchell, Guy K. *Global Warming: The Great Deception—The Triumph of Dollars and Politics Over Science, and Why You Should Care*. Savannah: Literary Management Group, 2022.

Montfort, A.W. *The Hockey Stick Illusion*. London: Anglosphere Books, 2020.

Pasin, Patrick. *The FBI Accomplice of 9/11*. Dublin: Talma, 2019.

Perkins, John. *Confessions of an Economic Hitman, 3rd Edition*. Oakland: Berrett-Koehler Publishers, 2004, 2023.

Reisman, John. *Exposing the Climate Hoax: It's All About the Economy*. Lyra Books, 2011.

Roberts, Paul Craig. *Empire of Lies*. Korsgaard Publishing, 2023.

Rose, Larken. *The Most Dangerous Superstition*. Independently published, 2012.

Scott, Peter Dale. *Drugs, Oil, and War: The United States in Afghanistan, Colombia, and Indochina*. Lanham, MD: Rowman & Littlefield, 2003.

Trebing, William. *Good-Bye Germ Theory: Ending a Century of Medical Fraud and How to Protect Your Family*. Independently published, 2006.

Sangster, M. J. *The Real Inconvenient Truth—It's Warming: But It's Not CO_2*. Independently published, 2018.

Scheff, Liam. *Official Stories: Counter Arguments for a Culture in Need*. Independently Published, 2016.

Schwab, Klaus. *The Fourth Industrial Revolution*. New York: Crown Publishing, 2016.

Sibrel, Bart. *Moon Man. The True Story of a Filmmaker on the CIA Hitlist*. Independently published, 2021.

Smith, C. Paul. *The Climate Change Hoax Argument*. Fredrick, MD: Fredrick, 2021.

Stiles, Michelle. *One Idea to Rule Them All: Reverse Engineering American Propaganda*. Independently published, 2022.

Taibbi, Matt. *Hate, Inc.: Why Today's Media Makes Us Despise One Another*. New York: O/R Books, 2019.

Tisdale, Bob. *Dad, Why Are You a Global Warming Denier?* Independently published, 2018.

Ulfkotte, Udo. *Presstitutes in the Pay of the CIA*. Progressive Press, 2019.

Webb, Whitney. *One Nation Under Blackmail: The Sordid Union between Intelligence and Organized Crime that Gave Rise to Jeffrey Epstein.* Walterville, OR: Trine Day, 2022.

Wigington, Dane. *Geoengineering: A Chronicle of Indictment.* Independently published, 2020.

Wood, Judy. *Where Did the Towers Go? Evidence of Directed Free-Energy on 9/11.* (The New Investigation, 2010).

Wood, Patrick. *The Evil Twins of Technocracy and Transhumanism.* Mesa: Coherent, 2022.

Online Resources

Anima Mundi School: animamundi.school

Architects & Engineers for 911 Truth: www0.ae911truth.org

Bright Light News: brightlightnews.com

Cellular Phone Task Force: cellphonetaskforce.org

Citizens for Safer Tech: citizensforsafertech.ca

Climate Intelligence: clintel.org

Collective Evolution: collective-evolution.com

The Conscious Resistance Network: theconsciousresistance.com

The Corbett Report: corbettreport.com

Dawn of Peace: dawnofpeace.org

The Epoch Times: theepochtimes.com

The Exposé: expose-news.com

The Freedom Cell Network: freedomcells.org

Global Research: globalresearch.ca

Geoengineering Watch: geoengineeringwatch.org

Kindness and Science in Action: kindnessandscience.org

National Citizens Inquiry: nationalcitizensinquiry.ca

Real Climate Science: realclimatescience.com

Switch4Good: switch4good.org

Stop World Control: stopworldcontrol.com

Sustainable Society: sustainable.media

Truth Comes to Light: truthcomestolight.com

Woke Watch Canada: wokewatchcanada.substack.com

Brand, Russell: russellbrand.com

Chuter, Robyn: robynchuter.substack.com

Icke, David: davidicke.com

Gage, Richard: richardgage911.substack.com

Mann, Clare: claremann.com

Marazzo, Tom: tommarazzo.ca

Maria, Henna: hennamaria.community
Rancourt, Denis: denisrancourt.ca
Rappoport, Jon: jonrappoport.substack.com
Roberts, Paul Craig: paulcraigroberts.org
Sheehan, Cindy: cindysheehan.substack.com
Wolf, Dr. Naomi: naomiwolf.substack.com
Z., Mickey: mickeyz.substack.com

NUTRITION AND HEALTHY LIVING

RESOURCES

⌒⌒

Bibliography

Barnard, Neal. *Power Foods for the Brain: An Effective 3-Step Plan to Protect Your Mind and Strengthen Your Memory*. New York: Grand Central, 2013.

_____. *Your Body in Balance: The New Science of Food, Hormones, and Health*. New York: Grand Central, 2020.

Bragg, Paul and Patricia. *The Miracle of Fasting: Proven Throughout History*. Bragg Fifty-Second edition, 2021.

Brulé, Dan, *Just Breathe: Mastering Breathwork*. New York: Simon & Schuster, 2017.

Burnett, Graham. *The Vegan Book of Permaculture*. Hampshire: Permanent Publications, 2014.

Campbell, T. Colin and Campbell, Thomas. *The China Study: Revised and Expanded Edition: The Most Comprehensive Study of Nutrition Ever Conducted and the Startling Implications for Diet, Weight Loss, and Long-Term Health*. Dallas: BenBella, 2016.

Campbell, T. Colin. *Whole: Rethinking the Science of Nutrition*. Dallas: BenBella, 2013.

Cheeke, Robert and Espinoza, Vanessa. *Plant-based Muscle: Our Roadmap to Peak Performance on a Plant-Based Diet*. Los Angeles: Gaven Press, 2017

Christy, Martha M. *Your Own Perfect Medicine*. Mesa, AZ: Wishland, 1994.

Clement, Brian and Clement, Anne Marie. *Killer Clothes: How Seemingly Innocent Clothing Choices Endanger Your Health...and How to Protect Yourself.* Summertown, TN: Book Publishing, 2011.

_____, *Self-Healing Diet: A Scientifically Supported, Life-Awakening Guide Revealing the Impact Our Lifestyle Choices Have on Our Health, Longevity, and Environment.* Independently Published, 2023.

Cousens, Gabriel. *Conscious Eating.* New York: North Atlantic Books, 2000.

Davis, Brenda, and Melina, Vesanto. *Becoming Vegan: Comprehensive Edition.* Summertown, TN: Book Publishing Company., 2014.

Delorme, Geoffroy. *Deer Man: Seven Years of Living in the Wild.* Greystone Books, 2022 (English translation).

Eddy, Mary Baker. *Science and Health with Key to the Scriptures.* Boston: Christian Science Publishing, 1904, 1934

Ferguson, Anna. *World Peace Yoga.* Cincinnati: Heart Books, 2018.

Fillmore, Charles. *The Twelve Powers.* Unity Spiritual Center: 2015.

Fronsdale, Gil, tr. *The Dhammapada.* Boulder: Shambhala, 2006.

Fuhrman, Joel. *Fast Food Genocide: How Processed Food Is Killing Us and What We Can Do About It* New York: HarperCollins, 2017.

_____. *Fasting and Eating for Health: A Medical Doctor's Program for Conquering Disease.* New York: St. Martin's Press, 1995.

Gannon, Sharon, and Life, David. *Jivamukti Yoga: Practices for Liberating Body and Soul.* New York: Random House, 2002.

Greger, Michael. *How Not to Die: Discover the Foods Scientifically Proven to Prevent and Reverse Disease.* New York: Flatiron Books, 2015.

Hall, Jenny and Tolhurst, Iain. *Growing Green: Animal-Free Organic Techniques.* White River Junction: Chelsea Green, 2006.

Hanh, Thich Nhat. *Peace is Every Step: The Path of Mindfulness in Everyday Life.* New York: Bantam, 1991.

Heruka, Tsangnyon, tr. *The Hundred Thousand Songs of Milarepa.* Boulder: Shambhala, 2016.

Kahn, Joel. *The Plant-Based Solution: America's Heart Healthy Doc's Plan to Power Your Health.* Boulder: Sounds True, 2018.

Logan, Karen. *Clean House, Clean Planet: Clean Your House for Pennies a Day, the Safe Nontoxic Way.* New York: Simon & Schuster, 1997.

Lisle, Douglas and Goldhamer, Alan. *The Pleasure Trap: Mastering the Hidden Force That Undermines Health & Happiness.* Summertown, TN: Book Publishing, 2003.

McDougall, John. *The Healthiest Diet on the Planet*. New York: HarperOne, 2016.

_____. *The Starch Solution*. New York: Rodale Press, 2012.

Megré, Vladimir. *Anastasia*. Kahului: Ringing Cedars press, 1996, 2004. This is Book One in this nine-book series, and a tenth book is available as an e-book.

Ober, Clinton, Sinatra, Stephen, and Zucker, Martin. *Earthing: The Most Important Health Discovery Ever?* Laguna Beach: Basic health Publication, 2010.

Ota, Lisa. *The Sacred Art of Eating: Healing Our Relationship with Food*. Sacred Exploration, 2017.

Pitcairn, Richard and Susan. *Dr. Pitcairn's Complete Guide to Natural health for Dogs and Cats*. New York: Rodale, 2017.

Radzienda, Thomas. *Hands-on Spiritual Liberation*. Chiang Mai: Sovereign Word Publishing, 2023.

Sharma, N.K. *Milk: A Silent Killer*. New Delhi: Life Positive, 2013.

Shelton, Herbert: *Fasting Can Save Your Life*. American Natural Hygiene Society, 1978.

Sherzai, Dean & Ayesha. *The Alzheimer's Solution: A Breakthrough Program to Prevent and Reverse the Symptoms of Cognitive Decline at Every Age*. New York: HarperOne, 2019.

Stevenson, Douglas. *The Farm Then and Now: A Model for Sustainable Living*. Gabriola Island, BC: New Society Publishers, 2014.

Van der kroon, Coen. *The Golden Fountain*. New Delhi: P. Jain Publishers, 1995.

Wigmore, Ann. *The Hippocrates Diet and Health Program*. New York: Avery, 1983.

Online Resources

Environmental Working Group (for checking toxicity of ingredients): ewg.org

Fasting: Dr. Frank Sabatino: drfranksabatino.com

Fasting: Dr. Alan Goldhamer: True North Health Center: healthpromoting.com

Fasting: True North Health Foundation: truenorthhealthfoundation.org

Feel Fabulous with Food: feelfabulouswithfood.com

Healing Power of Flowers with Dr. Rupa Shah: drrupashah.com

Herbal vegan nutrition with Dr. Steve Blake: drsteveblake.com

Hippocrates Wellness: hippocrateswellness.org

Naked Food Magazine: nakedfoodmagazine.com

Organic Consumers Association: organicconsumers.org
Plant-based pharmacist with Dr. Dustin Rudolph: plantbasedpharmacist.com
The Real Truth About Health: therealtruthabouthealth.com
Remineralize the Earth: remineralize.org
School of Lost Borders: schooloflostborders.org
Super Healthy Children with Karen Ranzi: superhealthychildren.com
T. Colin Campbell Center for Nutrition Studies: nutritionstudies.org
Vegan Fusion Institute (cooking school): chefmarkreinfeld.com
Vegan nutrition with Evita Ochel: evitaochel.com
Vegan Veterinarian with Dr. Armaiti May: veganvet.net

Foods and Nutrition Sources—U.S.

Azure: organic fresh and packaged food: azurestandard.com
Banyan Botanicals: organic foods, teas, extracts: banyanbotanicals.com
Blue Lotus Chai: organic chai teas: bluelotuschai.com
Chemical-Free Body: organic green powders, de-tox, health: chemicalfreebody.com
Eden Foods: organic grains, beans, seeds, nuts, soy, Japanese products: store.edenfoods.com
Evolution: vegan dog and cat food and treats: petfoodshop.com
Food to Live: organic nuts, seeds, grains, breads, snacks, superfoods: foodtolive.com
Garden of Life: organic meal replacement powder, herbal essences: gardenoflife.com
Go Raw: organic seeds, sprouted bars, granola: goraw.com
HealthForce: organic green powders, cleansing, health: healthforcesuperfoods.com
Hippocrates Wellness: organic raw seeds, foods: store.hippocrateswellness.org
Lotus Foods: organic rice and noodles: lotusfoods.com
Malama Mushrooms: organic mushroom powder: malamamushrooms.com
Mocu: organic seeds, mixes, powders, superfoods: mocuhealth.com
Pleasant Hill Grains: organic grains, legumes, seeds: pleasanthillgrain.com
Real Mushroom: organic mushroom extracts and powders: realmushrooms.com
Simply Organic: organic spices, herbs, extracts: simplyorganic.com
Sprout People: sprouting seeds: sproutpeople.org

Sun Warrior: organic green powders: sunwarrior.com
Terra Soul: organic seeds, nuts, superfoods: terrasoul.com
True Leaf Market: sprouting seeds, microgreens: trueleafmarket.com
V-Dog: vegan dog food and treats: v-dog.com
Vitacost: organic packaged foods: Vitacost: vitacost.com
Vitamin Sea Seaweed: wildcrafted sea vegetables: vitaminseaseaweed.com

Household Sources—U.S.

Azure Clean: all types of organic household and cleaning supplies: azurestandard.com

Chemical-Free Body: sprouting, saunas, water structuring, juicers: chemicalfreebody.com

Clearly Filtered: water purification: clearlyfiltered.com

Coyuchi: organic towels, sheets, blankets, apparel: coyuchi.com

DefenderShield: EMF protection: defendershield.com

E-Cloth: cloth window cleaning kit; sponges: us.e-cloth.com

Epic Water Filters: water purification: epicwaterfilters.com

Fresh and Alive: EMF protection: freshandalive.com

Full Circle Home: kitchen brushes, sponges, compostable food wrap: fullcirclehome.com

Gramicci: organic apparel: gramicci.com

Green Forest Paper: recycled toilet paper, paper towels, facial tissues: greenforestpaper.com

Healthcraft: Surgical steel cookware: healthcraft.com

Hippocrates Wellness: organic bedding, EMF protection, juicing: store.hippocrateswellness.org

If You Care: recycled aluminum foil, compostable parchment paper: buyifyoucare.com

Maggie's Organics: organic socks, apparel, home goods: maggiesorganics.com

Natural Action: water structuring devices: naturalaction.com

Pact: organic towels, sheets, blankets, apparel: wearpact.com

Pleasant Hill Grains: flour mills, flakers, dehydrators, cook's tools: pleasanthillgrain.com

Responsible Products: compostable bags: responsibleproducts.com

Saladmaster: Surgical steel cookware and food processors: saladmaster.com

The Soapy Tree: soap nuts: soapnuts.us

Tribest: juicers, blenders, sprouters, dehydrators, plant-milk makers: tribest.com

Vitamix: blenders, food processors: vitamix.com

Personal Care Sources—U.S.

Desert Essence: shampoo, body care, personal care: desertessence.com

Dr. Bronner: soap, body lotion, lip balm, shampoo, personal care: drbronner.com

Dr. Hauschka: facial, body cleansers, creams; makeup; shampoo, deodorant: drhauschka.com

Eco-Dent: tooth powder, floss: eco-dent.com

Heritage Store: rose water, skin care, shampoos, cosmetics: heritage-store.com

Hippocrates Wellness: skin care, cosmetics: store.hippocrateswellness.org

Nature's Answer: PerioBrite dental cleanse, herbal personal care products: naturesanswer.com

Nature's Brands: organic shampoo, facial creams, cosmetics: naturesbrands.com

OraMD: tooth oil, tooth care: oramd.com

Primal Life Organics: organic dental, toothbrush, cosmetics, skin care: primallifeorganics.com

Weleda: facial and body lotions, oils, and creams; deodorant: weleda.com

Animal Freedom and Sanctuaries

Animal Recovery Mission: animalrecoverymission.org

Animals 24-7: animals24-7.org

Edgar's Mission Animal Sanctuary: edgarsmission.org.au

Farm of the Free Sanctuary: farmofthefree.org

Fish Feel: fishfeel.org

Lei Lanni Farm Sanctuary: leilanifarmsanctuary.org

Peaceful Prairie Sanctuary: peacefulprairie.org

Rowdy Girl Sanctuary: rowdygirlsanctuary.org

United Poultry Concerns: upc-online.org/

Woodstock Farm Animal Sanctuary: woodstockfas.org

NOTES

⁓⁓

Introduction

1. The Farm in Summertown, TN, is still thriving. See https://thefarmcommunity.com and Douglas Stevenson, *Out to Change the World* (Summertown: Village Media, 2014)

2. Some primary examples of ancient wisdom texts from Eastern traditions: *Upanishads, Vedas, Bhagavad-Gita, Viveka Chudamani (Crest-Jewel of Discrimination), Ramayana, Yoga Sutras of Patanjali, Tao Te Ching, I Ching, Chuang Tzu, Dhammapada, Diamond Sutra, Platform Sutra of the Sixth Patriarch, Blue Cliff Record, Lankavatara Sutra, Vimalikirti Nrdsa Sutra, Mahaparinirvana Sutra, Mulamadhyamakakarika, Awakening of Faith, Jewel Ornament of Liberation, Tibetan Book of the Great Liberation, Bardo Thodol (Tibetan Book of the Dead).* Some examples of ancient wisdom texts from Western traditions: *The Bible, The Talmud, Hesiod's Theogony, Hymns of Orpheus, The Argonautica, Dramas of Aeschylus, Euripides,* and *Sophocles, Dialogues of Plato, Golden Verses of Pythagoras, Enneads of Plotinus, Meditations of Marcus Aurelius, Ovid's Metamorphoses, Pistis Sophia, The Gospel of Thomas, Confessions of Saint Augustine, Cloud of Unknowing, Imitation of Christ, Summa Theologica.*

Chapter 1—Health and Freedom for All

1. See, for example, Jonathan Chadwick, "More Than a Quarter of the World's Rivers Contain 'Potentially Toxic Levels' of Over-the-counter and Prescription Drugs Including Antihistamines, Antibiotics and Caffeine, Study Warns," *MailOnline*, February 14, 2022. https://www.dailymail.co.uk/sciencetech/article-10511875/Worlds-rivers-suffer-toxic-levels-pharmaceutical-pollution-study-warns.html

2. David Nibert, *Animal Oppression and Human Violence: Domesecration, Capitalism, and Global Conflict* (New York: Columbia University Press, 2013). Chapters 3 and 4.
3. Galatians 6:7.
4. "Total Number of People Taking Psychiatric Drugs in the United States," *Citizens Commission on Human Rights*, January 2021. https://www.cchrint.org/psychiatric-drugs/people-taking-psychiatric-drugs/

Chapter 2—The Five Dimensions of Health and Freedom

1. Hannah Ritchie, "If the World Adopted a Plant-Based Diet We Would Reduce Global Agricultural Land Use from 4 to 1 Billion Hectares," *Our World in Data*, March 4, 2021. https://ourworldindata.org/land-use-diets
2. Frances Moore Lappé, Joseph Collins and Peter Rosset, "The Myth: Scarcity. The Reality: There IS Enough Food," *Food First*, January 22, 2015. https://archive.foodfirst.org/the-myth-scarcity-the-reality-there-is-enough-food/
3. "UN Report: Global Hunger Numbers Rose to as Many as 828 Million in 2022," *World Health Organization*, July 6, 2022. https://www.who.int/news/item/06-07-2022-un-report--global-hunger-numbers-rose-to-as-many-as-828-million-in-2021
4. Thich Nhat Hanh, *Creating True Peace* (New York: Simon & Schuster, 2003), p. 77.
5. Andrew Gough, "The Disturbing Link Between Slaughterhouse Workers and PTSD," *Surge*, January 24, 2023. https://www.surgeactivism.org/articles/slaughterhouse-workers-and-ptsd
6. Andrea Donaldson, "Biochemistry Changes That Occur after Death: Potential Markers for Determining Post-Mortem Interval," *PLOS One*, November 21, 2013. https://journals.plos.org/plosone/article?id=10.1371/journal.pone.0082011
7. See, for example, Michael Greger, *How Not to Die* (New York: Flatiron Books, 2015). Cogent summary of nutrition research.
8. This is also true for those we categorize as "entertainment animals," "laboratory animals," and so forth, though our reduction of animals to mere food commodities is foundational to the others.
9. Sandra Laville, "Dumped Fishing Gear is Biggest Plastic Polluter in Ocean, Finds Report," *The Guardian*, November 5, 2019. https://www.theguardian.com/environment/2019/nov/06/dumped-fishing-gear-is-biggest-plastic-polluter-in-ocean-finds-report
10. See Will Tuttle, "Beyond Herderism," *In Defense of Animals*, January 2015. https://www.idausa.org/beyond-herderism/
11. See Will Tuttle, *The World Peace Diet* (New York: Lantern Books, 2005, 2016), Chapter Two, "Our Culture's Roots," for a more in-depth treatment of this subject.

12. Jim Mason, *An Unnatural Order: The Roots of Our Destruction of Nature* (New York: Lantern Books, 2021 – originally published in 1993 by Simon & Schuster).

13. Ahsan Butt, "Has a 'Fifth-Generation War' Started Between India and Pakistan?" *Al Jazeera*, January 4, 2021. https://www.aljazeera.com/opinions/2021/1/4/are-india-and-pakistan-in-a-fifth-generation-war

14. David Nibert, *Animal Oppression and Human Violence*, op. cit.

Chapter 3—The Unyielding Dilemma

1. Kary Mullis, *Dancing Naked in the Mind Field* (New York: Random House, 1998), p. 119.

2. Ray Arora and Jay Bhattacharya, "The Dangerous Illusion of Scientific Consensus," *The Illusion of Consensus*, May 28, 2023. https://www.illusionconsensus.com/p/the-dangerous-illusion-of-scientific

3. See, for example: Will Tuttle (Ed.), *Circles of Compassion: Essays Connecting Issues of Justice*. Vegan Publishers, 2014.
   David Nibert, *Animal Oppression & Human Violence*. Columbia University Press, 2013.
   David Nibert, *Animal Rights, Human Rights*. Rowman and Littlefield Publishers, 2002.
   David Nibert, (Ed.), *Animal Oppression and Capitalism*, Volumes 1 & 2. Praeger, 2017.

4. Christina Sewell, "Removing the Meat Subsidy: Our Cognitive Dissonance Around Animal Agriculture," *Columbia Journal of International Affairs*, February 11, 2020. https://jia.sipa.columbia.edu/news/removing-meat-subsidy-our-cognitive-dissonance-around-animal-agriculture

5. David Gillette, "The True Cost of a Hamburger," *The American Institute for Economic Research*, April 20, 2022. https://www.aier.org/article/the-true-cost-of-a-hamburger/

6. Erich Fromm, *Escape from Freedom* (New York: Avon) 1941, 1969. Pp. 157-231 passim.

7. Alistair Walsh, "What to Expect from the World's Sixth Mass Extinction?" *Deutsche Welle*, January 11, 2022. https://www.dw.com/en/what-to-expect-from-the-worlds-sixth-mass-extinction/a-60360245

8. This is also discussed in Will Tuttle, *Your Inner Islands*. Karuna, 2017.

9. Carl Jung, *Modern Man in Search of a Soul* (New York: Harcourt, Brace) 1933.

10. Paul Clarke, "How to Grow 6,000 Pounds of Food on 1/10th Acre," *Walden Labs*, December 10, 2015. https://waldenlabs.com/how-to-grow-6000-lbs-of-food-on-110th-acre/

11. See Vladimir Megré, Leonid Sharashkin, ed., John Woodsworth, tr., *Anastasia* (Ringing Cedars Press, 2005)

Chapter Four—Awakening from Materialism

1. Lecture at the Goetheanum, Dornach, Switzerland, August, 1924.
2. Bertrand Russell, *The Impact of Science on Society*, 1953, p. 50.
3. See Will Tuttle, *The World Peace Diet*, op.cit., Chapter Four, "Inheriting Our Food Choices," for a fuller discussion of as cultural indoctrination rituals.
4. Ibid., for a fuller discussion of these mentalities that are required by our herding culture's materialistic orientation: Chapter Eight, "The Metaphysics of Food."
5. Ansel Anders, "Biocyclic Vegan International: 'Purely Plant-Based Farming is Possible Without Any Losses in Yield,'" *Vegconomist*, January 23, 2023.
6. See Will Tuttle, *The World Peace Diet*, op.cit., Chapter Two, "The Herding Revolution."
7. Ibid., Chapter Eleven, "Profiting from Destruction," for a fuller discussion of the connection between herderism and corporate capitalism.
8. Melanie Joy, *Why We Love Dogs, Eat Pigs, and Wear Cows*. Conari, 2010. See also Sherry Kolb, *Mind If I Order the Cheeseburger?* Lantern Books, 2013.
9. Ibid., Chapter Three, "The Nature of Intelligence," for more on intelligence as the capacity to make connections.
10. The globalist plutocrats constitute a cabal as defined by Wikipedia thus: "a group of people who are united in some close design, usually to promote their private views or interests in an ideology, a state, or another community, often by intrigue and usually unbeknownst to those who are outside their group." See Iain Davis, *New World Order: Many Tongues One Voice* (2019) https://iaindavis.com/books/

Chapter 5—Liberating Our Minds

1. Edd Gent, "The Government Is Serious About Creating Mind-Controlled Weapons," *Live Science*, May 23, 2019. https://www.livescience.com/65546-darpa-mind-controlled-weapons.html
2. Dario Anderez et al, "The Rise of Technology in Crime Prevention: Opportunities, Challenges and Practitioners Perspectives," *ResearchGate*, February 2021. https://www.researchgate.net/publication/349125315_The_Rise_of_Technology_in_Crime_Prevention_Opportunities_Challenges_and_Practitioners_Perspectives
3. Mark Scialia, "It Could Take centuries for EPA to Test All the Unregulated Chemicals under a New Landmark Bill," *PBS News*, January 22, 2016. https://www.pbs.org/newshour/science/it-could-take-centuries-for-epa-to-test-all-the-unregulated-chemicals-under-a-new-landmark-bill
4. "National Toxicology Program Finds No Safe Level of Fluoride in Drinking Water; Water Fluoridation Policy Threatened," *Fluoride Action Network*, March 21, 2023. https://fluoridealert.org/articles/national-toxicology-program-finds-no-safe-level-of-fluoride-in-drinking-water-water-fluoridation-policy-threatened/

5. Devvy Kidd, "Germans and Russians Used Fluoride to Make Prisoners 'Stupid and Docile,'" *News with Views*, May 4, 2005. https://newswithviews.com /Devvy/kidd102.htm

6. Casey J. Krohl, "Fluoride's Effect on the Pineal Gland," *Truth About Fluoride*, April 1, 2023. https://truthaboutfluoride.com/fluorides-effect-on-the-pineal-gland/

7. Dane Wigington, "They've Made Weather a Weapon," YouTube Interview, April 13, 2023. https://www.youtube.com/watch?v=EgaTLlN_cbo

8. Ibid.

9. Arthur Firstenberg, et al, "'Electrosmog' is the Totality of the Electric Fields, Magnetic Fields, and Electromagnetic Radiation," July 26, 2023. https://arthurfirstenberg.substack.com/p/emfpolicybrief

10. See, for example, Arthur Firstenberg, *The Invisible Rainbow* (White River Junction, VT: Chelsea Green) 2020.

11. Robert F. Kennedy, Jr., *The Real Anthony Fauci: Bill Gates, Big Pharma, and the Global War on Democracy and Public Health* (New York: Skyhorse, 2021), p. xix.

12. Steve Kirsch, "New Paper: An Estimated 13 million People Worldwide Killed by the COVID Vaccine," *Steve Kirsch Newsletter*, February 11, 2023. https://stevekirsch.substack.com/p/new-paper-an-estimated-13-million

13. Markus Alden et al, "Intracellular Reverse Transcription of Pfizer BioNTech COVID-19 mRNA Vaccine BNT162b2 In Vitro in Human Liver Cell Line," *National Library of Medicine*, Feb. 25, 2022. https://pubmed.ncbi.nlm. nih.gov/35723296/

14. William F. Jasper, "CIA's Mockingbirds and 'Ruling Class Journalists,'" *New American*, May 8, 2017. https://thenewamerican.com/print/cia-s-mocking-birds-and-ruling-class-journalists/

15. See for example *Presstitutes in the Pay of the CIA* by Dr. Udo Ulfkotte (Progressive Press, 2019).

16. Edward Bernays, *Propaganda* (1928; 2004).

17. Carl Jung, *The Undiscovered Self*, "The Plight of the Individual in Modern Society," (New York: Signet, 1957, 2006), pp. 4-5.

18. Peter Breggin and Ginger Breggin, *Covid-19 and the Global Predators: We Are the Prey*. Lake Edge Press, 2021.

19. Shannon Thaler, "Americans with PhDs Are the Most Reluctant to Get Vaccinated Against Covid-19, Study Finds," *The Daily Mail*, August 14, 2021. https://www.dailymail.co.uk/news/article-9893465/Americans-PhDs-reluctant-vaccinated-against-COVID-study-finds.html

20. For more in-depth documentation of the history and insidious effects of public education, see John Taylor Gatto's books, *The Underground History of American Education; Weapons of Mass Instruction;* and *Dumbing Us Down.*

21. To read Dr. Tuttle's 1988 doctoral dissertation, "The Role of Intuition in Education," see http://willtuttle.com/images/DissertationUCB.pdf

22. H. L. Mencken, *In Defense of Women* (1918), Chapter 13.

Chapter 6—The Benefits of Deep Veganism

1. Joel Achenbach, "In Search of the Wild Cows," *The Washington Post*, September 9, 1994. https://www.washingtonpost.com/archive/lifestyle/1994/09/09/in-search-of-the-wild-cows/53828222-a01a-4cc1-8f55-d963c59b0310/

2. Olivia Rosane, "Humans and Big Ag Livestock Now Account for 96 Percent of Mammal Biomass," *EcoWatch*, May 23, 2018. https://www.ecowatch.com/biomass-humans-animals-2571413930.html

3. Solomon Asch, *Scientific American*, 1955; See Michele Reilly, "Conformity's History," *Medium,* August 2016. https://medium.com/@michelereilly/conformity-a7f8db72c7f5

4. Kevin Ryan, "The Top Ten Connections Between NIST and Nano-Thermites," *Journal of 9/11 Studies*, July, 2008. http://www.journalof911studies.com/the-top-ten-connections-between-nist-and-nano-thermites/ See also Edward Curtin, "Peace, War, and 9/11," *The Unz Review*, October 19, 2023. https://www.unz.com/article/peace-war-and-9-11/

5. Steven Jones, "Active Thermitic Material Discovered in Dust from the 9/11 World Trade Center Catastrophe." *911 Blogger*, April 4, 2009. http://911blogger.com/node/19761

6. Mark Gaffney, "The Demolition of the World Trade Center on September 11, 2001: 'The Devil's Trick'" *Global Research*, August 27, 2023. https://www.globalresearch.ca/demolition-world-trade-center-devil-trick/5829424

7. Ibid. See also Dr. Judy Wood, Where Did the Towers Go? (The New Investigation, 2010). See also "Dr. Judy Wood – 9/11 Directed Energy Weapon," https://www.youtube.com/watch?v=NZJZRxBrS4I

8. Dr. Judy Wood, *Where Did the Towers Go?* (The New Investigation, 2010). See also "Dr. Judy Wood – 9/11 Directed Energy Weapon," https://www.youtube.com/watch?v=NZJZRxBrS4I

9. Architects & Engineers for 9/11 Truth, *Beyond Misinformation: What Science Says about the Destruction of World Trade Center Buildings 1, 2, and 7* ((Berkeley, 2015). https://www.ae911truth.org/evidence/beyond-misinformation

10. Graeme MacQueen and Tony Szamboti, "The Missing Jolt: A Simple Refutation of the NIST-Bazant Collapse Hypothesis," *Journal of 9/11 Studies*, January, 2009. http://www.journalof911studies.com/the-missing-jolt-a-simple-refutation-of-the-nist-bazant-collapse-hypothesis

11. Brief overview: Janey Davies, "6 Shocking Social Psychology Experiments That Show How Far People Go to Fit in," *Learning Mind*, June 20, 2017. https://www.learning-mind.com/social-psychology-experiments/

12. Nestar Russell, "The Obedience to Authority Variations and Milgram's Agentic State Theory," *Springer Link*, September 18, 2018. https://link.springer.com/chapter/10.1007/978-3-319-95816-3_5

13. Bob Fennis, "Revisiting the Agentic Shift: Weakening Personal Control Increases Susceptibility to Social Influence," *European Journal of Social Psychiatry*, October 15, 2012. https://onlinelibrary.wiley.com/doi/10.1002/ejsp.1887

14. Étienne de la Boétie, *The Politics of Obedience: Discourse on Voluntary Servitude* (France, 1553)

15. Scott Armstrong, "Net Harm: Peer-Reviewed Science Shows COVID Injection Harm Outweighs Potential Benefit," *The Last American Vagabond*, December 22, 2022. https://tlavagabond.substack.com/p/net-harm-peer-reviewed-science-shows

16. Mark Trozzi, "Dr. Scott Jensen – Medical Journals Are Being Deleted," June 23, 2023. https://drtrozzi.org/2023/06/23/dr-scott-jense-medical-journals-are-being-deleted/

17. Russell L. Blaylock, "Covid Update: What Is the Truth?" *National Library of Medicine*, April 22, 2022. https://www.ncbi.nlm.nih.gov/pmc/articles/PMC9062939/

18. See Dawn Lester and David Parker, *What Really Makes You Ill?* (London: Lester & Parker, 2019)

Chapter 7—Dark Institutions, Food, and Freedom

1. *Goodreads.* Chris Hedges. https://www.goodreads.com/author/quotes/15438.Chris_Hedges

2. James Corbett, "Bilderberg 2019," *The Corbett Report*, June 1, 2019. https://www.corbettreport.com/?s=bilderberg

3. See Martin Gilens and Benjamin Page, "Testing Theories of American Politics: Elites, Interest Groups, and Average Citizens." *American Political Science*, September 2014, Vol. 12, No. 3. See also "Corruption is Legal in America." https://www.youtube.com/watch?v=5tu32CCA_Ig

4. Peter Dale Scott, *Drugs, Oil, and War* (Lanham, MD: Rowman & Littlefield, 2003).

5. John and Nisha Whitehead, "Masters of Deceit: The Government's Propaganda of Fear, Mind Control & Brain Warfare," *Truth Comes to Light*, September 21, 2022. https://truthcomestolight.com/masters-of-deceit-the-governments-propaganda-of-fear-mind-control-brain-warfare/

6. Jon Rappoport, "How the CIA Hid Their MK-Ultra Mind Control Program," *Truth Comes to Light,* March 30, 2018. https://truthcomestolight.com/how-the-cia-hid-their-mkultra-inmd-control-program/

Chapter 8-—The Vacca-cination of Humanity

1. Del Bigtree, "Episode 337: Let Freedom Sing," *The Highwire*, September 14, 2023. 12:45: https://thehighwire.com/ark-videos/let-freedom-sing/

2. Suzanne Humphries and Roman Bystrianyk, *Dissolving Illusions: Disease, Vaccines, and The Forgotten History.* 2013.

3. Dogs, cats, and other animals in the pet industry, which reaches into two-thirds of homes in the U.S., are not only recipients of annual vaccines and other drugs, but also of commercial pet foods that are well-recognized to be profitable, but not healthy for the animals. See Marion Nestle, *Pet Food Politics* (Oakland: University of California Press, 2010) and Richard Pitcairn, DVM, "A New Look at the Vaccine Question," https://www.drpitcairn.com/lectures-and-talks/new-look-at-vaccines/

4. Brian Buntz, "GSK, Pfizer and J&J Among the Most-Fined Drug Companies, According to Study," *Pharmaceutical Processing World*, November 18, 2020. https://www.pharmaceuticalprocessingworld.com/gsk-pfizer-and-jj-among-the-most-fined-drug-companies-according-to-study/

5. Peter Breggin, "What Should We Really Call Psychiatric Drugs?" *Mad in America*, January 17, 2018. https://www.madinamerica.com/2018/01/what-really-call-psychiatric-drugs/
See also https://breggin.com/Dr-Peter-Breggins-Scientific-Papers

6. For an overview of Pfizer's 2021 contributions, see https://www.document-cloud.org/documents/23787007-pfizer-2021-report

7. Joseph Mercola, "How Pfizer Bribes Led to Vaccine Mandates," *Lew Rockwell.com; Russell Brand.* May 3, 2023. https://www.lewrockwell.com/2023/05/joseph-mercola/how-pfizer-bribes-led-to-vaccine-mandates/

8. "Brought to You by Pfizer" video compilation: https://www.youtube.com/watch?v=QAkQlZgnbUQ

9. Pfizer's ad spending from 2008 to 2022," *Statista.* https://www.statista.com/statistics/254404/us-ad-spending-of-pfizer/

10. Sophie Putka, "Top Patient Advocacy Orgs Have Industry Ties in Leadership, Study Shows," *MedPage Today*, August 21, 2023. https://www.medpagetoday.com/publichealthpolicy/ethics/105976

11. Larry Dossey, *Reinventing Medicine: Beyond Mind-Body to a New Era of Healing* (New York: Harper, 2009).

12. Tony Fahkry, "This Is Why the Power of Love Will Heal Your Life," *Mission*, October 9, 2017. https://medium.com/the-mission/this-is-why-the-power-of-love-will-heal-your-life-f649b037ce78
See also Peter Breggin, "Are Emotional Disorders Really Disorders of Love?" *Mad in America, November 26, 2018. https://www.madinamerica.com/2018/11/disorders-of-love/*

13. Peter Breggin, "How Love Can Reformat Our Lives," *Mad in America*, January 8, 2019. https://www.madinamerica.com/2019/01/love-reformats-lives/

14. Bernie Siegel, *Love, Medicine, and Miracles* ((New York: Harper, 1998).

15. Inci Sayki, "Despite Record Federal Lobbying Spending, the Pharmaceutical and Health Product Industry Lost their Biggest Legislative Bet in 2022," *Open Secrets*, February 2, 2023. https://www.opensecrets.org/news/2023/02/despite-record-federal-lobbying-spending-the-pharmaceutical-and-health-product-industry-lost-their-biggest-legislative-bet-in-2022/

16. Marcia Angell, "Drug Companies & Doctors: A Story of Corruption." *The New York Review*, January 15, 2009.

17. Giulia Carbonaro, "How Is the World Health Organization Funded, and Why Does It Rely So Much on Bill Gates?" *EuroNews*, March 20, 2023. https://www.euronews.com/next/2023/02/03/how-is-the-world-health-organization-funded-and-why-does-it-rely-so-much-on-bill-gates

18. Peter McCullough, MD, "One Bio-Pharmaceutical Complex, Two Waves of Injury, Disability, and Death Driven by Three False Narratives," *Courageous Discourse*, September 16, 2023. https://petermcculloughmd.substack.com/p/one-bio-pharmaceutical-complex-two

19. Hannah Ritchie, "If the World Adopted a Plant-Based Diet We Would Reduce Global Agricultural Land Use from 4 to 1 Billion Hectares," op. cit., https://ourworldindata.org/land-use-diets

20. Carey Gillem, "Glyphosate: Cancer and Other Health Concerns," *U.S. Right to Know*, July 13, 2022. https://usrtk.org/pesticides/glyphosate-health-concerns

21. Tim Brown, "G Edward Griffin: 'The World Is Now in the Hands of the Banking Institutions,'" *The Washington Standard*, June 8, 2023. https://thewashingtonstandard.com/g-edward-griffin-the-world-is-now-in-the-hands-of-the-banking-institutions-video/

22. Tim Gielen, "MONOPOLY - Who owns the world?" Documentary, *Stop World Control*, October 1, 2021. https://rumble.com/vn7lf5-monopoly-who-owns-the-world-must-see.html

23. See Shiva Ayyadurai, "Shatter the Swarm: How the Few Control the Many (15:11)" *YouTube*, https://www.youtube.com/watch?v=OEkgZtu_Q2Q

24. "Oxfam Says Wealth of Richest 1% Equal to Other 99%," *BBC News*, January 18, 2016. https://www.bbc.com/news/business-35339475?SThisFB=

25. "Richest 1% Bag Nearly Twice as Much Wealth as the Rest of the World Put Together Over the Past Two Years," *Oxfam International*, press release, January 16, 2023. https://www.oxfam.org/en/press-releases/richest-1-bag-nearly-twice-much-wealth-rest-world-put-together-over-past-two-years

26. Hyun Hong Shin, "CBDCs: An Opportunity for the Monetary System," *Bank for International Settlements Economic Report*, June 23, 2021. https://www.bis.org/publ/arpdf/ar2021e3.htm

27. Pieter Borger et al., *Corman-Drosten Review Report*, International Consortium of Scientists in Life Sciences (ICSLS – Jan. 2021). https://resetheus.org/wp-content/uploads/2022/12/corman-drosten-review-report.pdf

Chapter 9-—The Metaphysics of Masks

1. Radha Burnier, *The Way of Self-Knowledge*, (Adyar: Theosophical Publishing House, 1979), p. 17.

2. Paul E. Alexander, "More than 150 Comparative Studies and Articles on Mask Ineffectiveness and Harms," *Brownstone Institute*, December 20, 2021.

https://brownstone.org/articles/more-than-150-comparative-studies-and-articles-on-mask-ineffectiveness-and-harms/

3. Paul Krugman, "What to Do with our Pandemic Anger?" *New York Times*, February 7, 2022. https://www.nytimes.com/2022/02/07/opinion/covid-unvaccinated-anger.html
4. See Will Tuttle, *The World Peace Diet*, p. 60.
5. Andrew Loewenthal, "The Censorship-Industrial Complex," *Brownstone Institute*, April 27, 2023. https://brownstone.org/articles/the-censorship-industrial-complex/
6. Sayer Ji, "Breaking: A 'Vast Censorship Enterprise' Funded by Taxpayers Knowingly Suppressed Vaccine Injury Content," *GreenMedInfo*, March 10, 2023. https://greenmedinfo.com/blog/breaking-vast-censorship-enterprise-funded-taxpayers-knowingly-suppressed-vaccine1
7. Andrew Loewenthal, "The Censorship-Industrial Complex," op. cit.
8. Paula Jardine, "Anatomy of the Sinister Covid Project," *TCW*, March 10, 2023. https://www.conservativewoman.co.uk/anatomy-of-the-sinister-covid-project-part-5/
9. Nita Bhalla, "40% of Global Crop Production is Lost to Pests. And it's Getting Worse," *World Economic Forum*, June 8, 2021. https://www.weforum.org/agenda/2021/06/climate-change-insects-pests-crops-agriculture/
10. Dr. Medardo Avila Vazquez, "Report from Physicians in the Crop-Sprayed Villages Regarding Dengue-Zika, Microcephaly, and Mass-spraying with Chemical Poisons, February 3, 2016. https://reduas.com.ar/wp-content/uploads/downloads/2016/02/Informe-Zika-de-Reduas_TRAD.pdf
11. Stephen Knight, "The Zika Virus Conspiracy," *Volunteer Latin America*, June 5, 2016. https://www.volunteerlatinamerica.com/blog/posts/the-zika-virus-conspiracy
12. Robert F. Kennedy, Jr., op. cit., p. xv.
13. For a concise illumination of the Federal Reserve's tactics, see Larken Rose, "Make It Happen," https://www.youtube.com/watch?v=8-tw_m3y3HY
14. Robert Malone, "Leading Economic Indicators," *Who Is Robert Malone?* August 10, 2023. https://rwmalonemd.substack.com/p/leading-economic-indicators
15. William Shakespeare, *Hamlet*, I, iii, 77.
16. Lucas Kawa, "How the Rothschilds Created Modern Finance and a Vast Fortune that Has Lasted for Centuries," *Business Insider*, December 23, 2012. https://www.businessinsider.com/the-early-rothschilds-built-a-fortune-2012-12
17. For example, I was listed in Wikipedia for about nine years, for my writing, music, and animal advocacy work, until 2015, when I wrote an article that had a few sentences questioning the ethics of vaccines. Within a few weeks, I disappeared forever from Wikipedia.
18. Dawn Lester and David Parker, *What Really Makes You Ill?* op.cit. p. 89.
19. Mark Grove, "Engineering Our Future with Dr. Zach Bush," *Mark Groves Podcast*, April 19, 2021. https://old.dexa.ai/markgroves/episodes/doc_16998

20. Mark Bailey, *A Farewell to Virology (Expert Edition)*, September 15, 2022; self-published. https://drsambailey.com/a-farewell-to-virology-expert-edition/

21. Britt Lind, "The Virology Fraud and its Disastrous Effect on our Well Being," *People for Reason in Science and Medicine*, July 18, 2023. https://www.peopleforreason.org/article_40.html

22. T. Colin Campbell, interview, "Holistic Nutrition, Academic Freedom, and the Profitability and Perils of Reductionist Science," *Worldwide Vegan Summit for Truth and Freedom with Dr. Will Tuttle*, October 2021. https://vimeo.com /646557976/ef953dfe16 See also T. Colin Campbell, *Whole: Rethinking the Science of Nutrition* (Dallas: Benbella, 2013).

23. Plato, *Laws*, translated by Benjamin Jewett. Book IV.

24. Ibid.

25. James Corbett, "Political Pedophilia," *The Corbett Report* April 16, 2015. https://www.corbettreport.com/episode-304-political-pedophilia/

26. Tom Jefferson et al, "Physical Interventions to Interrupt or Reduce the Spread of Respiratory Viruses," *Cochrane Report*, January 30, 2023. https:// www.cochranelibrary.com/cdsr/doi/10.1002/14651858.CD006207.pub6/full

27. Joe Pinkstone, "No Evidence Face Masks Protected Vulnerable from Covid, Health Officials Admit," *The Telegraph*, April 12, 2023. https://www.msn.com/en-my/health/other/no-evidence-face-masks-protected-vulnerable-from-covid-health-officials-admit/ar-AA19MEGT

28. Emily Joshu, "Mask Study Published by NIH Suggests N95 Covid Masks May Expose Wearers to Dangerous Level of Toxic Compounds Linked to Seizures and Cancer," *The Daily Mail*, August 23, 2023. https://www.dailymail.co.uk/health/article-12443319/Mask-study-published-NIH-suggests-N95-Covid-masks-expose-wearers-dangerous-level-toxic-compounds-linked-seizures-cancer.html

29. Calvin Freiburger, "New Study Finds Extended Use of 'Best' COVID Masks May Cause Cancer, Liver Damage, *LifeSite News*, August 28, 2023. https://www.lifesitenews.com/news/new-study-finds-extended-use-of-best-covid-masks-may-cause-cancer-liver-damage

30. "Face Masks Cause Permanent Brain Damage According to Neurologist," *The Exposé*, February 2, 2021. https://expose-news.com/2021/02/02/face-masks-cause-brain-damage/comment-page-1/

31. Lizzie Parry, "Could You Breathe Away Those Excess Pounds? 80% of Fat Leaves the Body Via the Lungs, Say Experts," *Daily Mail*, December17, 2014.

32. Geer Wallace, J.D. Pleil, "Evolution of Clinical and Environmental Health Applications of Exhaled Breath Research: Review of Methods: Instrumentation for Gas-Phase, Condensate, and Aerosols." *Anal. Chim.* Acta 2018, 1024, 18–38.

33. Kai Kisielinski et al, "Is a Mask That Covers the Mouth and Nose Free from Undesirable Side Effects in Everyday Use and Free of Potential Hazards?" *International Journal of Environmental Research and Public Health*. April 20, 2021. https://pubmed.ncbi.nlm.nih.gov/33923935/

34. Ibid.
35. Ian T. Liu, Vinay Prasad, and Jonathan J. Darrow, "How Effective Are Cloth Facemasks?" *Cato Institute,* Winter 2021/2022. https://www.cato.org/regulation/winter-2021/2022/how-effective-are-cloth-face-masks
36. Bowen Du et al, "Indoor CO_2 Concentrations and Cognitive Function: A Critical Review, *PubMed,* November, 2020. https://pubmed.ncbi.nlm.nih.gov/32557862
37. Kai Kisielinski et al, "Possible Toxicity of Chronic Carbon Dioxide Exposure Associated with Face Mask Use, Particularly in Pregnant Women, Children and Adolescents – A Scoping Review," *Heliyon,* March 3, 2023. https://www.cell.com/heliyon/pdf/S2405-8440(23)01324-5.pdf
38. Ibid.
39. Patricia Harrity, "Study Shows: Mask-Induced Exhaustion Syndrome May Be Misinterpreted as 'Long COVID'" *The Exposé,* August 21, 2023. https://expose-news.com/2023/08/31/study-shows-mask-induced-exhaustion-syndrome-may-be-misinterpreted-as-long-covid/
40. Denis Rancourt, "Review of Scientific rReports of Harms Caused by Face Masks, up to February 2021," February 22, 2021. https://denisrancourt.ca/entries.php?id=15
41. "47 Studies Confirm Ineffectiveness of Masks for COVID and 32 More Confirm their Negative Health Effects," *LifeSite News,* July 23, 2021. https://www.lifesitenews.com/news/47-studies-confirm-inefectiveness-of-masks-for-covid-and-32-more-confirm-their-negative-health-effects/
42. Paul E. Alexander, "More than 150 Comparative Studies and Articles on Mask Ineffectiveness and Harms," *Brownstone Institute,* December 20, 2021. https://brownstone.org/articles/more-than-150-comparative-studies-and-articles-on-mask-ineffectiveness-and-harms/
43. Melissa Shepard, "How to Combat Mask Anxiety," *Psychology Today,* June 5, 2020. https://www.psychologytoday.com/us/blog/erasing-stigma/202006/how-combat-mask-anxiety
44. Mick Cooper, An Empirical and Theoretical Investigation into the Psychological Effects of Wearing a Mask," 1999. https://strathprints.strath.ac.uk/43402/
45. "Babies Born in the Covid Pandemic 'Have Lower IQs', Research Says," *New York Post,* August 13, 2021. https://nypost.com/2021/08/13/babies-born-during-covid-19-pandemic-have-lower-iqs-study-says/
46. Kathleen Phillips, "Augmented Tech Can Change the Way We Live, But Only with the Right Support and Vision," *World Economic Forum,* Aug. 16, 2022. https://www.weforum.org/agenda/2022/08/ethics-not-technological-limits-will-be-the-guiding-factor-for-an-augmented-age/
47. Tyer Durden, "Klaus Schwab: Great Reset Will 'Lead to Fusion of Our Physical, Digital, & Biological Identity'" *Zero Hedge,* November 17, 2020. https://www.zerohedge.com/geopolitical/klaus-schwab-great-reset-will-lead-fusion-our-physical-digital-biological-identity

48. John Perkins, *Confessions of an Economic Hit Man,* (Oakland: Berrett-Koehler, 2004, 2023).
49. Robert F. Kennedy, Jr., p. xix.
50. Ibid., p. xx.
51. John Tierney, "Lockdowns: The Self-Inflicted Disaster," *City Journal,* July 6, 2023. https://www.city-journal.org/article/lockdowns-the-self-inflicted-disaster
52. "Lockdowns Were a Costly Failure, Finds New IEA Book," *Institute of Economic Affairs,* June 5, 2023. https://iea.org.uk/media/lockdowns-were-a-costly-failure-finds-new-iea-book/
53. John Tierney, "Lockdowns: The Self-Inflicted Disaster," *City Journal,* op. cit.
54. Robert Frank, "Most of America's Extra Savings During the Pandemic Are Going to the Wealthy," *CNBC,* August 3, 2021. https://www.cnbc.com/2021/08/03/most-of-americas-extra-pandemic-savings-are-going-to-the-wealthy-.html
55. Kara-Marie Hall, "6 Ways Sunlight Can Benefit Your Health," *Good Rx Health,* July 26, 2023. https://www.goodrx.com/health-topic/environmental/benefits-of-sunlight
56. Thomas Ling, "A plant-based Diet May Lower Severity of COVID-19 Infection by 73 Percent," *Science Focus,* June 9, 2021. https://www.sciencefocus.com/news/plant-diet-covid-19/
57. Bridget M. Kuehn, "More Severe Obesity Leads to More Severe COVID-19 in Study," *JAMA Network,* April 27, 2021. https://jamanetwork.com/journals/jama/fullarticle/2779186
58. Mike Yeadon, "Why I Don't Believe There Ever Was a Covid Virus," *TCW Defending Freedom,* March 22, 2023. https://www.conservativewoman.co.uk/why-i-dont-believe-there-ever-was-a-covid-virus/
59. Conor Kerley, "Can Nutrition Help Prevent Common Cold & Flu Viruses?" *T. Colin Campbell Center for Nutrition Studies,* April 12, 2018. https://nutritionstudies.org/can-nutrition-help-prevent-common-cold-flu-viruses/
60. Mike Yeadon, "The PCR False Positive Pseudo-Epidemic," *The Daily Sceptic,* November 30, 2020. https://dailysceptic.org/2020/11/30/the-pcr-false-positive-pseudo-epidemic/
61. Ariana Cha, "In New York's Largest Hospital System, Many Coronavirus Patients on Ventilators Didn't Make It," *The Washington Post,* April 26, 2020. https://www.washingtonpost.com/health/2020/04/22/coronavirus-ventilators-survival/
62. Denis Rancourt, "There Was No Pandemic," June 22, 2023. https://denisrancourt.ca/entries.php?id=130

Chapter 10—Circle of Slavery

1. David Ray Griffin and Elizabeth Woodworth, *9/11 Unmasked: An International Review Panel Investigation* (Northampton, MA: Interlink), 2018.

2. Robert Jobson, "Prince Charles Announces 'Great Reset Programme' in Bid to Save Planet after Coronavirus Pandemic," *Evening Standard of London,* June 3, 2020. https://www.standard.co.uk/news/uk/prince-of-wales-announces-great-reset-programme-global-economy-a4458631.html

3. For details, including England's royal connections with pedophilia, see James Corbett, "Meet King Charles, The Great Resetter," *The Corbett Report,* May 5, 2023. https://www.corbettreport.com/charles/

4. "Klaus Schwab: Great Reset Will 'Lead to a Fusion of Our Physical, Digital and Biological Identity'" November 16, 2020. https://www.youtube.com /watch?v=iru9oVn0wI8

5. Paul Joseph Watson, "Klaus Schwab: Great Reset Will 'Lead to a Fusion of Our Physical, Digital and Biological Identity,'" *Summit News,* November 16, 2020. https://summit.news/2020/11/16/klaus-schwab-great-reset-will-lead-to-a-fusion-of-our-physical-digital-and-biological-identity/

6. Schwab, Klaus. *The Fourth Industrial Revolution* (Crown, 2017) p. 121.

7. James Corbett, "Your Guide to 5th-Generation Warfare," *The Corbett Report,* April 18, 2023. https://www.corbettreport.com/5thgen/

8. Robert Malone, "5th-Gen Warfare Terms and Tactics," *Global Covid Summit,* January 26, 2023. https://globalcovidsummit.org/experts /drrobertmalone/global-issues/5th-gen-warfare-terms-and-tactics

9. Ibid.

10. Mary Fanning and Alan Jones, "Klaus Schwab Brags that Trudeau, Merkel, Putin Are Former World Economic Forum Young Global Leaders; 'We Penetrate the Cabinets'" *The American Report,* January 30, 2022. https://theamericanreport.org/2022/01/30/klaus-schwab-brags-that-trudeau-merkel-putin-are-former-world-economic-forum-young-global-leaders-we-penetrate-the-cabinets/

11. Rio Times Staff Reporters, "Meet all 3,800 Graduates of Klaus Schwab's Globalist WEF education Programs by Name," *The Rio Times,* May 10, 2022. https://www.riotimesonline.com/brazil-news/modern-Eay-censorship/meet-all-3800-graduates-of-klaus-schwabs-globalist-wef-education-programs-by-name/

12. "History," *The Vegan Society.* https://www.vegansociety.com/about-us/history

13. Mahatma Gandhi, *A Guide to Health* (Madras: Ganesan Publisher, 2021). pp. 107-110, passim. For the full text of this book, see https://www.gutenberg.org/ebooks/40373

14. "Shining a Light on Polio: Was Polio Eradicated?" *Stand for Health Freedom.* https://standforhealthfreedom.com/blog/polio/

15. Robert F. Kennedy, Jr., p. 341.

16. Judy Mikowitz, Kent Heckenlively: *Plague: One Scientist's Intrepid Search for the Truth about Human Retroviruses and Chronic Fatigue Syndrome, Autism, and Other Diseases* (New York: Skyhorse, 2017), p. xii.

17. Ibid., p. xii.

18. "A Glimpse into the Scary World of Vaccine Adjuvants," *Vaccine Choice Canada*, 2008. https://vaccinechoicecanada.com/vaccine-ingredients/a-glimpse-into-vaccine-adjuvants/

19. Deirdre Imus, "Toxic Vaccine Ingredients: The Devil is in the Details," *Children's Health Defense*, March 6, 2018. https://childrenshealthdefense.org/news/toxic-vaccine-ingredients-the-devils-in-the-details/

20. Bruesewitz v. Wyeth LLC, 562 U.S. 223, *Justia*, Feb. 22, 2011. https://supreme.justia.com/cases/federal/us/562/223/

21. "Undeniable Vaccine Facts," *Children's Health Defense*. https://childrenshealthdefense.org/wp-content/uploads/Undeniable-Vaccination-Facts-for-Legislators.pdf

22. Robert F. Kennedy, Jr., p. xxi.

23. "Chronic Diseases in America," *Centers for Disease Control and Prevention*, December 13, 2022. https://www.cdc.gov/chronicdisease/resources/infographic/chronic-diseases.htm

24. "Vaccines for Your Children," *Centers for Disease Control and Prevention*, May 10, 2019. https://www.cdc.gov/vaccines/parents/by-age/index.html

25. Andrew Wakefield, Director, *Vaxxed: From Coverup to Catastrophe*, 2014, Cinema Libre. https://vaxxedthemovie.com/
See also *Vaxxed II: The People's Truth*, 2019. https://live.childrenshealthdefense.org/chd-tv/videos/vaxxed-2/

26. Brian S. Hooker, "Measles-mumps-rubella Vaccination Timing and Autism Among Young African American Boys: A Reanalysis of CDC Data," *BMC: Translational Neurodegeneration*, August 27, 2014. https://translationalneurodegeneration.biomedcentral.com/articles/10.1186/2047-9158-3-16

27. Immunization Coalitions, "CDC Whistleblower: The Timeline." https://www.immunizationcoalitions.org/content/uploads/2017/01/Timeline-for-CDC-Whistleblower.pdf

28. Mark Murray, et al, "Panel Size: How Many Patients Can One Doctor Manage?" *FPM Journal*, April 2007. https://www.aafp.org/pubs/fpm/issues/2007/0400/p44.html

29. Robert W. Malone, "Vaccine Provider Incentive Program," *Who Is Robert Malone?* August 14, 2023. https://rwmalonemd.substack.com/p/vaccine-provider-incentive-program
See also "COVID-19 Information from Anthem Blue Cross and Blue Shield Medicaid (Anthem)," *Anthem Medical*, https://providers.anthem.com/kentucky-provider/communications/covid-19-updates

30. Vernon Coleman, *Anyone Who Tells You Vaccines Are Safe and Effective Is Lying* (Independently published, 2019)

31. Richard Pitcairn, DVM, "A New Look at the Vaccine Question," https://www.drpitcairn.com/lectures-and-talks/new-look-at-vaccines/

32. David Grimm, "Supply of Monkeys for Research is at a Crisis Point, U.S. Government Report Concludes," *Science*, May 4, 2023. https://www.science.org

/content/article/supply-monkeys-research-crisis-point-u-s-government-report-concludes

33. Brenda Baletti, "Big Pharma Is Bleeding Horseshoe Crabs Dry to Meet Growing Demand for Vaccines," *The Defender*, June 16, 2023. https://childrenshealthdefense.org/defender/big-pharma-bleeding-horseshoe-crabs-testing-vaccines/

34. Julia Musto, "US Invests Millions to Breed More Test Monkeys in Wake of COVID-19," *Fox News*, July 16, 2021. https://www.foxnews.com/science/us-breed-test-monkeys-covid-19

35. AnnaMaria Cardinalli, "Catholic Conscience and the COVID-19 Vaccine." *Crisis* Magazine, January 19, 2021. https://www.crisismagazine.com/opinion/catholic-conscience-and-the-covid-19-vaccine

36. Olamide Ologunagbe, "Inside the $1.7 Billion Global Organ Trafficking Industry," *Business Day*, June 24, 2022. https://businessday.ng/health/article/inside-the-1-7-billion-global-organ-trafficking-industry/

37. Robert F. Kennedy, Jr., p. 323.

38. James Lyons-Weiler and Paul Thomas, "Relative Incidence of Office Visits and Cumulative Rates of Billed Diagnoses Along the Axis of Vaccination," *MDPI*, November 22, 2020. https://www.mdpi.com/1660-4601/17/22/8674

39. Paul Thomas, "Dr. Paul's Fight for Medical Freedom." https://www.drpaulsfight.com/

40. Teresa Carey, "How Pfizer Became the First in Big Pharma History to Break $100B in Sales," *Fierce Pharma*, April 21, 2023. https://www.fiercepharma.com/pharma/top-line-how-pfizer-became-first-company-industry-history-100-billion-dollars-sales-plus

41. Pfizer: Pfizer Reports Fourth Quarter and Full-year 2021 Results. https://s28.q4cdn.com/781576035/files/doc_financials/2021/q4/Q4-2021-PFE-Earnings-Release.pdf

42. Pauly MV, Sepe S.J., Sing M., Willian M.K. *Supplying Vaccines: An Economic Analysis of Critical Issues* (IOS Press, 1996) p. 19.

43. Paul Wilde, Grant Robertson. "How Vaccines Became Big Business," The Globe and Mail, December 29, 2009.

44. Ibid.

45. "The Growing Crisis of Chronic Disease in the United States," *Partnership to Fight Chronic Disease*. https://www.fightchronicdisease.org/sites/default/files/docs/GrowingCrisisofChronicDiseaseintheUSfactsheet_81009.pdf

Chapter 11—Pandemics, Faux Veganism, and Eugenics

1. See Elana Freeland, *Chemtrails, HAARP, and the Full Spectrum Dominance of Planet Earth* (Port Townsend, WA: Feral House), 2014.

2. See Hope Bohanec, *The Ultimate Betrayal* (Bloomington, IN: iUniverse), 2013.

3. Jo Clavaglia, "Backyard Farms Drive Increase in Farm Animal Cruelty Cases," *Wisconsin State Farmer*, September 1, 2020. https://www.wisfarmer.com

/story/news /2020/09/01/backyard-farms-drive-increase-farm-animal-cruelty-cases/5661582002/

4. William Telford, "Investigation Launched after Video Shows Cows Being Hit with Pipes," *Plymouth Live,* September 18, 2018. https://www.plymouthher-ald.co.uk/news/business/investigation-launched-after-video-shows-2016609

5. Joby Warrick, "Modern Meat: A Brutal Harvest – They Die Piece by Piece," *Washington Post,* April 11, 2001. For more information on slaughterhouse abuse of animals, see Chapter 10, "The Dilemma of Work," in *The World Peace Diet.*

6. Animal Aid, "Humane Slaughter in British Abattoirs a 'Sham'" 2023. https://www.animalaid.org.uk/the-issues/our-campaigns/slaughter/humane-slaughter-british-abattoirs-sham/

7. CAFO is an industry acronym: Confined Animal Feeding Operation

8. Merritt Clifton, "What Wildlife Services Did Not Say About the Newly Re-leased 2021 Body Count," *Animals 24-7,* March 23, 2022. https://www.animals24-7.org/2022/03/23/what-wildlife-services-did-not-say-about-the-newly-released-2021-body-count

9. "USDA Wildlife Services Posts Fiscal Year 2022 Data on Management Actions and Funding Sources," *USDA Wildlife Services,* March 23, 2023. https://www.aphis.usda.gov/aphis/newsroom/stakeholder-info/stakeholder-messages/wildlife-damage-news/ws-fy22-pdr

10. Markus Alden et al, op. cit., https://pubmed.ncbi.nlm.nih.gov/35723296/

11. Jon Cohen, "Further Evidence Supports Controversial Claim that SARS-CoV-2 Genes Can Integrate with Human DNA," *Science,* May 6, 2021. https://www.science.org/content/article/further-evidence-offered-claim-genes-pandemic-coronavirus-can-integrate-human-dna

12. Rhoda Wilson, "Is it Possible to Patent Genetically-Modified Humans?" *The Exposé.* October 24, 2022. https://expose-news.com/2022/10/24/possible-to-patent-genetically-modified-humans/

13. Mark Trozzi, "Covid shots make Thalidomide look like Flintstone Vitamins" *Newsletter,* July 27, 2022. https://drtrozzi.org/2022/07/27/covid-shots-make-thalidomide-look-like-flintstone-vitamins/

14. Sucharit Bhakdi MD, Karina Reiss PhD and Michael Palmer MD, "The Eternal Dangers of RNA-Vaccines," *Peter and Ginger Breggin Exposing the Global Predators,* August 25, 2023. https://gingerbreggin.substack.com/p/dr-sucharit-bhakdi-and-colleagues

15. "COVID-19 Vaccines Were Never Made With mRNA," *GreatGameIndia Journal on Geopolitics and International Relations,"* August 1, 2023. https://greatgameindia.com/covid-19-vaccines-were-never-made-with-mrna/

16. Karina Reiss & Sucharit Bhakdi, *Corona, False Alarm?* (White River Junction: Chelsea Green), p. 111.

17. Sucharit Bhakdi, "Worrying Developments with Michael Palmer, M.D. & Su-charit Bhadki, M.D.," Children's Health Defense TV, October 21, 2021.

Rumble: 0:45 – 28:00. https://rumble.com/v1p3855-friday-roundtable-worry-ing-developments-with-michael-palmer-m.d.-sucharit-b.html
See also Michael Yeadon, M.D., (11:00 – 16:00) - https://sp.rmbl.ws/s8/2/o/3/7/w/o37wi.caa.mp4

18. Sucharit Bhakdi MD, et al, "The Eternal Dangers of RNA-Vaccines," op. cit.
19. Ibid.
20. Megan Redshaw, "9-Year-Old with no Pre-existing Conditions Died 2 Weeks After Pfizer Shot, Latest VAERS Data Show," *The Defender,* July 29, 2022. https://childrenshealthdefense.org/defender/9-year-old-child-died-pfizer-covid-shot-vaers-data/
21. Ross Lazarus et al., "Electronic Support for Public Health–Vaccine Adverse Event Reporting System," (*Grant Final Report.* 2010. https://digi-tal.ahrq.gov/sites/default/files/docs/publication/r18hs017045-lazarus-final-report-2011.pdf
22. Lynn Allison, "New Study Claims COVID-19 Vaccine Adverse Events Are Un-derreported," *iNews,* January 25, 2023. https://www.ieyenews.com/new-study-claims-covid-19-vaccine-adverse-events-are-underreported/
23. "MPs Warned Yellow Card System and Vaccine Damage Payment Scheme Failing Injury Victims." *Pandemic Response and Recovery,* July 17, 2023. https://appgpandemic.org/news/yellow-card
See also Dr. John Campbell, "2% of Vaccine Reactions Reported," August 12, 2023. https://www.youtube.com/watch?v=kGmOLkmfWIU
24. Frank Wright, "Swiss Study Finds That COVID Vaccine Heart Injury up to 20 Times More Common Than Previously Claimed," *LifeSite News,* August 1, 2023. https://www.lifesitenews.com/opinion/swiss-study-finds-that-covid-vac-cine-heart-injury-up-to-20-times-more-common-than-previously-claimed
25. Mark Crispin Miller, "Are the 'Vaccines' Also Driving People Crazy?" *News from Underground,* May 9, 2023. https://markcrispinmiller.substack.com/p/are-the-vaccines-also-driving-people
26. Russell L. Blaylock, "Vaccines, Neurodevelopment, and Autism Spectrum Dis-orders," March 12, 2008. https://vaccinechoicecanada.com/wp-content/uploads/blaylock-vaccines-neurodevelopment-autism-spectrum-disorders-2008.pdf
27. "Doctors Are 'Baffled' By the Increase in Sudden Adult Death Syndrome (SADS)," *We the Pundit,* June 1, 2022. https://wethepundit.com/doctors-are-baffled-by-the-increase-in-sudden-adult-death-syndrome-sads/
28. Dr. Chris Shoemaker, "DNA Is in the Vaccines," *Dr. Mark Trozzi,* August 11, 2023. https://drtrozzi.org/2023/08/11/dr-chris-shoemaker-global-whistle-blower/
29. Vinu Arumungham, "Leaked EU-Pfizer Agreement Reveals Cover-up of Bac-terial Proteins, Endotoxins, DNA, dsRNA, Other Contaminants and up to 50% Truncated, Modified, Recombined, Junk mRNA in the Vaccine," *Can-ada Health Alliance,* October 14, 2022. https://canadahealthalliance.org/leaksed-eu-pfizer-agreement-reveals-cover-up-of-bacterial-proteins-

endotoxins-dna-dsrna-other-contaminants-and-up-to-50-truncated-modified-recombined-junk-mrna-in-the-vaccine/

30. Naomi Wolf, "The Covenant of Death," *Outspoken with Dr. Naomi Wolf*," August 26, 2023. https://naomiwolf.substack.com/p/the-covenant-of-death?

31. Ibid.

32. National Security Study Memorandum 200: "Implications of Worldwide Population Growth for U.S. Security and Overseas Interests," (The Kissinger Report), December 10, 1974. https://static1.squarespace.com/static/61910a2d98732d54b73ef8fc/t/64bfd6e7f5ca8d4e8192bdbb/1690293992297/Kissinger+report+declassified.pdf

33. Robert Malone, "The Kissinger Report & U.S. Government Policy to Depopulate the Planet," *The Exposé*, August 25, 2023. https://expose-news.com/2023/08/25/kissinger-report-depopulation-us-gov-covid/

34. See How Bad Is My Batch: https://howbad.info/
See also Mike Yeadon, "The Variability in Serious Adverse Events by Vaccine Lot is 'The Calibration of a Killing Weapon' *The Expose*, January 11, 2022. https://expose-news.com/2022/01/11/mike-yeadon-the-variability-in-serious-adverse-events/
And Mark Trozzi, "Dr. Yeadon – The Calibration of a Killing Weapon," https://drtrozzi.org/2022/02/12/dr-yeadon-the-calibration-of-a-killing-weapon/
Covid-19 Vaccine Ingredients (Nobulart) https://nobulart.com/covid-19-vaccine-ingredients/
Mark Trozzi, "What's Really in the Covid Vaccines" *Dr. Mark Trozzi MD*, September 23, 2022. https://drtrozzi.org/2022/09/23/whats-really-in-the-covid-vaccines/

35. Children's Health Defense Team, "Inventing Diagnoses to Cover Up Vaccine Injury—A Con as Old as Vaccination Itself," *The Defender*, July 27, 2022. https://childrenshealthdefense.org/defender/vaccine-injury-cover-up-covid-vaccination/

36. Michael Shellenberger, "Exposed: America's Secret Censorship-Industrial Complex," *Public,* March 8, 2023. https://public.substack.com/p/exposed-americas-secret-censorship

37. Susan Schmidt, et al, "Report on the Censorship-Industrial Complex: The Top 50 Organizations to Know," *Racket News*, May 10, 2023. https://www.racket.news/p/report-on-the-censorship-industrial-74b

38. Mattias Desmet, "The UN's Digital First Responders – or The UN's Virtual Brownshirts?" *Mattias Desmet Substack*, June 23, 2023. https://mattiasdesmet.substack.com/p/the-uns-digital-first-responders

39. Ibid.

40. "The Censors' Henchmen," *Brownstone Institute*, August 7, 2023. https://brownstone.org/articles/the-censors-henchmen/

41. Peter McCullough and John Leake, *The Courage to Face Covid-19: Preventing Hospitalization and Death While Battling the Bio-Pharmaceutical Complex* (Dallas: Counterplay, 2022).
42. Peter McCullough, "Video: Dr. Peter McCullough Speech at the ReAwaken America Tour," *GlobalResearch*, December 10, 2021. https://www.globalresearch.ca/video-dr-peter-mccullough-speech-reawaken-america-tour/5767121
43. Peter McCullough, MD, "One Bio-Pharmaceutical Complex, Two Waves of Injury, Disability, and Death Driven by Three False Narratives," *Courageous Discourse*, September 16, 2023. https://petermcculloughmd.substack.com/p/one-bio-pharmaceutical-complex-two
44. Ibid.
45. Ibid.
46. Ibid.
47. Ibid.
48. Alan Reynolds, "How One Model Simulated 2.2 Million U.S. Deaths from COVID- 19," Cato Institute (Apr. 21, 2020)/ https://www.cato.org/blog/how-one-model-simulated-22-million-us-deaths-covid-19. See Kennedy, op. cit., for more information, pp. 4-5
49. Celia Farber, "Was the COVID-19 Test Meant to Detect a Virus?" *UncoverDC, April 7, 2020.* https://www.uncoverdc.com/2020/04/07/was-the-covid-19-test-meant-to-detect-a-virus/. See also https://www.youtube.com/watch?v=VHmVj3LTqrU
50. WaySide, "Kary Mullis: Nobel Prize Winning Scientist on the PCR Test," *Truth in Plain Sight?* November 29, 2021. https://truthinplainsight.com/kary-mullis-nobel-prize-winning-scientist-on-the-pcr-test/
51. Stella Paul, "Why Are Hospitals Still Using Remdesivir?" *Brownstone Institute,* May 30, 2023. https://brownstone.org/articles/why-are-hospitals-still-using-remdesivir/
52. Holly McKay, "Hospitals Are Paid More for Medicare Patients Confirmed or Presumed to Have Coronavirus," *Fox News,* May 4, 2020. https://www.foxnews.com/health/hospitals-medicare-patients-cost-coronavirus
53. Elizabeth Lee Vliet and Ali Shultz, "Biden's Bounty on Your Life: Hospitals' Incentive Payments for COVID-19," *Association of American Physicians and Surgeons,* November 17, 2021. https://aapsonline.org/bidens-bounty-on-your-life-hospitals-incentive-payments-for-covid-19/
54. Joseph Mercola, "Doctors Were Bribed for COVID Vaccination Coercion," April 27, 2023. https://media.mercola.com/ImageServer/Public/2023/April/PDF/doctors-bribed-covid-vaccination-coercion-pdf.pdf
55. James Corbett, *The Corbett Report.* https://www.corbettreport.com
56. Carol Roth, "We're Living Through the Greatest Transfer of Wealth from the Middle Class to the Elites in History," *Newsweek,* October 24, 2021. https://www.newsweek.com/were-living-through-greatest-transfer-wealth-middle-class-elites-history-opinion-1641614

57. Will Tuttle, ed., *Circles of Compassion: Essays Connecting Issues of Justice* (Boston: Vegan Publishers, 2014).

58. See, for example, JoAnn Farb, "How Co-option of Grass-Roots Activism Played Out in Kansas City's First VegFest." August 24, 2017.

59. "Mercy For Animals Opposes and Promotes Animal Exploitation, Somehow," *Vox Vegan*, October 23, 2017. https://voxvegan.com/2017/10/23/mercy-for-animals-opposes-and-promotes-animal-exploitation-somehow/

60. James Laveck, "Invasion of the Movement Snatchers: A Social Justice Cause Falls Prey to the Doctrine of Necessary Evil," *HumaneMyth*, October 2006. https://www.humanemyth.org/invasion.htm

61. Bryan Jung, "Lab Grown Artificial 'Meat' May Actually Be Worse for the Environment," *The Epoch Times*, July 20, 2023. https://www.theepochtimes.com/us/lab-grown-artificial-meat-may-actually-be-worse-for-the-environment-5409562

62. Ibid.

63. Josh Mitteldorf, "Yes, Ecosystems Are Collapsing. No, It Has Nothing to Do with CO_2," *The Defender*, August 7, 2023. https://childrenshealthdefense.org/defender/ecosystems-collapsing-not-co2-emissions

64. Chris Morrison, "No Warming in U.S. for at Least 17 Years According to Rarely Referenced Urban Heat-Free Database," *The Daily Sceptic*, July 30, 2022. https://dailysceptic.org/2022/07/30/no-warming-in-u-s-for-at-least-17-years-according-to-rarely-referenced-urban-heat-free-database/

65. See Helen Joyce, *Trans: Gender Identity and the New Battle for Women's Rights* (London: Oneworld, 2021).

66. "What Does Soylent Green Mean?" *Slang Dictionary*. https://www.dictionary.com/e/slang/soylent-green/

67. Lars Chittka, "Do Insects Feel Joy and Pain?" *Scientific American*, July 1, 2023. https://www.scientificamerican.com/article/do-insects-feel-joy-and-pain/

68. Baxter Dmitry, "Stanford University: 'Harvesting Blood & Organs of Children' Could Help Achieve 'Immortality'," *AC News*, May 19, 2022. https://ac.news/stanford-university-harvesting-blood-organs-of-children-could-help-achieve-immortality/

69. Louisiana State University, "Cannibalism: A New Way to Stop the Spread of Disease," *American Academy for the Advancement of Science*, July 10, 2017. https://www.eurekalert.org/news-releases/476976

70. Tim Pierce, "Swedish Researcher Floats Cannibalism to Combat Climate Change," *Washington Examiner*, September 9, 2019. https://www.washingtonexaminer.com/news/swedish-researcher-floats-cannibalism-to-combat-climate-change

71. Jared Piazza and Neil McLatchie, "Cannibalism Is Common in the Animal Kingdom – Here's Why for Humans It's the Ultimate Taboo," *The Conversation*, August 16, 2019. https://theconversation.com/cannibalism-is-common-in-the-animal-kingdom-heres-why-for-humans-its-the-ultimate-taboo-121678

72. *The New York Times*, Twitter: July 23, 2022. https://twitter.com/nytimes/status/1550864590560546816

73. Joseph Mercola, "New Documentary Exposes WHO's 'Diabolical' Plan to Use Vaccines to Reduce Global Population," *The Defender*, July 11, 2022. https://childrenshealthdefense.org/defender/infertility-a-diabolical-agenda-chd-wakefield-documentary-who-vaccines-global-population-cola

74. Linsey McGooey, *No Such Thing as a Free Gift: The Gates Foundation and the Price of Philanthropy* (London: Verso, 2015), p. 152.

75. Rachana Dhiman et al., "Correlation between Non-Polio Acute Flaccid Paralysis Rates with Pulse Polio Frequency in India," *International Journal of Environmental Research and Public Health* (Aug., 2018), ncbi.nlm.nih.gov/pmc/articles/PMC6121585/

76. James Corbett, "How and Why Big Oil Conquered the World," *The Corbett Report*. October 6, 2017. https://www.corbettreport.com/bigoil/

77. Ibid.

78. Ibid.

79. Ibid.

80. "American Eugenics Research — Racism Masquerading as 'Science'" *Alliance for Human Research Protection*, May 7 2023. https://ahrp.org/1913-u-s-eugenics-research-association/

81. "Buck v. Bell: Inside the SCOTUS Case That Led to Forced Sterilization of 70,000 & Inspired the Nazis," *Democracy Now!* March 17, 2016. https://www.democracynow.org/2016/3/17/buck_v_bell_inside_the_scotus

82. See Vera Sherav, *Never Again Is Now Global*, documenting parallels between the holocaust and the Covid response. https://neveragainisnowglobal.com/
See Charles Patterson, *Eternal Treblinka: Our Treatment of Animals and the Holocaust* (New York: Lantern) 2002.

83. "Buck v. Bell," *Democracy Now*, op. cit.

84. Ibid.

85. *Reichgessetzblatt.* https://upload.wikimedia.org/wikipedia/commons/b/b9/Reichsgesetzblatt_25_Juli_1933.jpg

86. James Corbett, "Who Is Bill Gates?" *The Corbett Report*, May 1, 2020. https://www.corbettreport.com/gates/

87. Ibid.

88. Samuel Smith, "Catholic Doctors Claim UN Aid Groups Sterilized 1 Million Kenyan Women With Anti-Fertility-Laced Tetanus Vaccinations," November 27, 2014, *The Christian Post*. https://www.christianpost.com/news/catholic-doctors-claim-un-aid-groups-sterilized-1-million-kenyan-women-with-anti-fertility-laced-tetanus-vaccinations-129819/

89. Andrew Wakefield, *Infertility: A Diabolical Agenda*, https://infertilitymovie.org/resources/

90. James Corbett, "Who is Bill Gates?" *The Corbett Report*, op. cit.

91. Andrew Wakefield, *Infertility: A Diabolical Agenda,* https://infertilitymovie.org/about-film/

92. Carol M. Swain, "Systemic Racism at Planned Parenthood" *First things,* February 5, 2021. https://www.firstthings.com/web-exclusives/2021/02/systemic-racism-at-planned-parenthood

93. Evie Fordham, "Melinda Gates: These People Deserve to Get Coronavirus Vaccine First," June 24, 2020, *FoxBusiness.* https://www.foxbusiness.com/technology/coronavirus-vaccine-bill-melinda-gates

94. Vera Sherav, "Unless All of Us Resist, Never Again Is Now," *Remember,* August 20, 2022. https://remember.org/nuremberg-code.html

95. Tamara Ugolini, "Parents Enraged after Saskatchewan School Features Perverse Presentation by Planned Parenthood," *RebelNews,* June 23, 2023. https://www.rebelnews.com/parents_enraged_after_saskatchewan_school_features_perverse_presentation_by_planned_parenthood

96. Tim Talley, "Official: Trafficking More Profitable than Drugs," *The Washington Times,* September 24, 2014. https://www.washingtontimes.com/news/2014/sep/24/oklahoma-house-to-study-human-trafficking-crimes/

97. Jillian Kubala, "What Is BPA? Should I Be Concerned About It?" *HealthLine,* April 12, 2022. https://www.healthline.com/nutrition/what-is-bpa

98. Robert Sanders, "Pesticide Atrazine Can Turn Male Frogs into Females," *Berkeley Research,* March 1, 2010. https://vcresearch.berkeley.edu/news/pesticide-atrazine-can-turn-male-frogs-females

99. Michael Greger, "How to Block Breast Cancer's Estrogen-Producing Enzymes," *Nutrition Facts,* April 17, 2017. https://nutritionfacts.org/video/how-to-block-breast-cancers-estrogen-producing-enzymes/

100. Michael Greger "The Effects of Hormones in Dairy Milk on Cancer," *Nutrition Facts,* September 25, 2019. https://nutritionfacts.org/video/the-effects-of-hormones-in-dairy-milk-on-cancer/

101. T. Colin Campbell, "What Does Research Indicate About Animal Protein and 'Reproductive' Cancers? *T. Colin Campbell Center for Nutrition Studies,* October 15, 2012. https://nutritionstudies.org/research-indicate-animal-protein-reproductive-cancers/

102. Lacey Muinos, "Does Drinking Milk Increase Estrogen Levels in Men?" (*Livestrong,* October 28, 2019. https://www.livestrong.com/article/554285-does-milk-raise-estrogen-in-men/

103. Kerrie Saunders, *The Vegan Diet as Chronic Disease Prevention* (New York: Lantern Books), 2019, p. 137. See also Will Tuttle, *The World Peace Diet,* p. 122.

104. Helen Joyce, *Trans: Gender Identity and the Battle for Women's Rights* (London: OneWorld, 2022). See also Jennifer Bilek, "Who is Behind the Trans Agenda?" https://www.youtube.com/watch?v=tLXdoqXbC6k&t=2338s

105. "If Everyone Ate an American Diet 'We Would Need Another Planet," *Yahoo News*, January 20, 2020. https://news.yahoo.com/western-diet-climate-change-destroying-planet-183103326.html

106. See also David F. Cechetto, Jane C. Topolovec, "Cerebral Cortex," *Encyclopedia of the Human Brain* (San Diego: Academic Press), 2002, p. 663.

107. "Video Interview with Yuval Noah Harari," July 12, 2023. https://www.cbcg.org/images/books/Yuval-Noah-Harari-07-12-2023.pdf

108. Jennifer Brown, "The WEF Part 2: Yuval Noah Harari," *Holding the Line with Dr. Funtimes*, April 2, 2022. https://docbrown77.substack.com/p/the-wef-part-2-yuval-noah-harari

109. Ibid.

Chapter 12—The Benevolent Revolution

1. Johanna Schroeder et al, "Psychiatric Impact of Organized and Ritual Child Sexual Abuse: Cross-Sectional Findings from Individuals Who Report Being Victimized," *National Library of Medicine*, October 31, 2018. https://www.ncbi.nlm.nih.gov/pmc/articles/PMC6266763/

2. Jeff Horwitz and Katherine Blunt, "Instagram Connects Vast Pedophile Network," *The Wall Street Journal*, June 7, 2023. https://www.wsj.com/articles/instagram-vast-pedophile-network-4ab718.

3. James Vincent, "Instagram's Recommendation Algorithms are Promoting Pedophile Networks," *The Verge*, June 7, 2023. https://www.theverge.com/2023/6/7/23752192/instagrams-recommendation-algorithms-promote-pedophile-networks-investigation

4. S. B. Matthews, "The Adrenochrome Pathway," *PubMed*, April 1985. https://pubmed.ncbi.nlm.nih.gov/2991537/

5. "Dr. Shiva Details Adrenochrome Horrors: Trafficked Children Tortured for Chemical in Their Blood, *Stew Peters Network*. July 12, 2023. https://rumble.com/v2zgstq-dr.-shiva-details-adrenochrome-horrors-trafficked-children-tortured-for-che.html. See also Bjornn Hofmann, "Young Blood Rejuvenates Old Bodies: A Call for Reflection when Moving from Mice to Men," *PubMed Central*, January 3, 2018. https://www.ncbi.nlm.nih.gov/pmc/articles/PMC5836258/

6. Max Lobdell, "Adrenochrome," *Unsettling Stories*, https://unsettlingstories.com/2017/02/03/just-learned-horrible-impossible-truth-drug-called-adrenochrome/#more-1163. See also Patricia Harrity, "The Truth about Adrenochrome," *The Exposé*, December 13, 2023. https://expose-news.com/2023/12/13/the-truth-about-adrenochrome/

7. "Age of Animals Slaughtered," *Farm Transparency Project*, December 21, 2020. https://farmtransparency.org/kb/food/abattoirs/age-animals-slaughtered

8. David Icke, *The Trigger: The Lie that Changed the World – Who Really Did it and Why* (Derby, UK: Ickonic, 2019), pp. 578-588.

9. See Mark Passio, "De-Facto Satanism" December 202, 2022. https://odysee.com/@woeih:e/Mark-Passio-De-Facto-Satanism:a

10. Whitney Webb, *One Nation Under Blackmail: The Sordid Union Between Intelligence and Crime that Gave Rise to Jeffrey Epstein, Vol.1* (Walterville, OR: Trine Day Publishing, 2022).

11. Jeremy Howard et al, "An Evidence Review of Face Masks Against COVID-19," *Proceedings of the National Academy of Sciences,* January 11, 2021. https://www.pnas.org/doi/10.1073/pnas.2014564118

12. Emily Kopp, "Vaccine Industry Insider Peter Hotez Helped Fund Wuhan Gain-of-Function Study," *Children's Health Defense,* August 10, 2022. https://childrenshealthdefense.org/defender/vaccine-industry-peter-hotez-funded-wuhan-gain-of-function-study/

13. Dr. Mike Yeadon, "Why I Don't Believe There Ever Was a Covid Virus," *The Conservative Woman,* March 23, 2023. https://www.conservative-woman.co.uk/why-i-dont-believe-there-ever-was-a-covid-virus

14. Peter McIlvenna, "Dr. Mike Yeadon Concludes: There Are No Respiratory Viruses. It Is All a Fraud," *Hearts of Oak,* August 1, 2022. https://rumble.com/v1oef9h-dr-michael-yeadon-there-are-no-respiratory-viruses-it-is-all-a-fraud.html See also https://heartsofoak.org/dr-mike-yeadon-fraud-fear-and-how-herd-mentality-has-brought-us-to-the-edge/

15. Michael Yeadon, "Truth Be Told Rally," Trafalgar Square, London, U.K., May 13, 2023. https://gr8h8er.substack.com/p/final-copy-yeadon-at-trafalgar-square. See also https://www.bitchute.com/video/qzav98jBSOz4/

16. Michael Walsh, "The End is Close for the Covid Cultists Says Dr Reiner Fuellmich," Europe Renaissance, December 11, 2021. https://europerenaissance.com/2021/12/11/the-end-is-close-for-the-covid-cultists-says-dr-reiner-fuellmich/

17. United Nations: *Transforming Our World: The 2030 Agenda for Sustainable Development.* https://sustainabledevelopment.un.org/post2015/transformingourworld/publication

18. Michael Yeadon, "Technological Tyrannies Have no Natural Ending," June 28, 2023. https://interestofjustice.substack.com/p/former-vp-pfizer-dr-yeadon-tell-everyone

19. Sean Adi-Tabatabai, "CIA: 'Disinfo Program Is Complete' – They Actually Said This" *NewsPunch,* January 15, 2015. https://newspunch.com/cia-disinfo-program-is-complete-they-actually-said-this/

20. Louise Osborne, "Amazon Rainforest Study: Brazil Led Deforestation in 2022," *DW Global Media,* June 27, 2023. https://www.dw.com/en/global-forest-watch-report-tropical-forest-loss/a-66034028

21. "Impact of Deforestation: Local and National Consequences," *Mongabay,* July 22, 2012. https://rainforests.mongabay.com/0902.htm

22. David Ellison et al, "Trees, Forests and Water: Cool Insights for a Hot World," *Science Direct*, March 2017. https://www.sciencedirect.com/science/article/pii/S0959378017300134

23. Shanna Hanbury, "Scientists Measure Amazon Drought and Deforestation Feedback Loop: Study," *Mongabay*, July 21, 2020. https://news.mongabay.com/2020/07/scientists-measure-amazon-drought-and-deforestation-feedback-loop-study/
See also Judith Schwartz, "Forest Modeling Misses the Water for the Carbon: Q&A with Antonio Nobre & Anastassia Makarieva," *Mongabay*, February 7, 2023. https://news.mongabay.com/2023/02/forest-modeling-misses-the-water-for-the-carbon-qa-with-antonio-nobre-anastassia-makarieva/

24. Fred Pearce, "Rivers in the Sky: How Deforestation is Affecting Global Water Cycles," *China Dialogue*, August 30, 2018. https://chinadialogue.net/en/cities/10792-rivers-in-the-sky-how-deforestation-is-affecting-global-water-cycles/

25. Hannah Ritchie and Mark Roser, "Deforestation and Forest Loss," *Our World in Data*, December, 2021. https://ourworldindata.org/deforestation

26. Michael Bengwayan, "Deforestation Reduces Oxygen," *Eurasian Review*, June 24, 2020. https://www.eurasiareview.com/24062020-deforestation-reduces-oxygen-oped/

27. Rhoda Wilson, "Climategate is the Worst Scientific Scandal of our Generation," *The Exposé*, July 15, 2023. https://expose-news.com /2023/07/15/climategate-is-the-worst-scientific-scandal/

28. Ibid. See also Martin Durkin, *Climate: The Movie (The Cold Truth)*, Free Your Mind Documentaries, March 21, 2024. https://rumble.com/v4kl0dn-climate-the-movie-the-cold-truth-martin-durkin.html

29. Rhoda Wilson, "After Climategate I Realised I Had Fallen into Groupthink, Climate Expert Said," *The Exposé*, July 27, 2023. https://expose-news.com/2023/07/27/i-realised-i-had-fallen-into-groupthink/

30. Rhoda Wilson, "Climategate 2.0: "The Science" Is Dependent on Manipulation of Facts and Data," *The Exposé*, July 16, 2023. https://expose-news.com/2023/07/16/climategate-2-0-the-science-is-dependent-on/

31. Robert Malone, "It's Evil to Fake Deaths to Panic People," *Who Is Robert Malone?* July 24, 2023. https://rwmalonemd.substack.com/p/its-evil-to-fake-deaths-to-panic

32. Rachel Smolkin, Melissa Fleming, Adrian Monck, "Tackling Disinformation," *World Economic Forum Sustainable Development Impact Meetings*, September 20, 2022. 42:20 timestamp. https://www.weforum.org/events/sustainable-development-impact-meetings-2022/sessions/tackling-disinformation

33. "1921 Heatwave," *Real Climate Science*. https://realclimatescience.com/1921-heatwave/

34. P. Gosselin, "Europe's '48°C Horror That Never Was' - ESA, Media Sharply Criticized for Manipulative Reporting," *Watts Up With That?* July 19, 2023.

https://wattsupwiththat.com/2023/07/19/europes-48c-horror-that-never-wasesa-media-sharply-criticized-for-manipulative-reporting/

35. Rhoda Wilson, "When it Comes to Temperatures in Italy, BBC Lies and Lies and Then Lies Some More," *The Exposé*, July 29, 2021. https://expose-news.com/2023/07/29/when-it-comes-to-temperatures-in-italy-bbc-lies/

36. "Data shows There's No Climate Catastrophe Looming – Climatologist Dr. J. Christy Debunks the Narrative," *BizNewsTV*, February, 2023. https://www.youtube.com/watch?v=qJv1IPNZQao

37. C. Paul Smith, *The Climate Change Hoax Argument* (Frederick, MD: Frederick, 2021), p. 57-58.

38. Andy Thade, "Nobel Laureate: 'Climate Science Has Metastasized into Massive Shock-Journalistic Pseudoscience,'" *Ript*, May 21, 2023. https://gript.ie/nobel-laureate-climate-science-has-metastasized-into-massive-shock-journalistic-pseudoscience/

39. "Nobel Laureate John Clauser Elected to CO_2 Coalition Board of Directors," *CO@ Coalition*, May 5, 2023. https://co2coalition.org/publications/nobel-laureate-john-clauser-elected-to-co2-coalition-board-of-directors/

40. M. J. Sangster, *The Real Inconvenient Truth—It's Warming: but it's not CO_2* (Michael Sangster, 2018), p. 121-123.

41. Andy Thade, op. cit.

42. Ajit Naranjan, "'Era of Global Boiling Has Arrived,' Says UN Chief as July Set to Be Hottest Month on Record," *The Guardian*, July 27, 2024. https://www.theguardian.com/science/2023/jul/27/scientists-july-world-hottest-month-record-climate-temperatures

43. "Tonga Eruption Blasted Unprecedented Amount of Water into Stratosphere," *NASA*, August 2, 2022. https://www.nasa.gov/feature/jpl/tonga-eruption-blasted-unprecedented-amount-of-water-into-stratosphere

44. Jeff Childers, "Overheated," *Coffee & Covid 2023*, July 28, 2024. https://www.coffeeandcovid.com/p/overheated-friday-july-28-2023-c

45. Sergey Khaykin, et al, "Global Perturbation of Stratospheric Water and Aerosol Burden by Hunga Eruption," *Nature*, December 14, 2022. https://www.nature.com /articles/s43247-022-00652-x

46. J. Best, "Tonga Eruption May Temporarily Push Earth Closer to 1.5°C of Warming," *Eos*, March 16, 2023. https://eos.org/articles/tonga-eruption-may-temporarily-push-earth-closer-to-1-5c-of-warming

47. Ilya Sandra Perlingieri, "Dr. Ilya Sandra Perlingieri in 2010 on Weather Modification," 2010. https://www.youtube.com/watch?v=VjW8l5Zi-Qo

48. Ibid.

49. Mark Whiteside and J. Marvin Herndon, "Chemtrails and Covid-19: Two Faces of Evil," *Advances in Social Sciences Research* Journal, April 16, 29022. https://journals.scholarpublishing.org/index.php/ASSRJ/article/view/12191

See also Foster Gamble, "Chemtrails: How They Affect You and What You Can Do," *ThriveOn,* July 6, 2013. https://www.thriveon.com/media /chemtrails-how-they-affect-you-and-what-you-can-do

50. Dane Wigington, "Nanoparticle Contamination Cover-Up: Answers from a Scientist," *GeoEngineering Watch,* February 22, 2023. https://www.geoengi-neeringwatch.org/category/audio-video/video/

51. Killuminati, "HAARP," https://www.bitchute.com/video/G449PcS7D8e7/

52. Dane Wigington, "Graphene Rain, Scientist Sounds Alarm," https://www.youtube.com/watch?v=zm261O9BRB0

53. Dane Wigington, *The Dimming,* March 10, 2021. https://www.geoengineer-ingwatch.org/the-dimming-full-length-climate-engineering-documentary/

54. Laila Yuile, "Why Did the BC Government Repeal the Weather Modification Act?" *Westcoast Views,* July 28, 2011. https://lailayuile.com/2011/07/28/why-did-the-bc-government-repeal-the-weather-modification-act/

55. J. Marvin Herndon and Mark Whiteside, *Chemtrails Are Not Contrails* (2022), p. 6.

56. Wigington, "Graphene Rain, Scientist Sounds Alarm," op. cit.

57. David Keith, "Harvard's Solar Geoengineering Research Program," *Harvard University,* https://geoengineering.environment.harvard.edu/people/david-keith
See also "The Oxford Geoengineering Program," http://www.geoengineer-ing.ox.ac.uk/www.geoengineering.ox.ac.uk/

58. Dane Wigington, *Hacking the Planet,* June 13, 2017. https://www.geoengi-neeringwatch.org/hacking-the-planet-the-climate-engineering-reality/

59. Jane Flanagan, "Staying power of Kilimanjaro snow defies Al Gore's gloomy forecast," *The Times, U.K.,* February 17, 2020. https://www.thetimes.co.uk /article/staying-power-of-kilimanjaro-snow-defies-al-gores-gloomy-forecast-8x8l7s0v3

60. Larry Tomczak, "Al Gore's 10 Global Warming Predictions, 12 Years Later — None Happened!" *Prepare for Change,* January 1, 2018. https://pre-pareforchange.net/2018/01/01/al-gores-10-global-warming-predictions-12-years-later-none-happened/

61. Global Climate Intelligence Group, "World Climate Declaration: There Is No Climate Change Emergency." https://clintel.org/

62. C. Paul Smith, p. 70.

63. M. J. Sangster, p. 29.

64. Global Climate Intelligence Group, *op.cit.,* https://clintel.org/world-climate-declaration/

65. Ibid.

66. Anna Ratcliff, "Carbon Emissions of Richest 1 Percent More Than Double the Emissions of the Poorest Half of Humanity," *Oxfam International,* September 21, 2020. https://www.oxfam.org/en/press-releases/carbon-emissions-richest-1-percent-more-double-emissions-poorest-half-humanity

67. Rhoda Wilson, "WEF Plans to Smother Covid and Climate Change Information that Doesn't Favour Their False Narratives," *The Exposé*, January 21, 2023. https://expose-news.com/2023/01/21/wef-plan-to-smother-info-against-them/

68. For more information on the devastating environmental impact of so-called green energy, see the documentary film, *The Dark Side of Green Energy* by Al Jazeera, September, 2020. https://www.aljazeera.com/program/featured-documentaries/2020/9/7/the-dark-side-of-green-energy/
For more in-depth coverage of the "green energy" fraud, see the documentary film, *Planet of the Humans* by Jeff Gibbs, 2019. https://www.amazon.com/Planet-Humans-Al-Gore/dp/B08L4M94BR

69. Robin McKie, "Child Labour, Toxic Leaks: The Price We Could Pay for a Greener Future," *The Guardian,* January 3, 2021. https://www.theguardian.com/environment/2021/jan/03/child-labour-toxic-leaks-the-price-we-could-pay-for-a-greener-future

70. Joseph Mercola, "Deforesting the Amazon for green energy windmills?" *Nexus Newsfeed*, July 4, 2023. https://nexusnewsfeed.com/article/climate-ecology/deforesting-the-amazon-for-green-energy-windmills/

71. Mark Keenan, "Transcending the Climate Change Deception – Toward Real Sustainability," *Global Research*, July 8, 2023. https://www.globalresearch.ca/transcending-climate-change-deception-toward-real-sustainability/5805158

72. Rhoda Wilson, "Bill Gates Is Funding a Scheme to Cut Down 70 Million Acres of Forests in North America," *The Exposé*, September 2, 2023. https://expose-news.com/2023/09/02/bill-gates-cutting-down-70m-acres-forests/

73. Ibid.

74. Ibid.

75. Rhoda Wilson, "We Shouldn't Demonise Cows for Burping and Farting; We Should Be Thanking Them," *The Exposé*, June 2, 2023. https://expose-news.com/2023/06/02/we-shouldnt-demonise-cows-for-burping/

76. Ibid.

77. Rhoda Wilson, "The Fires in Greece and Spain Are Likely Due to Arson, Not Climate Change," *The Expos´*, August 31, 2023. https://expose-news.com/2023/08/31/fires-in-greece-and-spain-are-due-to-arson/

78. Mark Crispin Miller, ""All the Materials that Didn't Burn Should Have, & All the Materials that Did Burn Shouldn't Have": An Arborist and Firefighter(s) on what Hit Maui: 'That Ain't a Wildfire,'" *News from Underground*, September 6, 2023. https://markcrispinmiller.substack.com/p/all-the-materials-that-didnt-burn

79. "Why Are There So Many Fires? Dr. David Martin Unveils What He Thinks Is Behind It," *Vigilant News*, August 25, 2023. https://vigilantnews.com/post/why-are-there-so-many-fires-dr-david-martin-unveils-what-he-thinks-is-behind-it

80. Spencer Walrath, "How the Rockefellers Manufactured the Climate Liability Campaign," *Energy in Depth,* April 11, 2019. https://eidclimate.org/how-the-rockefellers-manufactured-the-climate-liability-campaign/
81. James Corbett, "How and Why Big Oil Conquered the World," https://www.corbettreport.com/bigoil/
82. See https://foodforestabundance.com/
83. "The History of the Dacha Movement," *The Earth,* August, 2013. https://www.ringingcedarsofrussia.org/vladimir-megre/dacha-move-ment.html#world1
84. Dan Witters, "US. Depression Rates Reach New Highs," *Gallup,* May 17, 2023. https://news.gallup.com/poll/505745/depression-rates-reach-new-highs.aspx
85. Dawn Lester and David Parker, *What Really Makes You Ill? op.cit.*
86. Earthing is the practice of connecting our bodies (usually our bare feet) directly with the earth. For more information: https://www.earthing.com/pages/what-is-earthing

Conclusion

1. Charles W. Leadbeater, *The Masters and the Path* (Adyar: Theosophical Publishing House, 1927) p. 229. Leadbeater attributes this saying to 'Lord Buddha.'

Printed in Great Britain
by Amazon

41499142R00208